THE GREAT INFIDEL

BY THE SAME AUTHOR

A Washington Story

The Blue Chips

(One or both of the above novels have appeared in the following editions: French, Italian, British, Czech, Dutch, Swedish, German, Yiddish, Hungarian, Swiss, Greek, Russian, Rumanian)

THE GREAT INFIDEL

A biographical novel

Joseph Jay Deiss

RANDOM HOUSE · NEW YORK

First Printing

 Published in New York by Random House, Inc., and simultaneously in Toronto, Canada, by Random House of Canada, Limited.

Library of Congress Catalog Card Number: 63-7123

Manufactured in the United States of America

by The Haddon Craftsmen, Inc., Scranton, Pa.

Design by Guy Fleming

To the memory of young

PRINCE HENRY OF BAVARIA,

with whom in conversation

this book began

"BY STARS, BY FLIGHTS OF BIRDS,
BY FATE WE SEE
OF ALL THE WORLD
ONE MAN SHALL HAMMER BE."

—*Oracle, 1239* A.D.

Of Men and Time

IN THE TREACHEROUS MIDDLE AGES, during the first half of the thirteenth century, there lived in Italy a "Modern Man"—Frederick the Second, Holy Roman Emperor and King of Sicily. His mother was Sicilian and his father German—a stormy combination of opposites. To the Italians he was known as Federico di Sicilia e d'Apulia, grandson of the Norman King Ruggero il Grande; to the Germans, as Friedrich von Hohenstaufen, grandson of the Emperor Friedrich I, "Barbarossa."

Among his contemporaries he was hated by many, loved by many; but because he was not a man of his own times, he seemed an enigma to all. He was, in fact, a man of antiquity born a thousand years too late, and a man of the Renaissance born two hundred years too soon.

From Hadrian, in the second century A. D., to Lorenzo the Magnificent in the fifteenth, no other European ruler was so outstanding as Federico Secondo. To a remarkable degree he combined many of the qualities of long-dead Hadrian and yet-to-be-born Lorenzo: their general intellectual curiosity; their admiration for Greek culture; their experimental interest in science and nature; their knowledge of art, architecture, and poetry; their conception of legal social reform; their ambiguous private and public religious attitudes; their mastery of the game of power politics; their astute diplomacy directed always toward peace; their bursts of violence when aroused; their biting, scintillating wit; and finally, their uninhibited, licentious, destructive loves.

This account of the life of Federico Secondo is both biography and novel—a "bio-novel" hewing closely to the historical facts, but frankly using the technique of the novel to recreate as fully as possible the man and the period.

Though I present this book with diffidence, I am wary of apology for historical errors—for at such a distance of years, who is to have final say about so controversial a figure? The chroniclers of the Middle Ages contradict each other; and the modern historians contradict not only each other on many points, but the chroniclers as well. I have followed what seemed to me the most probable course of events, and, where necessary, filled in the gaps. Some of the most debatable points at issue are indicated in the *Notes*, preceding the *Selected List of Sources*.

All the major characters, and most of the minor, existed in life. Psychological interpretations are, of course, my own. I have used actual names even down to court pages and a pet horse. Letters and documents quoted are verbatim, as are many fragments of conversation. Nevertheless, relatively little personal detail is known, for the medieval writers were more concerned with battles and miracles, hell and heaven, than with the ordinary daily life of men. The medieval artists, for their part, were more interested in demons and saints, gargoyles and angels, than in the likenesses of their contemporaries—though the miniaturists in illuminated manuscripts sometimes recorded lay clothing and customs. It is noteworthy that the faces of Hadrian and Lorenzo are both well known to us, but not one authentic portrait of Federico Secondo—painting or sculpture—today exists. We know his face only from written descriptions and a profile on a coin.

In the search for information, I have followed the trail from Sicily to the farther side of the Alps. I have visited the castles, the cathedrals, the museums. I have looked at the original manuscripts, the armor, the inscriptions. I have searched every major library in Italy, and some minor; and in Vienna, both library and the treasure chambers of the Holy Roman Empire. The thrones, the crowns, the jewels, the robes, the swords, the hose and shoes used on state occasions are accurately described; I have seen them with my own eyes, touched some of them with my own hands. Such are the physical externals. It is my hope that I have also touched something of the inner life—the mind and spirit—of an extraordinary man.

In the final analysis, Federico's tragedy derived from the fact that he could not escape from the medieval world which constricted him, nor remake it securely to the pattern of his own vision of the future. But his efforts to escape and remake never ceased. While he lived, a great light of rational intelligence shone through the murky medieval gloom of ignorance and superstition. When he died, writes a modern Italian, ". . . there died with him the idea of the State, which he had given body and life, and soon misery, squalor, obscurantism, feudal bondage returned to a land which had known, under him, prosperity, civilization, splendor." Tragic results, imposed by military force and clerical authority, which are still felt through all the south of Italy.

"Now let earth and heaven break forth into joy at this great deliverance!" exclaimed Pope Innocent IV at news of Federico's death. And orders went out to pursue Federico's "brood of adders" until the last descendant was exterminated.

To Dante, however, after fifty years had passed, Federico was not only father of the Italian language but a model emperor—though in the *Divine Comedy* confined to hell for religious heresies. So great was Federico's impact on the popular mind that many people refused to believe in his death. Impostors arose, and were enthusiastically acclaimed. For more than a hundred years, rumors were current of his reappearance, accompanied by a fantastic baggage train of camels, or riding abroad on a giant horse with thundering hoofs. Stories grew: he had taken refuge in the cone of Etna; he was slumbering in a cavern of the Kyffhäuser in Germany; he would return after death, to reform abuses and lead all peoples to peace.

And even now, fresh flowers are often found on his tomb in Palermo—not elaborate wreaths indicating official approval, but small bouquets from unknown hands.

Federico today is not forgotten.

JOSEPH JAY DEISS

Contents

THE GREAT INFIDEL

Prologue

To this day it is rumored that my mother was a nun who was seduced by a demon, and that my unnatural birth was attended by strange signs and portents.

At my birth, my mother was over forty. She had been married to my father almost ten years without a pregnancy. My father was only twenty-nine, and very anxious for a son; he announced my birth throughout the length and breadth of the Realm by a traveling band of Saracen trumpeters. As for my mother, it is said that, in spite of the winter wind (it was the day after Christmas), she bore me in an open tent in a market place, wishing all doubters to see both my normal arrival and her milk-filled breasts. Later it was reported throughout Italy that celestial music had been heard in the piazza, the earth trembled, and that holy men and wizards had been informed instantly of my first breath. The famed Abbot Gioachino of Calabria proclaimed that I was to become the "Scourge of the Earth"—while at the other end of Europe the Breton wizard Merlin hailed my birth as "wondrous and unhoped for," and declared that I was to become a second Saviour, an "Emperor of Peace."

My own reaction to my birth is another matter. I was born: that much is certain. I am not unaware of the value of glamorous legends in creating an authoritative personality, and I have taken good care not to discourage fabulous stories which I myself could never believe. On the other hand, it is no accident that far and wide I am known to men as *Stupor Mundi*—the wonder of the world. Now, in writing of myself to myself, I have no reason for the slightest concealment of my attitudes and opinions, or my pride in my achievements. As for the range of my passions, I accept them as a fact, just as I accept the fact of royal birth. All things considered, I am, truly, whatever else may be said of me, a wonder of the world.

At this moment I write in another tent, a royal tent not dissimilar, perhaps, to the one which allegedly sheltered me at birth. My camp is pitched in the cool foothills of the Alps above Torino, for the time is July and I prefer to escape the miasma and vapors and insects of the plains around the river Po. Aside from armed men, horses, and dogs, I have brought with me only books and my beloved falcons. For reasons of expediency I have left behind my usual traveling entourage of an elephant, a giraffe, a score of camels, five leopards on leash, bears, lions, apes, eunuchs, dancing girls, astrologers, Moors, dwarfs and jesters—such a company is too cumbersome for rapid emergency movement. And who knows what emergencies I may be called upon to face . . . ?

My picked Saracens stand guard outside the royal tent, and the silken entrance curtains are tightly drawn. For diverse reasons I write this personal history alone, secretly, in Arabic, by my own hand. I say "personal history" because the public history will be written by the chroniclers—both by my enemies and my partisans; and because a "private life," other than inward reflection, is hardly possible for a man in my position. Even petty kings are almost wholly public figures, with every coming and going recorded by chroniclers, gossips, ambassadors and spies. How much more intensely watched, then, are the actions of a man who is not only King of many Kingdoms but also Holy Roman Emperor—a Caesar in the ancient, classic sense?

At this moment as I scratch reed pen on paper, no other sounds can be heard except the familiar late-at-night noises of a military camp: barking of dogs, whinny of horses, fluttering of pennants in the wind, occasional clank of armor, pacing of sentries —all of which come to me diminuendo, like faraway surf. Now and then my wolfhound, Omar, twitches and utters a soft moan as he sleeps at my feet. He is named for that remarkable mathematician-poet, Omar Khayyám (as the priests frown on the use of Christian names for animals, I amuse myself by choosing Muslim names for those I love best). When my Omar moans, I sigh, and pause in my writing. I note how the great candle flickers when moths are drawn irresistibly into the flame; how shadows sway upon the purple-and-white striped tent fabric; how candlelight glistens on the gold chain I wear girt about my scarlet silk tunic; how the jewels glitter in the hilt of my dagger (such stones are said to work magic); how the veins swell and the tiny blond hairs stand out on the backs of my strong hands. . . .

I write: to clarify my life, to view myself from the perspective of time, to find whatever meanings may be found. I write to calm myself in a period of terrible tension, though I am less tense than those around me. And, finally, I write to escape from the use of the royal "We," the *pluralis majestatis*, and think of myself as essentially *Federico*. Thus whatever confessions I shall make are, like my dreams, for myself alone. And for posterity—who can say? So transient are the works of men that the words of the most powerful Caesars, graven on stone, are now covered by loam or vines or defaced by pigeon dung. Yet no one can affirm that I despise honor and fame, or hold contempt for my reputation in the future.

Except for the dangers involved, I would have preferred to write in the tongue I most relish, the everyday vernacular of my *bellissima Italia*—the language of my poems and love songs, the language of my adored Bianca, the language of beauty above all others. Or Latin, as a second choice, with its rhythm and cadence, the language of my chancery—but also, alas, the language of every prying priest or diplomatic secret agent. Next I would choose Greek, for its felicity and precision, a tongue still spoken by my subjects in Calabria, and which I learned in classic form from a Greek slave. Or, to the language of Provence, limpid and melodious in the mouths of the troubadours, I would offer little objection. This I prefer to the Norman French taught me by my mother before her fateful, early death when I was four; or the German taught me by order of my Hohenstaufen father, a Swabian who knew no Italian, and who preceded my mother to the grave by one year. I might, with some effort, have written in Spanish, the language I sometimes spoke with my first wife, the somber Costanza of Aragon—whom I married at the insistence of my guardian, Pope Innocent III, when I was fourteen and Costanza was not only a widow but ten full years older than I. Indeed, I might even have written a page or two in English, a complex, awkward, Anglo-Saxon language confusingly mingled with Norman French and Latin—a language I learned only in fragments from my third wife, the beautiful appleblossom-cheeked young princess Isabella, sister to King Henry III of England. Or, finally, for purposes of fully confusing spying eyes, I might have had a try at Hebrew, which I picked up as a kind of intellectual exercise during my Crusade in the Holy Land.

But, for my purposes, Arabic is not a bad choice. I learned Arabic during that most instructive period of my life, from seven to twelve, when, though a king, I might well have been a wandering beggar boy. Often I roamed the streets of Palermo unfed, uncared for, unloved, except when ordinary people from time to time took pity on me and shared both their food and affection. In the narrow *vicoli*, along the docks, in the *vucciria* (that clamorous market where all things salable—including men and women, boys and girls—were bought and sold), I listened to Arabic tongues. Soldiers, sailors, traders, slaves, holy men, magicians—from them I learned the *Arabian Nights* as told at the court of Harun al-Rashid, and the long poetic *Luzumiyat* of the skeptic al-Maarri. I mimicked perfectly the *mu'adhdhin* calling from the minarets, and the sleepy drone of the imam under the palm trees. With Arab boys I ran wild, thieving and indulging in sexual games. With an Arab girl my own age I discovered the tender words of first love; thus the child king became a man.

Ah yes . . . for me, Arabic is a language of many connotations. It was the tongue of choice in the bedroom of my second bride, the fourteen-year-old Yolanda of Syria; and also in the bedroom of her brother's wife, whom I made my mistress in spite of the husband's wildly insane jealousy. Arabic is a language of love and lyric beauty; and more significantly, is the present language of mathematics and astronomy, philosophy, and science. It has proved of supreme value to me, as when it enabled me to reach the mind of the powerful Sultan al-Kamil of Egypt, at a moment of great crisis for us both. It is the language of my bodyguard, who are incorruptible. But the importance of Arabic to me now lies in the fact that it is known fluently by few of my most intimate friends (not even by Piero, my *alter ego*)—and by none of my most virulent enemies.

As for this secret kept from the eyes of Pier della Vigna—my Piero—it is the only one. All else about me, except my dreams, he knows. Why then this sudden reticence on my part? He is my most trusted adviser, my private other self, my mirror. From the moment of our first meeting, in the prime of our youth, we have seen with the same vision and conversed with our eyes. Intuitively he has known how to write what I think. As lawyer and poet he has given my chancery a style and distinction unequaled in

Europe. I have created a special post for him: *Logothetes*—my "artist with words." He has become famous. I have heaped honors and wealth upon him; and, next to me, he is the most powerful man in the Empire. As is said at court, Piero "holds the two keys to Federico's heart"—as the Pope holds the two keys to Heaven. Those who would reach me must first reach Piero; and for this he is hated, feared, flattered. Again and again I have closed my ears to those who, through envy (that harlot of courts), would whisper against him. Even queens may turn traitor against their consorts; on the abiding loyalty of Pier della Vigna I would stake my own life.

But, these days, Piero is too emotionally and physically spent to bear another burden—even the smallest personal secret. He broods; the thin clean-shaven face darkens, the delicate mouth tightens, the sentient, so intelligent, pensive eyes overflow with melancholy. He talks little, paces much, refuses both wine and sex. He turns inward to feed upon himself. Perhaps all this is no more than the onset of middle life—for some men a terrible time, too old to be young and too young to be old. It grieves me sorely to note the deepening lines in his face, to record how thick is the gray in his short-cropped curls. He is but a shadow of that young, volatile, handsome Pier della Vigna who stimulated in me so great an intellectual and physical excitement. In this stranger I hardly recognize my Piero. I feel, too, that he is fatigued by more than the weight of time and the incubus of memories. I now detect in Piero a deep spiritual exhaustion, as though I have demanded too much and given too little.

Nor, as yet, have I been able to bring myself to speak about the emotional distress I sense in him. It would seem, I fear, an aspersion—almost an accusation of disloyalty. Alas, even between the closest of companions, the most inseparable of lovers, reservations remain—thoughts and feelings which may be implied but never said. And how shocking such thoughts and feelings would sometimes sound if translated into the harsh, irrevocable communication of words! I dare not, I will not! But not in words, not in actions—only in dreams does a man reveal himself fully; and a man's dreams are his alone . . . Piero's his . . . mine, mine. So—I keep this, my one secret.

I stroke my cheeks reflectively. They are smooth, for I am shaven every day. My German grandfather, the Emperor Friedrich I, called "Barbarossa," was famous for his red beard. It may be that, with passing centuries, the fame of his beard will transcend the fame of my deeds, but I hope not—for he was a savage conqueror, a violent man of fire and sword, hated the length and breadth of Italy. As I have not duplicated his beard, thus far I have tried not to duplicate his actions, striving to govern by persuasion and reason. My wars, without exception, have been forced upon me. But this is not to imply that I, too, cannot be ferocious when provoked; once with a single blow of my mailed foot I kicked open the belly of a trusted emir who had betrayed me. High have been some of the gallows I have erected.

While the character of Barbarossa was as evident to all men as his beard, my character is quite another matter. To some men I am one thing, and to some another. It is not surprising, though often annoying, that they describe my person and my habits in their own terms. Prostitutes, for example, complain that I have forbidden the use of love potions and magic charms for the phallus because I myself have no need of aphrodisiacs. (Actually, with wry humor I wear—like many men in Italy—a tiny coral *corno* alongside the cross on a golden chain around my neck; it is a horn shaped exactly like the phallus of a satyr, and is supposed to avert the Evil Eye, assure potency, bring good luck.) The mendicant friars, who are not notably fastidious, and whom I have forbidden to perform "miracles," complain that I bathe every day, even on Christmas and Easter. The monks, who are not noted for the absence of paunches, complain of the luxury of my court and the richness of the board—though I myself am temperate with the grape and eat but one simple meal each day. Doctors complain that I have jeopardized the relationship between physician and patient by regulating fees; wealthy landlords complain that I cripple incentive by confiscatory taxation; rich merchants complain that I destroy initiative by the organization of state monopolies for trade. But lawyers, happily, praise me as a monarch who relies not on whim but on law.

Bishops and cardinals, echoing the German barons, complain that I waste too much time on learning, and are aghast not that I read and write so many languages but that I read and write at all. They point out to me, accusingly, that the Emperor Charlemagne could barely write his name (in truth, he dabbled a goose quill in an inkpot, and the splotches were his signature). And more than one complaint has come from the Holy Father that I read Ovid and Catullus when I should be reading Scripture and Sant'

Agostino; that I encourage artists to paint secular pictures and stonecutters to carve the human form nude; that I dwell too much on the glory of ancient Greece and Rome and too little on *gloria in excelsis* and the "City of God."

One of my enemies, in a letter which was intercepted, described me as being ruthless, wily, subtle, evil and sensual—but he went on to compliment me by writing that I could be gracious, friendly and kind when I wished to show favor. He noted also that I speak with a compelling logic difficult to refute—though actually I say little in public, preferring to let others speak for me. One of my friends has been so candid as to describe my gaze into the faces of others as so direct, so steady, and so penetrating that my eyes resemble a snake's. This explains, perhaps, why some of my subjects persist in trembling with fear in my presence, though the prevailing explanation that I am surrounded by a supernatural—almost divine—aura is of course more gratifying.

Now that I have passed my fiftieth birthday I see myself, I hope, in the sober light of reality. Curiously, my appearance has not greatly changed since I was a young man, or even a boy, though with maturity I have become less slender. I have the same resilience of step, clarity of eye, steadiness of hand—and the same disarming smile, when I wish to charm or ingratiate. I remain tanned and weathered by sun and open air. I bear armor lightly, and *amore* as well. I can, now as then, spend twenty-four hours on horseback without excessive fatigue, shoot an arrow straight to the bull's eye, thrust a sword with sufficient force to pin a man to the wall. I am now much better at solving abstruse problems in mathematics; I have read in detail the ancient poets and philosophers, and I have attempted many experiments to explain difficult questions in science. Now, as then, I am in love with all things beautiful. So my body has not lost its youthful zest, nor my mind its native curiosity. As my body has grown stronger, my mind has broadened and enlarged its scope. With all this I have retained my sense of *jovialitas* and serene self-confidence—proven of value in many dark and dangerous hours.

As a youth I was called "the golden-haired boy from Apulia." It is true that I was vain about my hair, then worn shoulder-length, as I am now vain about the majesty of my Empire. It is symptomatic that when I came to cast the golden coins known as *augustales*, bearing my image, I cut and combed my locks to resemble the Emperor Augustus, and wore a laurel wreath and toga. Nevertheless the sinewy neck, the outthrust jaw, the ironic but sensuous mouth, the straight nose, the wide-set, suggestively smiling eyes are uniquely mine. Is it a handsome face? Yes, I think so—for certainly by prevailing standards it could not be called ugly. Is it a noble face? Yes, I think so—not because I am the son and grandson of kings, but because it bears an expression of nobility.

But the noblest of kings spills ink like the commonest of scribes. Mine smears, and I wait for it to dry. My gaze wanders, tracing the oriental patterns in the thick Persian rug on the tent floor . . . the elaborate Arabic embroidery on the stuffed silk cushions . . . the diverse watermarks in my writing paper. In the paper are figures: a castle, an eagle, a six-pointed star. I ponder the significance of the symbols, and marvel that the secret of paper manufacture came from far-distant China by way of the Arabs. My mind floats with memories evanescent as dreams: blond boy-King . . . bronzed Emperor in young manhood . . . empurpled Caesar . . . triumphs, triumphs . . . love and glory. . . .

And now . . . ?

Ah! For me the luxury of fantasy is past. I must weigh with my own cool logic, as opposed to the hot passion of my enemies, the events which have brought me to this point. I must contemplate with candid realism those powerful forces which, counterposed through the years, have carried me with seeming inevitability like the moth to the flame. Even the boldest of the astrologers now shrinks from casting my horoscope. But not I! I foresee a struggle of titans; but the outcome—the outcome is obscure.

Tonight, as for days past, I am waiting. I wait for news which will determine the course of all the rest of my years. I wait with impatience, and a clear premonition of danger. I wait for the return from France of emissaries I have sent to the Council called in Lyons by Pope Innocent IV. Innocent, my former friend, who fled from Rome clad in armor—to become my present nemesis. The Council of a handful, hand-picked by the Pope and anointed with the gall and wormwood of hatred! Invidious gathering—expressly designed to seize secular authority and depose me from the Roman throne! We—*Fridericus Secundus, Holy Roman Emperor, august Caesar, King of Germania and Lombardia, Toscana and Italia, Calabria and Sicilia, King of Jerusalem, sustainer of the Roman pontificate, champion of the Christian faith.*

So—an Innocent Council indeed! Secure behind the bastion of the Alps, the Pope's hirelings already have drawn up an indictment against me, an indictment cleverly designed to confuse the basic issue of Church versus State. Piously and for the greater glory of God, they proclaim publicly such a list of crimes as to make even the criminal himself gasp:

The Emperor has murdered his wives—they charge. Surrounded by eunuchs and Saracen guards, the Empresses one by one have disappeared into the "labyrinth of the Emperor's Gomorrah," and have perished by witchcraft or poison.

The Emperor maintains a harem of lascivious Saracen women—they charge. The harem is called the "labyrinth of Gomorrah," and in it are perpetrated all sins of the flesh. (But not one word about the Emperor's Christian mistresses, the sin of adultery, or his natural sons and daughters.)

The Emperor practices "scarcely veiled sodomy"—they charge. He has not only a Gomorrah but a Sodom as well. They point at the handsome boy pages drawn from all classes, noble to slave, at the overall youthfulness of the court, at the State maintenance of exceptional students, at the elegant young Negro musicians richly costumed and taught to blow silver trumpets exclusively for the Emperor's pleasure. Mentioned also is the name of Pier della Vigna, by innuendo, or openly but in whispers; thus friendship is transformed into calumny.

The Emperor has murdered his first-born son—they charge. After rising in armed revolt, as King of Germany, against his father, the heroic youth was captured, thrown into a dungeon, and cruelly put to death by his father's bloodthirsty orders.

The Emperor has built no churches or monasteries—they charge. Instead, he has erected luxurious castles for his many concubines; constructed an entire town, complete with mosques, inhabited only by Saracens; established a school of medicine for the dissection of cadavers; founded a university where freethinking and apostasy are encouraged. In a Pope's own words, "he has built schools for the perdition of souls."

The Emperor has accepted costly gifts from Mohammedan princes—they charge. He has ignored the tragic slaughter of Christian crusaders; his own Saracen warriors brutally rape Christian women and girls in the mosques. Worse, he willingly traffics with infidels.

The Emperor harbors heretics, tolerates Muslims, defends Jews

—they charge. He has deliberately brought to his court scholars, mathematicians, astronomers, philosophers who have written new and heretical books; or from Arabic, Hebrew and Greek, translated many ancient books—pagan, un-Christian, and surely inspired by the Devil. He draws no significant line between Christians, Muslims and Jews—treating all as equal.

The Emperor, by associating with heretics, is himself guilty of heresy—they charge. His laws against heresy do not atone for his heretical personal views: he has denied the immortality of the soul, doubted the Virgin birth, scoffed at the Holy Sacraments. With his wizards, he has performed blasphemous experiments, seeking to disprove the existence of the human soul. He believes neither in God nor in the dogmas affirmed by the one Holy Church.

The Emperor has willfully made war on the Church—they charge. He has taken up arms against the Holy Father, the cardinals and bishops, wishing that they should be poor and go on foot. He would seize the riches and treasures of the Church, which has showered him with blessings and divine grace, for himself and his sons. He has seized and imprisoned high prelates, and driven a Pope to the grave.

The Emperor is the Antichrist, as foretold—they charge. "The Emperor," writes the Cardinal Raniero, venting Papal hatred, "has three rows of teeth in his jaws, for the monks and the clerics and the blameless laity, and mighty claws of iron. Some he has devoured, others he has slain with torments, and the remnant he has trampled underfoot in his dungeons. Hell-hound shall he be called, like Herod! Crueler than Nero shall he be known! He has in his forehead the horn of power, and a mouth which spews monstrous things. He thinks himself able to transform the laws and the times and to lay truth in the dust. Destroy the name and fame, the seed and sapling of this Babylonian! Let mercy forget him!"

I pause in wrath, I gag on such words. I remove the heavy gold signet ring from my left little finger; I study it. It shows an eagle in half flight. Is the Papal tiara, I wonder, to become the political signet for the whole world? Twice already, in my struggles against the temporal power of the Papacy, I have been excommunicated. In all the churches of Christendom, except in my own Realm, the sentence of excommunication was read by priests amid flickering tapers and the sounding of bells. All persons adhering to me were excommunicated. No masses, no marriages, no absolutions, no rites for the dead could be celebrated in any town loyal to my standard. The very gates of Hell were opened; the heat of leaping flames became a fearsome threat. Nor have I yet received absolution. What is left to face—damnation timed with deposition from the throne? This is the ultimate blow—but one!

Only one instrument of fury remains to be invoked against me: murder. More than once have I escaped assault by the narrowest of margins, and I wonder if my enemies again will have recourse to the technique of dagger or of poison. I take reassurance from the oracle which predicted my death *sub flore*, with no hint of the loss of my crown. More bitter than the prospect of death itself is the apocalyptic image of an Emperor who is both moral leper and physical monster—an image to become firmly fixed in men's minds for generations to come, no doubt. For the hosts of priests—if not devils—will give my soul no rest.

My life itself, the record of my deeds, is the best answer to the crimes charged against me. In every half-truth is a lie, and in every lie a half-truth. Demons, it is said, were once angels who fell from grace. Neither demon nor angel am I—but a man.

I

AGNELLO FRA I LUPI

I

IN TRUTH, there are many unexplained mysteries about my birth, but they touch more on the personal and political than on the supernatural. How was my mother extracted from a nunnery and forced to marry my father? Why did so many years pass before I was conceived? (I cannot believe this delay was accidental.) How did it happen that I was born not at court or in one of the cities, but hidden away in a tiny village near Ancona, far, far from Sicily? Why did my mother hardly wait to recover from her confinement before whisking me off to a castle in Foligno, placing me under the care of the Duchess of Spoleto while she herself hurried back to Palermo? Why did my father see me only once? Why did my mother leave me in Foligno until after my father's death? And why did she call me Costantino, though I was baptized Fridericus?

All these questions I have asked the good Archbishop Berardo of Palermo; but, though he was a friend of my mother's, he can give me little satisfaction. At the time of these events he was Bishop of Bari, only later being appointed to Palermo, after my mother had used her influence with the Pope. It was not, actually, until my coronation—when I was so tender of age—that he came fully into my life. Other persons who might give answers have either died or vanished, or profess to know nothing.

My mother was a Hauteville: Costanza, daughter of Ruggero II, last memorable Norman king of Sicily. When I was an impoverished boy, wandering about the streets of Palermo, I used to go sometimes to the Church of the Martorana; with three conical domes on top it looked like a fairy-tale mosque. There, hoping for a miracle, I suppose, I sat in its cool recesses amid a forest of marble columns for an hour or more—all the while staring at the mosaic of Christ crowning my grandfather Ruggero.

The Christ was a giant figure; my grandfather much smaller, but clad in a brilliant Byzantine robe of gold. Yet, except for Christ's halo and the fact that my grandfather's beard was blond, the faces were little different; and I came to the conclusion that by no accident was my grandfather portrayed as so Christlike. More interesting still was my grandfather's crown. Just then I would have been thankful for a single one of its jewels. Methodically I calculated the worth of each stone in bread and clothing. (Perhaps the knowledge of poverty is one of the reasons I am noted today for my generosity.) Though I reminded myself that I too was a king, I could not help brooding on the decline of my family; and always I was filled with longing for the mother I had so briefly known.

After my grandfather Ruggero's death, the kingdom fell into confusion under a succession of weak rulers—a ripe invitation to new conquests. Within the span of thirty years my grandfather Barbarossa (through my father) stretched out an acquisitive hand. But though the fruit was ripe, it was not yet ready to fall.

The original Norman wrenching of Sicily from the Arabs had not been easy—unlike William's conquest of Britain from the crude Anglo-Saxons at about the same time. The Arabs had ruled Sicily for two hundred and fifty years, building an advanced civilization on the legacy of Byzantium, Rome, Carthage, and Greece, for civilization itself had come early to Sicilia. The Arab arms and strategy reflected the experience of techniques developed through centuries. But they succumbed. The Norman campaign began under Roger de Hauteville, who recorded for history that he had not so much as a horse, and so was forced to steal one. It must have been a very good horse, fully equal to its master, for Roger's campaign was remarkably successful. Once Palermo had fallen, the final decision was hardly in doubt, though many years were required to complete the conquest.

Some chroniclers have said that the Normans were but crusading adventurers who fell in love with a semitropical paradise, and conquered it to avoid going home. In a sense, this is true. But Normans landed in Apulia long before the first crusade. They were victorious in Sicily only because they came with fresh vigor into a decadent land, and their policies, along with their blood, infused a new strength and greatness. The Norman rule, for more than a century, was outstanding. Norman and Arab lived together in tolerance and harmony; learning flourished; a brilliant new architecture appeared; Norman arms seemed forever invincible. Yet by the end of my grandfather's reign, processes of disintegration were already at work; and rich, beautiful, languorous, tragic Sicily once more was on the verge of chaos.

My poor mother, who was born in the very year of her famed father's death (he had passed sixty), was wildly tossed by the winds of misfortune. Though she was the last legitimate heir to the throne, as she grew older the quarrels of the nobles forced her often to seek sanctuary in convents—or perhaps she really preferred a life of withdrawal and retreat from the troublesome world. Why had she spurned marriage? Had she finally taken the veil, as rumor says; or only first vows? From the Convent of Santa Chiara in Napoli she was snatched as a bride for my father. Once, when I was passing through Napoli, I went to the abbess and demanded the records. Alas and alack, I was told, the old records had been destroyed in a fire the very year of Queen Costanza's departure to marry the German Emperor's son. With no more substance than the wispy smoke from Vesuvio, I retreated from the cloister, no questions answered.

They were married in Milano, in the piazza of the Church of Sant' Ambrogio: beneath the church lay the bones of the saint, bleached and gruesome, wearing a scarlet robe, a jeweled crown, and embroidered gloves stuffed with wool. Under bare-branched elms and poplars as lofty as the bell tower, a special pavilion was constructed so that thousands could see. With all the pomp so loved by my grandfather Barbarossa, my mother was accompanied by a hundred and fifty mounted knights, their horses bedecked in gold and silver and draped with silk and furs.

In the old brick church itself was a magical figure, an awesome naked Hercules, a marble which had survived from ancient times. So long as the statue stood in the basilica, ran the legend, so long would the Empire stand. There is reason to believe that my mother, on her way to confession before marriage, strove with all her might to topple the statue from its base; and, failing, beat it with her fists and scratched it with her nails.

My mother, it seems, did not like Germans. She found them coarse and uncivilized, and is reputed to have said their guttural tongue sounded in her ears like the barking of dogs. Though she had never before met my father, who was so many years the younger, she must certainly have known that throughout Italy he was called "Heinrich the Cruel." He was a gloomy autocrat, somber of mood, gaunt of countenance, frail of body, with the manners and movements of an old man, though he was not yet twenty. His beard was scant, his face pale, his eyes the cold ice-blue of an Alpine glacier. Never was he known to smile or laugh. Such was my progenitor. I can never bear to think of the first night he took my mother to his bed—how coldly, without pleasure, he must have calculated my conception, how inwardly she must have repulsed him with all her heart.

My father became Emperor, as Heinrich VI, on the death of that impetuous old man, my grandfather Barbarossa. He was leading a crusade to the Holy Land, but never arrived because he was drowned while hastily fording a river just in sight of his goal. This event occurred only four years before my birth. Promptly my father launched into schemes of conquest which would make him the highest feudal overlord of lands from Britain and Normandy to Constantinople, from the Polish east to Morocco, from Antioch to Jerusalem and Egypt. It was he who captured Richard Coeur de Lion, and thus succeeded in reducing England temporarily to a tributary vassal state.

As for Sicily, its crown came to him as part of my mother's dowry—and that, of course, is why he married her. Nevertheless, he had to fight for the Sicilian lands, and the conquest took time—as well as most of the money he got from Richard's ransom. It was not until Christmas day, in the year of our Lord 1194, that he entered Palermo in triumph, to the ringing of bells, the clatter of armor, and the blare of trumpets.

Next day, though he did not know it, his Queen bore an heir. In the north of Italy, in the Marche of Ancona near the Adriatic Sea lies the village of Jesi, its serrated walls set like a crown of stone on a misty blue hill. There, far, far from Palermo, I was born. Since then Jesi has become a sacred place, a kind of second Bethlehem for many thousands of pilgrims each year. I myself went once, incognito, to observe it; and once again, with full panoply of Empire, to give it added dignity.

In Palermo, on my birth date, my father rounded up all my mother's Norman relatives, with all the Norman lords who disliked a German on their throne, and disposed of the lot by the simple process of burning them alive. He exhumed the body of Tancred—who, though illegitimate, had briefly held the throne—and publicly beheaded the corpse. The only surviving potential heir, Tancred's son and my mother's half-nephew, a boy of six or seven, was first blinded and then castrated—fortunately he did not survive the shock. At last my father felt safe in his new Sicilian dominion, though with the knowledge of my birth he felt much safer.

My father wasted no time in securing my election as King of the Germans, at a meeting of princes in Frankfurt—thus, with my hereditary Kingdom of Sicily, attaining a union of north and south. It was a policy not liked much by the Pope (Celestine III, then a feeble octogenarian), who recalled that the boundaries of the Kingdom of Sicily lay, not in Sicily, but close to Rome—and he felt the lands of the Church being squeezed between the jaws of a nutcracker. It was a policy not liked by my mother, either. She foresaw that soon I would be transported to Germany, to Swabia, the ancestral home of the Hohenstaufens—there to grow up in the dark castle of Waiblingen, learning little more than the handling of arms and how to "bark like a dog." Why did she leave me in Foligno, so far from Palermo, so far from her breast? I can only suppose that with my father I would have learned as my native speech German, the tongue she abhorred. (She persisted in confusing all Germans and the German language itself with her dislike of my father—an error I deplore.) As for my father, he was content to leave me alone—the closer to Germany the better, he thought.

Not long after my second birthday, my father commanded my uncle, Philipp of Swabia, a mild-mannered man who preferred singing the Hours and Responsories with choir boys to jousting with the knights—ordered him, I say, to come with all haste to Italy and fetch me back to Germany. But for some reason, perhaps love of the choir boys or dread of the road, Philipp was slow in coming. And suddenly my father fell ill, so ill that he lay close to death.

There seems little doubt, today, that the Pope, aided by my mother—or my mother, aided by the senile Pope—contrived to poison my father. Through his spies, my father learned of the truth. When he recovered, all those involved in the plot, nobles and clerics alike (with the two key exceptions), he put to public torture and death. He cluttered the landscape with gallows, hanging suspects two or three at a time. He forced my mother to attend while the conspirators were scalded with hot lead, broken on the rack, pulled apart by horses, mounted alive on wheels high on poles for carrion birds to pluck out their eyes.

She wept, and covered her face; but he demanded that she stare straight at the spectacle without flinching. When he called in his jesters to make sport with the jerking limbs, bloody heads, and quivering bodies, my mother fainted away. Afterward, she is said to have heard screams in the night for weeks on end, and she became wan and thin with deep-sunken eyes.

A few months later, in September, while hunting wild boar in the forests on the slopes of Mt. Etna, my father was seized with severe stomach cramps and dysentery. He was carried to Messina, by Markward von Anweiler, his interpreter, chief adviser, and hunting companion. He grew better for a number of days; then he died. He was only thirty-two. At once Markward von Anweiler, a bearded, beer-barrel of a man, who was ambitious in proportion to his size, proposed himself to my mother as Vice Regent, uttering threats and implying all sorts of disasters if his services were not accepted. First secretly, then in bold defiance, he hastened to organize as a fighting band all the German nobles in Sicily who had held fief under my father.

Finally my uncle Philipp of Swabia had undertaken his mission, and had not only reached Italy, but was resting on the reedy shores of Lake Bolsena, hardly two days' journey away from me. There, word reached him of my father's death, and simultaneously the news that all Italy was aflame against Germans. The point was made sharper by the arrows which flew from nowhere, by the stones which rolled down steep hillsides, by the fires set in bivouac. My uncle turned north on the Via Cassia, and fled.

Was this destiny? A direct intervention of fate? Or the stars, as some say? Thus, by only a few hours' march not marched, was the main course of my future decided; I was to be Italian, not German. I was to grow up among the tropical gardens of Sicily instead of the black forests of Germany; among riotous pink and red geraniums and purple bougainvillaea instead of edelweiss and cabbages; under blue and sun-hot skies instead of gray and snow-laden clouds; in elegant and beautiful palaces like the Castello della Zisa (in Arabic, *Aziz*—in Italian, *Splendido*), with its famous mosaic ramp designed as a shimmering fountain, instead of barren and ugly heaps of stone perched on craggy fastnesses; among the most cultured and polyglot people then existing in Europe, and not among knights rigid outside and in—with armor, ignorance and the stultifying code of chivalry.

Without delay my mother sent for me, and, though I was not

yet quite three years old, from our first meeting I derive my most vivid memory of childhood. She had me brought to her as Queen, seated on the Norman throne of multicolored Arab mosaic in the great hall of her ancestral palace. She was dressed all in black, wearing on her head a tall peaked cap from which a thin black veil descended. She drew aside the veil, revealing a pale face and deep-blue eyes ringed by dark circles.

"Take my hand and kiss it, Costantino," she said, "I am your mother, the Queen. I have banished all the Germans, and very soon you shall be crowned King of Sicily!" Then she clutched me in her arms and smothered me with hugs and kisses.

I felt deliciously secure, and returned the kisses. How was I to know that the Germans would not stay banished?

2

It was not until Whitsunday of the following year that I was crowned King. In the interval before my coronation, several events occurred—in Rome and in Germany—of the greatest significance to my future. But of them, of course, I knew nothing, feeling only the cumulative excitement of the approaching coronation itself—which I must have regarded as something like Epiphany, when the good witch, Befana, brings presents to children.

What did it mean to my childish mind when I heard the bells pealing news of the election of a new Pope? The news that the famous Cardinal, Lotario dei Conti, was to become Innocent the Third—a Pope young and vigorous, able and itching to rule? Or did I pay the slightest attention when a courier from Germany brought word to my mother that Otto the Welf, a hulking simpleton of a man, had risen to contest the claims of my uncle, Philipp of Waiblingen, to the Empire—both blandly ignoring the fact that *I* had been elected King of the Germans, and was next in line for the title of Emperor. Who could have foreseen, and explained to a child, that rivers of blood would flow between Welf and Waiblingen—or as they came to be called when the feud crossed the Alps, thanks to Innocent's meddling, *Guelf* and *Ghibelline*? Fire and water; black and white; cold and hot; death and life; Guelf and Ghibelline—opposites all. Not much time was to pass before even children my age played at the game, hurling names, then stones, at one another. And how short is the step from wooden sword to Damascus steel—You *Guelf!* You damned *Ghibelline!* Blind hate—for a name, a banner, a color, a party, a policy, a Pope, a King. It is love which gives life, but hate which brings death. Already the ugly winds of hate had begun to swirl around my coronation.

Meanwhile, preparations continued at a feverish pace. My mother, though lacking in knights and armed men, was determined to show the world what glories yet remained in the Norman Kingdom of Sicily. Artisans worked day and night setting jewels; weavers loomed clothes of gold and silver; tailors cut new gowns of silks and satins; bakers invented new recipes for cakes and *torte*; hunters sought the rarest birds and game; carpenters brought hammers and crosscut saws to build elevated stands along the palm-shaded route to the cathedral; rug-makers wove a single crimson carpet the entire length of the aisle. But the activity I liked best was my stealthy eaves-dropping on the *trovatori*, who were practicing new songs in my honor.

All this, in my honor! I felt, certainly, very important—bigger than a man already, stronger than a knight, smarter than a wizard. As powerful, maybe, as a sultan. When people bowed low to me (and everyone did, except my mother), I longed to *be* a sultan, so that I might command them to bump their heads against the fascinating multicolored tiles set in geometric patterns on the palace floors. All that I lacked, it seemed, was the ability to fly; and this I accomplished in my dreams—wondering, when I awoke, if I might not accomplish it in fact with artificial wings.

At last the great day arrived. I was bathed, perfumed, and dressed in a robe of purple and gold, adorned with six Byzantine enamels of saints and six golden eagles with wings of lapis lazuli. My mother, who had fasted and prayed the whole night through, was ecstatic: she said that I looked like an angel, and my short blond ringlets would be perfect to accommodate the crown. In the cavalcade to the cathedral, in the brilliant June sun of mid-morning, I was borne on a litter, that I might be seen and cheered by the thousands.

Behind me, carried aloft like a holy relic, was the coronation mantle, made for my grandfather King Ruggero and meant for my shoulders as a grown man. My mother had told me much about this mantle, and I was very excited at seeing it for the first time—many people thought it was a magic garment. So potent was its legend that I myself, years later, added it to the regalia of the Holy Roman Empire, and it became world famous as *der Kaisermantel.* It was a great cloak of heavy scarlet silk, showing two groups of beasts separated by a palm tree—no doubt the Tree of Life. In each group a lion was attacking a camel already fallen to its knees. They were embroidered in gold and outlined with blue silk thread and thousands upon thousands of tiny pearls. The only stones were three huge rubies; the clasps were of solid gold. Around the hem, worked in pearls, was a Cufic inscription which my mother had translated in part: "May the King be beloved and thrive, living in splendor, renown, and magnificence; may his hopes and wishes be fulfilled; may his days and nights be spent in enjoyment without end or change; may generosity, honor, and happiness go with him all the days of his life. Made in the capital of Sicilia in the year 528 of the Hegira." And, as the mantle passed in the procession, a sudden hush fell over the people, a feeling of awe for a holy thing.

As for me, I neither smiled nor waved, but, as instructed, sat solemn with the majesty of royalty and heavy with the dignity of the anointed of God. Only once did I feel small or insignificant, when by chance I gazed upward at the cathedral's mighty Norman towers. So many stones, I thought, set one upon another to reach so high; I was made dizzy at the thought, I who had wanted wings—and suddenly I was filled with concern for the stonemasons and was glad to be a king. But the chanting choir and the glittering magnificence of the gold-and-jewel-encrusted vestments of the priests drove all other thoughts from my mind. In moments I would be King . . . !

First I was given Holy Communion, so that when I was crowned I would have within me the flesh and blood of our Lord and Saviour Jesus Christ. As I passed down the aisle for Communion the faces blurred before me, and I recalled only that my mother walked behind me dressed in silver and carrying white lilies like a bride. The high-pitched chant of the priest reached me, and my Latin was so fluent that I followed easily all the words:

"*AGNUS DEI, qui tollis peccata mundi: miserere nobis.*
AGNUS DEI, qui tollis peccata mundi: miserere nobis.
AGNUS DEI, qui tollis peccata mundi: dona nobis pacem."

Agnus Dei? I thought. This puzzled me. Who was the lamb of God? Was it I? A lamb could be King? Or was Jesus the Lamb, He who was King of Heaven? Then His people must be sheep, not like the fierce knights I had seen, swaggering in chain mail or tossing bright plumes on their helmets. Just sheep? But I had become King only because of my father's death, while Jesus was King only because He Himself had been crucified.

I felt guilt for my father's death, guilt for Jesus' crucifixion. So confused did I become that I choked on my wafer and wine. And this is the first memory I have of Berardo.

"Easy, my son," I heard a voice—a kind and soothing voice—whisper, "take it slowly, slowly."

I looked at the rich vestments, at the crosier, the miter, the gloves and the ring; I looked up and straight into the bearded face of the Archbishop. His eyes, under eyebrows like two wide inverted V's, were solemn but smiling—and suddenly he winked! To me he seemed very old (though he was only about thirty), and I was astonished that a man of God should wink. Yet in the instant I was as certain as if it had been revealed by the Virgin that I would be his friend for life—and he mine. What a splendid father *he* would make, I thought; why hadn't my mother married *him*?

And from that instant my attitude toward him has been that of a son for a respected father—a respect beyond the powers of any natural father to inspire, because free of the emotion of jealousy or the more astringent emotion of hatred. Curiously, to me Berardo always has appeared old, even when his full beard was brown and silky—not, as it later became, pure white like a prophet's. Astute, worldly, patient, this was the man who would one day teach me to play chess, refusing to relinquish his instruction until I was capable of beating him three times out of five—with each victory exclaiming the Arabo-Persian words, *shah mat*—"the king is dead!"

But the king was not dead—the new king was very much alive. The Norman crown—a narrow band of iron, engraved and set with a few large simple jewels and surmounted by three ornamented points—I glimpsed before me. Then suddenly I felt its weight upon my head. I remember the face of the Archbishop Berardo: he smiled with reassurance. All was well. Of the ceremony I remember nothing else except the smell of incense and the multitudes of winking candles, winking, winking like the Archbishop himself. . . .

That night, after the pomp and wild excitement of the day, I dreamed that Berardo was both God and my father. I floated on the crimson coronation mantel as upon a magic carpet. And I continued to hear the joyous cries of my people: "*Christus vincit, Christus regnat, Christus imperat . . . !*"

3

MY MOTHER's death, a few months after my coronation, changed everything. It is a mystery that I was not immediately murdered—as is also the fact that I survived throughout boyhood. I can only conclude that, to certain conspirators, I was more valuable alive than dead. How helpless is a child king!

It was Berardo who brought me the news when the church bells were ringing for matins. I recall that suddenly they changed their rhythm, and began the solemn tolling of a dirge. Berardo bowed slightly, then hoisted me into his arms, holding me so that I caught a whiff of incense from his beard. "My esteemed young Lord," he said in a voice calm but nevertheless charged with emotion, "alas, my son, God took your mother unto Himself at dawn this morning. But as this is the will of God, we must not cry."

In spite of his injunction I wept profuse and bitter tears. "I want my Mama!" I shouted. "I don't want God to have her! You must tell Him so, Berardo, because I am the King!"

That night my nurse Lucia comforted me with warm kisses and soothing words. Lucia was small, dark, hairy, fat, and like all Sicilian women wore tiny gold circlets through the pierced lobes of her ears. "Your Mama is in Paradise, seated at the feet of Jesus with the blessed Virgin His mother," she whispered, giving me a crucifix to kiss. "Angels crowd around, angels with white feathers in their wings, waving palm fronds and singing hosannas. Your Mama sees and knows everything you do. Someday you'll be a great King, and she'll be very proud of you. . . ."

Slowly my sniffles ceased, and I began to dream vaguely of manhood—all the while wishing my nurse would not eat so much garlic in her *pasta*. And next day, even though the Archbishop Berardo officiated, I was much disturbed by the Requiem

Mass for the dead: it was all too much like my coronation, though it was my mother who lay motionless, with hands crossed, before the altar—not I. Perhaps that is why, ever afterward, I have been unable to sit through any Mass without a feeling of distress, an obscure unease almost amounting to anxiety. This I control by doing mathematical problems in my head, or speculating on art or on science. I do not, however, like to decide matters of policy while the priests are making such a din in my ears: I tend to become too severe. In retrospect I see my mother's dear, dead, trusting face. . . .

For she put her trust in no less person than the Pope. Innocent III was named in her will as my guardian; he become also feudal overlord of Sicily and Regent of the Kingdom—though of course he remained in Rome. Unaware that we had become woefully poor, my mother specified that Innocent was to be reimbursed for all his expenses, and paid in addition each year thirty thousand gold tarens—no small sum in any country. As for my person, I was given over to a Council of Bishops; and the Bishop of Troia, called Gualtiero di Palearia, was named Chancellor. Why was Berardo left completely out of the governing council? Obviously the will had been written with the approval of the Pope, and for some reason Berardo had not found favor in the Pope's eyes.

Hardly a week passed before Berardo was in fact put under what amounted to house arrest, forbidden to see me on pain of death. Actually he was helpless, and was himself in constant danger of murder. He told me afterward how, before tasting food, he fed reluctantly a portion of each meal to the cherished little black and white Volpino dog he kept at his side; but he was at a loss for a winetaster until he hit upon the scheme of forcing his parakeet to drink. (And it was not long before the luckless creature became a regular guzzler, burbling aloud with the joy of Silenus himself—poor *pappagallo!*)

Possibly my life was saved by the very fact that I was the Pope's ward. As I learned in later years, a Papal Legate, the Cardinal Cencio Savelli (afterward to become Pope Honorius III) was charged with my physical protection, though he had evinced little enthusiasm for the task. It is certain that Innocent, astute though devious, found me more useful alive than dead, for he was occupied with the grand design of a world empire in which I played a part. And as for those lesser men, those bishops who ran the affairs of the Kingdom in my name—they found my name a veritable "Open Sesame" when it came to acquiring lands, fiefs, titles and fortunes for their relatives and friends. Some years later it cost me much effort to undo their handiwork. There was another factor, too: the revolt of the Sicilian German barons under Markward von Anweiler. The bishops were very busy in my defense, they told the world; but in reality they were very busy defending the Pope's fief—as Markward bore as great enmity toward the Pope as he did toward me. I was not the Sovereign, said Markward, but only the "supposed" son of my father; and, apparently believing in the big lie, he put out the story that I had been sired by a butcher. He, Markward, had been designated by the Emperor Heinrich as Regent of the Kingdom—that was his claim. So the German knights took up arms, while my defenders payed not the slightest attention to me.

To get me out from under foot, the bishops shifted me, with my nurse, quietly out of the Royal Palace and into the Castello di Maredolce—for me, as it happened, a most fortunate move. There I discovered a friend—and the memory is as sweet as the waters of the Castello's artificial sea. The Castello itself had been one of the joys of the Normans, who had found it intact and exquisite when they conquered Palermo, and ever afterward had lavished upon it the utmost in care and attention. The Castello had been built by a Saracen emir, about the year 1000, in fulfillment of an exotic dream. It was designed to reflect, in the fresh clear waters of a man-made lake, not only the delicate arches and pink domes of the structure itself, but also the green palms, white oleanders, and scarlet hibiscus of the gardens. For two hundred years Arab voyagers sang of the delights of its fountains, the perfume of its flowers, the elegance of its peacocks and birds of paradise, the magic enchantment of its shimmering reflection.

When I arrived, I was greeted by a formal bow from the castellan, an old man who had been appointed by the last of the Normans. He was short-bearded, vastly dignified. From the bow he straightened himself with difficulty. "We are greatly honored, my grandson and I," he said, indicating the young man who stood behind him, "greatly honored by your Majesty's presence in the Castello. You will find us faithful and devoted to your person. We wish, with your permission, to welcome you with a small gift. . . ."

The young man stepped forward, bowed, and placed in my hands a scroll of papyrus with gilt knobs top and bottom, and a strip of yellowed parchment on which a word was written in red. I held it gingerly, as though it might be dangerous.

"It is an ancient book," the young man said, "the *Aeneid*, by the poet Vergil; it is the story of the greatest Roman hero, a man of destiny, Aeneas—"

Vergil—already I knew that name; it fell frequently from people's tongues. Vergil was regarded with awe and so were his works, for he was considered the greatest of all magicians. In one of his poems, the Fourth Eclogue (which later I was to read with fascination) he was said to have predicted the birth of Christ, though he lived and wrote in the time of the Emperor Augustus. And in years to come this very same poem was said to apply to me—oh far-sighted Vergil! But of this as yet I knew nothing.

"A book!" I said in dismay. "I cannot read—"

"We will read it together," the young man said, and reassured me further: "Soon you will read it for yourself. Then you will understand this gift."

"Only a book—" I murmured, and the young man laughed. I looked up, and seeing that he laughed not unkindly, I laughed too.

Guglielmo Franciscus was a student, for he wished to become, like his grandfather, a learned man. Though he was only eighteen or so, he seemed to me certainly the wisest person in the world, and certainly the most admirable. A scholar, but no monk, he wore hose of red and yellow, a red doublet, and a curling yellow feather in a red cap. His curls were black and tumultuous as lava, while his eyes were as dark and bright and inquisitive as a bird's. What was he? Saracen? Greek? Or ancient Siculian—a descendant of the people who inhabited the island long before the Greeks set foot upon it? This latter, I think, for he was very small in stature—though his body was perfectly formed, harmonious and graceful. I used to copy the motions he made with his hands while he was speaking, and the rhythm of his walk. His smile was habitual and exuberant, but his eyes became solemn when he bade me to get on with my studies. And I did so—for I had come to adore him.

His grandfather had pointed out to the bishops that I had no way of learning my ABC's except from a Saints' Calendar made in Ravenna, and young Maestro Franciscus could take on the job of instruction. The bishops did not bother to send so much as a friar to teach me gospel, but hired Guglielmo as my tutor for everything—paying him now and then when they felt like it. They must have considered the investment a waste of money, for surely they doubted I would live to grow up. As for me, I was quite lost with happiness, for I had acquired a complete family at last: Lucia, my nurse; the old man, whom I was soon calling *Nonno*; and Guglielmo, my idol. I learned to read in an astonishing hurry, and Guglielmo said I was precocious—but I did not know what the word meant, though I liked its cadence.

On Sundays, all the Christians dressed in their best clothes and walked abroad in the late afternoon, visiting, flirting, gossiping. The girls walked arm in arm; and the young men also walked arm in arm, staring at the girls. The streets always swarmed. Often Guglielmo took me with him. He said that I ought to know something of the world outside the Castello, if someday I would be a great ruler. When we went to the city we crossed the river Oreto by the Ponte dell'Ammiraglio, noted architecturally for its wide and harmonious arches, as Guglielmo carefully informed me.

"This bridge was built by your grandfather King Ruggero," Guglielmo said, "in honor of his famous admiral, Giorgio of Antioch. Many fine galleys were in your grandfather's fleet."

"Where," said I, "is Antioch?"

"In the Levante," Guglielmo said, "—a country of Arabs. The Holy City Jerusalem is there, too."

"Someday I'll go to Jerusalem," I said firmly. "You'll see!"

"I'll go with you," he said.

"You must never leave me, 'Lielmo," I said. "I command it!"

But my commands were worth little, for at playtime he frisked with me more as puppy than as king. Nevertheless I always sensed in him a certain respect, almost deference, as if I were no ordinary *fanciullo* but someone definitely apart. He never called me "My Lord," as did the others, but merely "Federico," yet there was a particular quality in the way he pronounced my name.

I forgot all my sorrows, and for three years worked and played with zest—and most of the time I could not tell work from play. Along with my letters I learned the elements of swordplay, how to bend a bow, and to ride bareback on a lovely little Arab mare. I leaped, ran, jumped, climbed, wrestled, swam, and practiced the *balestra* (though I could load the arrow with quick accuracy, my hands were not yet strong enough to crank the *girelle* which cocked the steel crossbow). Like the boys of ancient Greece, who exercised naked, my body was lithe and tanned. And, like the ancients, Guglielmo taught me to rub down with olive oil and scrape my body clean with a *strigilis*. Of illness I knew nothing. I was never lonely because ever at hand was my Guglielmo.

As for the coming of the new century, the year 1200, I have only the haziest memories. On *capo d'anno* I went with Nonno and Guglielmo to midnight Mass, and I recall much pealing of bells and the breaking of many pots, plates and bottles in the streets. Everyone was glad, apparently, that another hundred years had passed without the Judgment Day—for, at the millennium, two hundred years before, people were filled with such apprehension that cows went unmilked and looms untended, while all the pious made shrouds and prepared to die. But friars and hermits could not resist continuing to predict that the end of the world was at hand.

While I was busy with my childish games, the Pope was busy with games of another sort. I had forgotten my guardian, though he most assuredly had not forgotten me. Because I was King of Sicily, he wished at all costs to avoid the possibility of my becoming Holy Roman Emperior. He wished to avoid, also, any Staufen on the Imperial throne so long as another Staufen was King of Sicily. He believed in the principle of "divide and rule." Hence, though my Uncle Philipp of Waiblingen certainly had more claim to the Empire than Otto the Welf, Pope Innocent suddenly declared himself in favor of Otto, excommunicating my Uncle Philipp. For this favor, Otto defined in a document all the lands of the Church, and renounced all claims by the Empire forever. Thus was unleashed the beginning of the brutal wars between Welf and Waiblingen, Guelf and Ghibelline, in which I, too, was destined to let blood.

Later, I found most interesting the Pope's justifications for not having recognized me—his ward—as King of the Germans and as claimant to the Imperial throne. I was, he said, at the time of my election, unbaptized. Also the German princes who elected me had assumed that my accession would not occur until I was of age, and this was a condition I could not then fulfill. Also I had first been known, as my mother desired, by the name of Costantino—a Greek name, not a proper name for a German king. And, finally, he was not robbing me of my German inheritance, because his appointment as my guardian was not intended to secure the Imperium for me, but to defend my inheritance in Sicily.

Those were the statements he made publicly, while at the same moment he was writing privately: "If once the boy reaches years of understanding, and perceives that he has been robbed of his honors as Emperor by the Roman Church, he will surely refuse her reverence and will oppose her by every means in his power. He will free Sicily from feudal fetters, and deny homage to the Church of Rome. . . ."

So Innocent, without an astrologer, foresaw the future. To neutralize that future he had two alternatives: my death, or my submission from ward to vassal. The former would have released a witch's caldron of troubles for him. The latter seemed—when I was still so young and pliable—an easier way.

Never having seen me, how was he to know that I was I —or to assess the forces already astir within me? Had he been a more prudent man, he might have taken warning from certain events which occurred in the Castello di Maredolce one November afternoon, when I lacked but a month of being seven.

Wild disorder ruled in the streets of Palermo, for the German knights of Markward von Anweiler had entered the capital, seized the Norman Palace and driven away the bishops (years later I learned that Gualtiero di Palearia had sold out for German gold). At the Castello we had only a handful of men to defend us, and it remained for Guglielmo's grandfather to give the order to bar the gates. Guglielmo armed himself and gave me a dagger. Then we ran to a tower room overlooking the dusty road to the Ponte dell'Ammiraglio. I gazed down at that charmed pathway where I had trudged so often with my hand in Guglielmo's—where I placed it now. As we watched, Nonno made the sign of the cross, and nurse Lucia began to wail and cry. I could feel the veins throbbing in Guglielmo's hand, and my heart kept pace with a perfect rhythm.

We had not so very long to wait. First we heard the distant beat of the German drums . . . next we saw steel flashing in the autumn sun . . . then we saw the armored horses, the banners, the lances, the halberds, the maces, the axes . . . then the ravenous gaunt black eagles paired with dragons on long yellow shields . . . and finally the cold steel helms with blank narrow slits for eyes.

With a roar of hoofbeats, drums, and armor they swept into the courtyard before the gate . . . hundreds, it seemed, hundreds and hundreds of them . . .

4

WE WERE betrayed. So strong were the gates of the Castello that we might have held out for several days; but we were betrayed to the Germans by a chamberlain.

When we saw that the soldiers were entering through a small iron door which had been opened for them, we knew that shortly the gates would be flung wide and the mounted knights would storm into the emir's tranquil gardens. Already our few guards and many servants had prostrated themselves in servile surrender.

Guglielmo, Nonno, my nurse and I fled from the tower to an inner windowless room where the emir had kept his jewels. From this room a secret passage led outside the walls, and Nonno alone had a key to the passage. It was our only chance of escape from the Germans. To our dismay, when we arrived, sweating and breathless, we found the passage door barred from the other side. Our traitor had carefully prepared a trap.

Now we felt the horrifying frustration of the helpless who await doom. Lucia shrieked, fell on her knees before a crucifix, and muttered rapid Ave Marias while beating at her temples with her fists. Quickly Guglielmo kissed dear Nonno on both cheeks. The old man began crying, though in silence and in dignity, without sobs. Then more quickly Gugliemo kissed me too, and whispered very close to my ear, "You will be brave—I know you, my Lord!" And somehow this salutation of my kingship seemed to have enormous meaning.

We heard clearly the tramp of mailed feet on the tile pavements, relentlessly approaching. I thought how hot the Germans must be under the armor, and hoped they would smother to death. They did not. They arrived on the double, with drawn broadswords, breathing loudly through the holes perforated in their helms. The helms themselves resembled pointed pig snouts or frightful giant bird beaks. Their *Führer* was the largest man I had ever seen, with a width a third of his height, and a neck so thick his head was lost in his twin-horned tubolar helmet. He was encased in heavy black armor. I remember noticing the protrusion of his steel codpiece, the first such suit of armor in my experience; I also remember a crucifix engraved upon his breastplate, depicting a knight (himself, of course) in humble adoration of the Christ. A giant, I thought, a giant armored bull; afterward I learned he was Markward von Anweiler.

They shouted in German, and I found the words unintelligible. Lucia, screaming, was dragged away. Without warning, and for sheer pleasure it seemed, the leader cut down Nonno by splitting his head with a single direct blow of the heavy sword. Air rasped from the old man's lungs as he fell forward, blood spurting; his brains spattered across the beautiful, cool tile floor. For the first time I was witnessing death by murder; my heart pounded and a wild hot fury swept into my veins. I wanted to cry, but I could not. I was conscious of sweat in the palm of my hand, on the hilt of my dagger. Suddenly two soldiers turned on Guglielmo, seizing him from behind and twisting his arms so brutally that I feared they would break. He groaned in anguish. With rushing horror I realized that once again I was all alone in the world.

At a command from the *Führer* a captain sprang forward to seize me. Trembling, I drew back my dagger. "If you touch me I will kill you!" I cried, though I thought I could not breathe. "I am King by Divine right!"

To my amazement the captain hesitated, clearly in awe. I distinctly recall the twitch of his outstretched gloves, which were chain mail sewed upon linen and leather. In this moment the leader struck my arm with the flat of his sword, and the dagger flew out of my hand. I was helpless.

"*Hauptmann*," bellowed the leader, "do not hurt the boy!"

I heard the words through the clamor of my cries and the grunts of my adversary as I attacked with my bare hands, my feet, and my teeth. Guglielmo described the scene in a dispatch he later wrote to the Pope as my guardian; and when at last in person I confronted the Pope, he gave me the letter as a present. It is one of my treasures, and it exists to this day. But at that moment I had no concern for the way I appeared in the eyes of others. I realized, with the instinctive fear of a small animal, that I was cornered, and I was prepared to fight so long as any spark of life remained in me. I bit, kicked, gouged, striving constantly to reach the captain's face and eyes, for he wore a cap of chain mail without helm. Had he not been protected by steel, I would have torn at his genitals; even so I landed one blow that made him howl. I was snatched away by another soldier. As it was now apparent that escape was impossible, I ripped off my clothing and, trembling in humiliation, rage, and indignation, raked my own flesh with my nails—as if to destroy myself before my enemies could again set hands on me. I could not, would not, suffer that indignity to my person!

Nevertheless, finally I was subdued. But they did not bind me with the cords they had brought, nor did they carry me away. I walked—between four soldiers—tattered and bleeding, but proudly, on my own feet.

5

I WAS HOUSED in a garden storeroom with a dirt floor—a room crude but pungent with the scent of lemons and blood-red oranges fresh-picked, melons in storage, and twisted strands of garlic hanging on the walls. On all sides mimosa was in fresh and yellow bloom; lavender bougainvillaea cascaded from terrace to terrace; white butterflies drifted on languid wings among the flowers. Nowhere was any sign of crisis, turmoil, or tyranny.

The furnishings of my room were a table, an oil lamp fashioned of clay and shaped exactly like the lamps of antiquity, a battered charcoal brazier, a three-legged stool with one leg uneven, and a wooden bed laced with hemp rope and covered with a mattress of dry grass. I was lucky to have a bed, the gardeners all said; most prisoners slept on stone floors and a little straw. But was I a prisoner? No bars covered my windows; I had been shoved into the room and told by the soldiers to shift for myself.

The gardeners were rough but not hostile—though they stole from me whatever I had left of any value, and drew lots among themselves. Whatever sympathy they may have felt, they were afraid to show, for Germans garrisoned the Castello. Each day, however, the gardeners brought me a bowl of *pasta* and indifferent sauce, though they had not been given orders to feed me. In spite of this I seemed never to get enough to eat. I became ravenous. Thus it was hunger which drove me stealthily the first time into the city; and then again and again, after I realized that the gardeners deliberately took no notice of me.

So began that most extraordinary period of my life, when I wandered about as the winds listed—a child, with the heart of a man; a beggar, with the crown of a king. For five years, hardly noticed by my captors, I was to live among my people—eating their food, wearing their clothes, smelling their smells, suffering their hurts, speaking their tongues. In all history, I believe, no other prince ever had such an education as I.

I was, as people said, an *agnello fra i lupi*—a lamb among wolves. *Agnus Dei*—I added to myself, ironically. Already the Pope's legates had been busy, and Markward was accepted as Regent in my behalf, though Markward had banished his accomplice Gualtiero di Palearia and the bishops who ruled in my name. During the turmoil of the city's occupation, Berardo had escaped in the disguise of a peasant, riding an *asino*. And one day a message was brought to me by an old monk, who whispered mysteriously from under his cowl: "Your dear friend, the one who liked to wink and whose beard reeked of incense, is alive and in hiding; do not despair, for someday you will see him again!"

This cheered me, but I mourned day and night for Guglielmo. Everywhere I inquired about him, and finally learned from a friend of his grandfather's that Guglielmo was in prison. But, no matter how hard I tried, I could not discover in which fortress. He was not sufficiently important for people to have paid much attention to his destiny. The flame in my heart nothing could extinguish.

The first lesson I was to learn from the streets was the value of food. I ate whatever came to hand. Fruit of some variety was always maturing in the vast royal parks. Not once did a gardener forbid me to help myself to *nespoli*, strawberries, cherries, plums, mulberries, peaches, pears, grapes, persimmons, oranges, pomegranates, and endless figs white and purple. In season there were melons of all types, olives, dates, almonds, walnuts, and the raisins called *zibibbo*. Because my body burned with a fierce energy, I needed other foods as well, and I delighted in the *gamberi* or *calamari* or deep sea fish which occasionally came my way. More and more often, as I grew bigger and handsomer, some kind *donna* would note the hungry glint in my eye, and I found myself in the kitchen waiting and brushing off flies while a great pot of *minestrone* bubbled and simmered on the tile-inlaid charcoal stove. Or sometimes a pretty young girl would let down a basket on a cord from some upper-story window, to receive from me a stolen trinket in exchange for a portion of *capretto*—though I have never much liked the taste of goat, even when young and tender. Most of the time, however, like any peasant or fisherman, I munched on the chickpeas called *ceci,* or on black bread spread with olive oil and a few sardines. Once in a while, when I was very lucky, I had sweet almond paste formed and colored to resemble fruit.

My clothing (what was left of my fine silks and soft woolens) was soon worn out or outgrown. I then counted myself lucky when someone tossed me a tattered cloak or a linen tunic not yet scrubbed thin on the stone tubs of a community *lavatoio* or rocks on the bank of a stream. Even today I cannot pass a group of women washing clothes without recalling my nakedness as a child, and I know as well as they the refrains of their songs. Not long since I paused to listen to a Neapolitan washwoman sing:

> *"Tu m'aje prommiso quatto moccatora*
> *oje moccatora, oje moccatora . . ."*

My feet, which had been covered in winter with pointed shoes of leather soft as doeskin, and in summer with tooled and gilded sandals, now had only the protection of *zoccoli*—those clumping wooden clogs which beat out their telltale staccato at every step. No thief or brigand wears *zoccoli:* of that you may be sure. And I, like a thief, most often ran barefoot—until the soles of my feet so hardened that I feared to develop the hoofs of an *asino.*

As for dirt, I have no consciousness now of having been dirty. Perhaps I was, for dirt is meaningless even to a royal child; perhaps I was not, for I swam often in fresh water and in the sea. I am sure that, in either case, my mother would not have approved of my appearance, for I rarely combed my hair and I was close to nakedness.

My constant companion was a ridiculous short-haired yellow dog, silly and playful, who attached himself to me as another stray. His uncertain ancestry was as plebeian as mine was royal, and we understood one another perfectly. I named him "Rex," in unwitting irony, I suppose, of my situation. His legs were long and gangling, his body hardly more than skin over ribs, his muzzle thin and pointed, his erect ears much too large for his head, his tail a perpetually wagging mockery. When he stood on his hind legs he was as tall as I, and with his big yellow eyes he looked soulfully into mine. His favorite pastime was to place his paws on my shoulders, lick my face lavishly with his generous pink tongue, grin, whiffle, slurp, bounce, and—unless I was firmly resistant—attempt to make love. *Amore*, I thought, was the sole aim of his life; for even though half-starving, he would optimistically leave a fresh bone for diversion. He seemed always happy—and I loved and envied his happiness.

These were the years of first discovery and exploration—years in which everything was wonderful to behold. All unawares I developed my powers of observation. I watched whiskered old women carding wool and winding distaff and spindle. I watched restless young girls rolling macaroni around the tough stems of *busa*, while humming songs of love and babies. I watched muscular near-naked men, *trappitara*, turning the heavy stone presses which crushed olives for oil. I watched bronzed young Bacchi, whose arms and feet were stained by the grapes; while they washed wine casks in sea water they sang, "I want to drop a sweet red grape into your mouth . . . your mouth of a thousand kisses." I watched goatherds who looked and smelled and sounded like Pan himself as they played the pipes. I watched artisans painting carts in brilliant reds and yellows with scenes of the *paladini*. I watched with total absorption the *Opera dei Pupi* as the puppet knights, day after day, fought out the wars of Charlemagne—and I thought of him as only slightly preceding my grandfather Barbarossa as Holy Roman Emperor, though four hundred years had passed. I thought, too: someday when I am grown . . . why not me . . . ?

For a time I haunted the waterfront, mingling with sailors and fishermen. I learned the fittings of a galley as thoroughly as an admiral, studying the rigging, the oars, the lights as if I surely intended to have my own fleet. As for the sea, I learned to know its moods, as well as some of the creatures in it. Since I swam like a dolphin, I had no trouble bringing up *frutta del mare*, those sweet and delicious shellfish hardly bigger than a thumbnail; or capturing *polipi*, so iridescent and beautiful under water that I regretted biting out the eyes of the squid—the surest and quickest way to kill before the parrot-like beak can harm you. I learned how to take the sea urchin without piercing my hands with the spines, and how to distinguish the inedible male from the edible female. I learned, too, a knowing laugh (though I was still too young to understand why the joke was quite so funny) when a big sea cucumber came up in the nets. The creature was called in fisherman's dialect, *cazzo del mare*—penis of the sea.

My curiosity drove me to all sorts of exploration. I searched for green lizards among the rocks, watching the lightning flick of their tongues as they fed on insects, and their method of fighting by seizing each other's tails in their jaws. They are said to be the souls of people who cannot enter Heaven, but I saw no evidence of it. I climbed giant ficus trees entwined with roots like jungle snakes, and swung like an ape from one dangling root to another. I sat quietly by the hour watching birds, especially the long-legged herons, skylarks, finches, and even nightingales. I wondered, I remember, why I never saw cuckoos building nests —a question I was not to have answered until many years had passed.

I explored Monte Pellegrino, clambering over its slopes, in and out among the century plants and the bristling cactus called *fichi d'India*. Below me, from the mountain, lay the city in its far famed golden shell, the opalescent *Conca d'Oro*. Spires of Norman churches and minarets of Saracen mosques towered above even the tallest palms and ficus trees. Sometimes, at sunset, when the sky changed from mauve to gold, I thought that Palermo was a magic eastern city, conjured from a genii's lamp, with no limit to its wonders.

Once I climbed a cliff to a falcon's aerie, and hurriedly stole from the nest one precious egg. I wrapped it in a cloth and tied it close to my body under my tunic, to keep it warm. Then, oh so carefully, I climbed down and ran straight away to place the egg under a setting hen. I watched every day for the egg to hatch, and when at last it did, I took the fledgling away from the hen and fed it scraps of meat because I saw it could not run about like a chick. I wondered, though, whether it would grow up with the habits of a chicken, since this orphan eyas had no other parent to show it what to do. I got it to the point of full feathers before it died. It looked like a falcon, though it did not behave like a falcon, nor like a chicken, either. It was my pet, and responded to my commands. It loved to play with marbles and bits of bright glass, and to admire itself in a mirror. It greeted me always with a loud *skreek skreek*, and would peck at my hand with affection. The claws on the bright yellow feet were like razors, and I had to learn to avoid them. I named it *Freccia*, because it flew like an arrow. I wept when it died, and wondered what disease caused the illness—for I was sure disease, not witchery, was at fault. Who would wish to cast an evil spell upon a mere bird owned by a king so forgotten as I . . . ?

As events transpired, I was not so forgotten as I thought. One day I heard in the *vucciria*, amid its babble of tongues, that Markward von Anweiler was dead. He had fallen into great pain from a gallstone, people said, and had implored his doctors to cut open his stomach and take out the stone. From the operation he succumbed, his last breath a scream of agony.

At the news my heart pounded, but I felt more fear than joy. Certainly my fortunes would change, I thought; and probably not for the better. Who, without Guglielmo and Berardo, was left to aid or protect me? My aloneness was frequently reimpressed upon me. At the Feast of the Dead no dead returned to bring me toys and other presents; and even the *festa* of San' Giuseppe aroused no feeling of surety that the good saint was watching over me.

I stood on tiptoe to increase my height; I flexed the muscles in my arms and legs. I had faith only in myself—in my ability to dodge and run and hide, for these are nature's gifts to all animals continually hunted. . . .

6

Perhaps foreboding was the reason for my restlessness that night of Markward's death, the reason I awoke suddenly to the sound of footsteps on the graveled path. For the footsteps had not the sound of gardeners' *zoccoli*.

I leaped from my bed and pulled up the linen coverlet as though I had not slept there, seized my clothes (I slept naked under the linen), and like Ali Baba clambered into one of the huge garden jars stored in my room. I crouched in the bottom of the jar, shivering, my clothes a protective wad over my head. Through a crack in the jar I saw, moments later, two men tiptoe through the doorway. They were clearly defined in the moonlight. They wore hoods instead of gardeners' smocks, and the moonlight glinted from their daggers. The hair on my neck rose, my spine tingled: murderers!

I breathed hardly at all. So rigid was I that a cricket in the jar began chirping—in my ears a shattering sound. The men started, as though in surprise at the cricket. Then one struck the bed with his dagger. A gesture of futility, I wondered, or a test to make sure I was not hidden under the mattress? They jostled one another, turned and ran.

I was astonished at their eagerness to be gone. Since then I have learned that murderers of a divinely sanctioned king run great risks of torture—in both this world and the next. Such was the first attempt on my life. At its failure I felt a great relief; and I cannot say that I have ever learned to take such attempts as a matter of course. Next day the rip in the sheet earned me a scolding from a gardener's wife. I offered not a murmur of objection. . . .

With some difficulty I assembled paper and ink, for I planned to write a letter of protest. Once written, I would dispatch it by couriers—if I could find any such who would carry messages without payment. I wrote in a most elegant style:

> To *all the Kings of the world, and to all the Princes of the universe, from the innocent boy, King of Sicily, called Federico—greetings in God's name.* Assemble yourselves, ye nations; draw nigh, ye kings; hasten hither, ye princes, and see if any sorrow be like unto my sorrow! My parents died before I could know their caresses; did I not deserve to see their faces? And I, like a gentle lamb among wolves, fell into slavish dependence upon men of various tribes and tongues. I, the offspring of so august a union, was handed over to servants of all sorts, who presumed to draw lots for my garments and for my royal person. Germans, Tuscans, Sicilians, barbarians conspired to worry me. My daily bread, my drink, my freedom, all were measured out to me in scanty proportion. No king am I; I am ruled instead of ruling; I beg favors instead of granting them. My nobles are silly and quarrelsome. Since my Redeemer liveth, and can raise me out of such a pool of misery, again and again I beseech you, O ye princes of the earth, to aid me to withstand slaves, to set free the son of Caesar, to raise up the crown of my kingdom, and to gather together again the scattered people! Unless you avenge me, you yourselves will fall into like dangers. . . .

I did not return to my bed for more than a month, prefering a remote spot hidden in a thicket of oleanders. I cleared a hollow to protect me from scorpions; I slept rolled in my linen sheet, to protect me from mosquitoes at night and flies in the early morning. When, finally, I returned to my storeroom, I rigged up a system of traps, with hidden strings and bells, to give me warning of intrusion. And never again was I separate from a dagger, day or night.

Actually my precautions served no purpose, for the Germans who succeeded Markward were so occupied with destroying one another that they had little time to consider my existence. Probably, had I been under foot, they would have disposed of me. But out of sight is out of mind, as the old saying goes, and I drifted along in oblivion and safety. Logically, I should have been taken into the castle of some noble Norman family; but of those remaining, not one cared to run such a risk. So I continued to roam the streets—when I was not reading.

I had access to all the libraries established by my grandfather Ruggero. He had caused many works of Plato, Aristotle and Ptolemy to be translated from Greek into Latin, and many others from Arabic into Latin. He had also commissioned the now famous *Geography*, which required fifteen years of work by the scholar al-Idrisi, and revived the Greek idea that the earth is a sphere. In the Latin original, I read the *Satyricon* of Petronius Arbiter, and, with help, *The Golden Ass* of Apuleius (though I was for more skeptical than Sant' Agostino that the hero literally had been transformed into an ass, I had no doubt that his paramour loved him better as ass than as man). Actually, some years were to pass before I could savor either of these works to the full; no boy is as fully equipped as a man . . . much less an ass.

At this period, however, my chief interest lay in the realm of history. I was particularly avid to learn all that I could of Rome, and the lives of Augustus, Hadrian, and Justinian kept me reading many a night by flickering oil lamps. My *Aeneid*—for me the most precious of all books—I reread again and again. The words *Caesar Imperator* often recurred in my dreams. . . .

Aside from many languages, I learned as much from the streets as I did from books, including much specific instruction. Little effort was required to lie on a wall during sleepy afternoons and listen to an iman droning on about the Sharia, or Islamic law, and the Five Pillars of Islam. The word *Muslim* merely means "believer." All that was necessary to become a Muslim was to recite: "I believe there is no god but Allah, and that Mohammed is the Messenger of Allah." And the other four Pillars, as I learned to know by heart, were the five daily prayers; the annual fast—abstaining totally from food, drink, sexual intercourse between dawn and sunset during the month of Ramadan; the pilgrimage to Mecca; the giving of alms to the poor. I found, when I listened outside the windows of a synagogue, that the rabbis' teaching of the Mosaic law was much the same as the Sharia. Both forbade the eating of pork, gambling, and the representation of animals or the human figure in art.

For my part, I considered foolish the prohibition of graven images; nor did I like the Catholic emphasis on mortification of the flesh. Already I had developed an eye for the beauty of the human form as represented by Greek statuary, and could find no evil in it. I did not like, either, the Muslim aversion to wine, for I had felt its heady benefits. On the other hand, I was more than a little interested in Islam's provision of four legal wives and unlimited concubines per man; and in the remarkable simplicity of divorce for both Mohammedans and Jews. "I divorce you, my wife," said the man—and that was about the substance of it.

In the market place I heard followers of Francesco d'Assisi—at that time regarded with great suspicion and hostility by the Pope—plead for a return to poverty, penitence, and prayer within the Roman Church. Had I guessed that one day I would have an extraordinary conversation with this man, I could not have followed the arguments of his followers more closely. Others, heretics like the Waldenses and Albigenses, had fled from the Pope's inquisitors in the north, though so numerous were the Albigenses in France that the Pope had launched a great crusade against them. Eyes alight with the fires of reform, and in voices like trumpet blasts, these heretics protested that there was no need for the priest to serve between God and man, that the word of God and not the word of the Pope should be believed. The Waldenses even denied the existence of Purgatory.

To me, the most interesting of all was a man who professed to follow Fra Arnaldo da Brescia, who had been hanged by my grandfather Barbarossa on the urgent request of the Pope. Fra Arnaldo had preached from the Scriptures—against greed, war, hatred, lust, perjury, murder, theft, deception, and the evil desires of the flesh. More important from the Pope's point of view, he preached against corruption in the Church. Now Fra Arnaldo's disciple, who had seen him and known him, carried on his work. He spoke like this:

"The Roman Church is corrupt! It smells of money, it stinks of greed! Benefits and absolutions can be bought with gold. Even Holy Mass itself is for sale! For thirty consecutive Masses paid in advance, a soul can be wafted straight from Purgatory into Heaven. Every prayer, every marriage, every death, every candle, has its price! And in the end it is not God, nor the poor, who get the money—but the priests! In all the monasteries and nunneries the tables groan with meat and cheese and wine, while the serfs who work the Church lands go hungry. The Church has become rich and worldly, possessing great lands, palaces and treasures. While we pick our teeth with our fingers, the cardinals use a new silver instrument called a fork! The Church no longer speaks with the voice of God, but of the Pope! The Pope is a clerical emperor, lusting to rule the world . . . !"

Much murmuring greeted his words, mingled with cries of "Shame!" and "Sedition!" and "This man speaks truth!" I remember that the Brother said the Emperor Barbarossa was moved too late by compassion and mourned that he had taken the life of Arnaldo. I did not identify myself; but I felt sorry, too.

My street course in comparative religions did not stop, however, with the contemporary varieties. More than once I heard a Persian rug merchant say that our Christian blood cult of a crucified god was but a variant on their ancient sun-god religion of Mithra, and that nothing was new under the sun—even gods. Others were travelers who had been in many countries, and called themselves agnostics, doubting the existence of any god. Still others said that to eat and drink the body of a god, even in symbolism as Christians do at Communion, was cannibalism—and they would have none of it. Some said Christ was like Dionysus, devoured by his followers—but in misery, and not in frenzied joy. And the Greeks who reputedly were members of the Eastern Orthodox faith had forgotten nothing of their ancient myths.

Once I trotted along beside a woman carrying on her head a jug of water from a public fountain. She had the great eyes and smooth olive skin of the Dorians. She told me that I resembled the boys of long ago who competed in the Olympian games, and I would surely have been a winner. She was moved, somehow, to set down the jug from her head to talk to me. I still recall the blond, luxuriant hair of her armpits. She told me all about Greece, where she had been born, and how to her surprise she had found the ancient Greek temples of Sicilia—of which I could see ruins aplenty—as great as the temples of Athens. In Siracusa, though, the temple had not been destroyed but converted into a Christian church. So Jesus now hung from His cross among the Greek gods. No matter, for Jesus was a name derived from the Greek "Joshua"—meaning merely "Jah is deliverance," a cry, probably, of slaves in revolt. As for the Madonna, she was a goddess much like Hera. Often each was represented carrying a babe in arms, wearing the blue star-spangled robe of the night, holding a pomegranate (an ancient symbol of fertility), standing on the horns of the new moon (as also the Egyptian goddess Isis) with the clouds of heaven pulled aside by a cherub (a baby Eros). Well!

"So you see," my informant finished, adjusting the pad to balance the water jug on her head once more, "the Italian women really worship Hera." And I can yet remember the ribald, knowing laugh when she added, "And as for the Italian men, they worship Priapus!"

She was too busy to explain about Priapus, and it was quite some time before I discovered his identity—though in fact all the boys and men of my acquaintance had been busy in his behalf, privately and sometimes publicly. So had I; but I was not aware just yet that such pleasures were associated with religious worship.

Sex was a subject which was not a subject, because it was so much a part of everyday life. So, of course, was the poverty, the stench, and the filth of the back streets and narrow alleys. All teemed with mutilated beggars, bloated naked babies, mangy yellow dogs, wizened *asini* bedecked with tinkling bells, ferocious half-starved cats (*brutti gatti*), song birds and parakeets in cages hanging from the lintels, flies in clouds, pimps and prostitutes. In the midst of all this, men swore and laughed and spit, women squawked in harsh voices like jungle birds, young people sang love songs and made love. From the earliest ages, children were fully aware of everything sexual. Love-making occurred continually in their presence: parents in the beds, lovers in the gardens, casual pickups in the streets at night or backed against the garden walls. Boys held contests to determine who could ejaculate the fastest; little girls lifted their ragged sacks up to their bare middles, touched each others' vulvas and giggled with delight. Bigger children drew pictures on the walls with chalk—pictures which evoked from their elders salacious laughter at such precocious wisdom.

As I wandered through the streets, many times I was accosted by men who wished to use my body; and, as I approached the age of twelve, also by women who mistook my mature bearing for that of an older boy. Indeed, at the age of nine I knew everything without knowing anything, and, as yet, had experienced nothing.

7

As I grew older I lived less with nature and books and more with people. Because it was well known by everyone that I was the heir to the throne, and had been displaced by the hated Germans, I was generally well treated—though not treated like a king. Salutations of majesty would have been too much to expect, under the circumstances, and in fact degrading. Imagine a fisherman calling, "Here, your Majesty, catch this sardine!" or some woman saying, "Here, your Majesty, is a cast-off tunic my son has outgrown—a few patches, true, but good enough to turn the rain. . . ." The somewhat uneasy problem of my name was solved by the simple word "Boy." Thus I was addressed by everyone older than I—*Ragazzo* this or *Ragazzo* that; but by my young contemporaries I was called Costantino—it came more easily to their tongues.

Gradually I fell under the influence of an Arab boy a couple of years older than I. He was known to his six or eight followers as simply *al-Kaid*—the leader. He was daring, alert, and had an engaging, slightly twisted smile which revealed remarkably white teeth. I remember particularly his thin, beaked Arabic nose and long, thin, facile fingers. He must have been very handsome, because he continually attracted attention from adults. Often he wore a tattered, flowing *taghis* which gave him a dramatic, semi-*bedāwi* air like a desert *shaikh*.

He taught us how to steal sweets and small objects in the market without being caught, and how to dissemble when we were questioned too closely by armed men. Once we found in shale the mysterious bones of a long-dead animal. It had a single horn sprouting from the skull. Some of the boys said it was a dragon; but I thought it resembled a heavy African animal I had read about. Al-Kaid settled the argument: it was, he said, a unicorn in process of growing a new horn. Notwithstanding his authority, I continued to have my doubts.

I admired al-Kaid greatly, and for a while my greatest ambition was to be like him, then to supplant him as leader. I practiced carefully the exact cadence of his greeting, *salam aleikum*, and managed to infuse into it, I think, something of his attraction. He taught me a much more fluent Arabic, how to dive deeply by holding my breath in a certain way, and how to explore cautiously the green and blue underwater grottoes which he said might be filled with treasure. He taught me how to play the lute. I practiced seriously every day, harassing my listeners. I was much interested in the word as well as in the instrument. From the Arabic *al'ūd* was derived the Italian *liuto* and the French *leüt*. I kept a sharp lookout for words which thus transformed themselves.

Al-Kaid taught me other things as well—specifically, how pleasant was the worship of Priapus—though I do not recall that he ever pronounced the name of this quasi-divinity, the son of Dionysus and Aphrodite, condemned to perpetual erection. After swimming, we would run along the shore, shivering, until we came to our favorite cluster of massive rocks. We liked to lie on their smooth surface, nude except for necklaces of shells, baking in the hot rays of the late afternoon sun and clinging close together for companionship. We were fascinated by our own bodies, with their little animal hairs which the sun transformed into a sprinkle of gold. Wholly spontaneously we began to play with our male organs, snickering as they erected and flopped about like weighted toys. From ourselves we turned to one another, and the sport of the game was increased. Passing fishermen merely laughed at our impudence, or cheered us on to greater efforts, saying that if we practiced enough we would become big as men. In this primitive state, tanned and naked as we were, except for the single fact that the Christian boys (but not I) crossed themselves before leaping into the water, there was nothing to distinguish Christian from Saracen. I think it is not too much to say that we loved one another as brothers.

By the time I was eleven I had grown restless under al-Kaid's leadership, and wished to choose myself the paths to follow over Monte Pellegrino or the underwater caverns to explore. Once or twice we quarreled, then fought; but strong and agile as I was, he, with his greater age, was more than a match for me.

Of necessity I acceded to his commands. Then, suddenly the whole situation changed.

We were swimming underwater, near a grotto which was unfamiliar, when without warning al-Kaid was attacked by a killer as deadly as any shark—a moray eel as long as the arm of a man. First a flurry in the water, then swirling clouds of blood. Somehow we got him to the surface. His right arm and hand were terribly lacerated, and he would have bled to death upon the sand but for the aid of fishermen who stayed the blood with tourniquets. I watched . . . trembling with rage, fury, love, fear.

With compulsive concentration I backed away from the sobbing, moaning boy, and all my subsequent movements were dreamlike. I found a driftwood staff and, with a fishline, bound my dagger to it. Without a word to anyone I plunged back into the sea and sought the entrance to the dangerous grotto. All was calm and clear; then in a flash of green light I saw mottled brown and yellow—the moray's face and teeth grotesquely exaggerated. I struck with my spear full force. I pierced him through the gills and brought him, writhing, upward. As I broke the water's surface with the lashing eel I gave a triumphant shout. And the shout was echoed in the cheers from ashore.

After that, during the many months required for al-Kaid's arm to heal, I was the leader. But it was not until I climbed the aerie and brought back the falcon's egg that I was given a title of leadership. Then I was called *al-Tair*—the Eagle.

It so happened that al-Kaid had a twin; but his twin was a girl. She was called Aïsha, a name associated with life. The Saracens kept their women segregated, veiled, and off the streets as much as possible—though among the poor such restrictions did not function very well. Al-Kaid's twin had not yet put on the veil, and the features which made him handsome made her a beauty. When I came to visit him in the family's half-domed stone house of two small rooms, the girl was constantly with us, and I was very much aware of her lovely face. As for her body, she wore a robe which hid her form. But had she been a dancing girl in thinnest veils she could not more keenly have aroused my curiosity. I sensed, rather than saw, what lay beneath. Always to my dismay, when I tried to speak to her, she shyly turned her head and answered nothing.

One evening I came to urge al-Kaid to go with me to

see a troupe of traveling performers. I hoped to cheer him. The wounds had caused much trouble, and he was very gloomy because he feared his hand would be so stiff that he could not become, like his father, a mosaicist. That night he had fever again, and lay tossing in bed.

"Take my sister Aïsha," he said. "She has been begging me all day for permission. I can't stand any more of her! My father has gone to Monreale to repair the mosaics. He took my mother, as he can afford only one wife and no concubines."

My heart made a sudden extra beat. "If your sister will go with me—"

"Oh yes, yes yes!" she said. "I will wear a veil of my mother's, a black one. No one will see me. . . ."

I can see you, I thought; I can see through the veil—and also the robe. . . .

The performances were given in the square garden near the front of the Norman Palace, a garden so thick with palm trees that it seemed an oasis. I hardly glanced at the bulk of the Palace, for now it seemed to me quite unreal that I had ever lived within those walls—and to have said so to Aïsha would have seemed slightly ridiculous, like boasting, or actually untrue. And who among the performers would have believed they displayed their talents before a king?

Curtains surrounded a small stage lighted with oil lamps, and the audience—those who could pay more—sat on benches. I was fortunate to have coins for standing room. I did not mind standing, because I was close to Aïsha, and in the shadows we held hands. The pressure of our fingers expressed our enchantment with the performance. I am sure our mouths fell open as we watched the tumblers in baggy pants, the fire-eaters blackened with smoke, the snake-charmers in piled-up turbans, the drummers who were naked to the waist and wore coils of bracelets. Best of all we liked the singer accompanied by a lute, for this was when our hands were clasped the tightest. In a high, monotonous, but to our ears beautiful voice, the singer chanted the verses of a love poem by the Sicilian-Arabic poet Abu al-Hasan:

"Long drinks of cooling water
Cannot compare with my contentment
When I kiss the lips of my beloved . . .
Her breath is scented with amber,
And by its fragrance
I know she is here. . . ."

Dreamy, a little dazed, after the performance Aïsha and I, hardly speaking, wandered among the palms of the garden. From vendors I bought, with the remains of my money, sweetmeats and salted almonds; but somehow we had no appetite.

Then from behind the black veil I heard a whisper: "I don't want to go home . . . !"

"Come with me," I whispered in reply. I led her by the hand, and the touch was all the communication either needed.

We went to another garden, not far from the Palace walls—the tiny garden of San Giovanni degli Eremiti. The church not long before had been a mosque, and even now there were no hermits. The intricately worked wrought-iron gate was closed and locked; but, street urchin that I was, I knew a way—for I had slept in peace under the luxuriant foliage through many a sultry afternoon.

Now the pink squat domes of the mosque and the small dome atop the square tower could be seen only by the flares in the street. The repose of centuries pervaded the shadowy garden. Tall cypresses waved gently against the sky, blocking the stars. The sweet scent of lemon blossoms and jasmine was the fragrance of my beloved. We settled together, wrapping her robe about us as in a silk cocoon. It seemed we had been waiting all our lives for this moment, but we did not hurry. The savor was too sweet.

Then, at last, when we were utterly finished, after having tasted the delight again and again, murmurings ceased and words formed.

"How old are you, al-Tair?" Aïsha whispered. "I'm thirteen."

"I—?" I hesitated, then I said in a tone of dignity, "Soon I shall be twelve."

That night, from the so brilliant stars, could either of us have foreseen that she was destined to become a king's first concubine?

8

ONE RAW, rainy January morning not long after my twelfth birthday, I awoke shivering from lack of cover. I stumbled up from bed to strike fire for the charcoal in my brazier. Then suddenly the sleep left my eyes and I saw two armed men posted at my door.

"*Hòi!*" I cried. "What's this?"

I had ceased to rig my traps, for I had come to the opinion that I alone remembered I was King. Besides, I had come to depend on that other Rex, my gangling yellow dog; but not long since he had disappeared in the pursuit of some ephemeral affair. In those moments, that morning, I realized conclusively that lack of vigilance only once in a lifetime was enough. Hence today I am so impatient with my representatives who come to me airing long-winded excuses about their failures, begging in maudlin tones for a second chance. When I give a second chance, it is in a lower, less responsible post, and the offenders count themselves lucky to remain in my service.

Happily, my apprehensions were unfounded. A third man appeared, a man with a plump and pleasing face. He shook the rain from his cloak and bowed. "My Lord," he said in a tone so humble that I guessed instantly that my abandonment was at end, "my Lord, I am Riccardo, the chamberlain of the Norman Palace, appointed originally by your blessed mother, the Queen. I have been sent to beg your presence at the Palace. Your friend and protector Gualtiero di Palearia has returned, and craves an audience with your Majesty."

My friend and protector! Riccardo of course was repeating what he had been told, but in a negative sense he was right. The sins of Gualtiero toward me were more of omission than commission, and I counted myself lucky to be alive. So I went back to my earlier home, the Royal Palace of the Norman Kings, where I had lived so briefly with my mother. This time it did not seem so vast, nor the rooms so grand; and, though it was full of people, for me there was a certain emptiness.

My old nurse Lucia had disappeared in the turmoil of so many changes of rulers. I found assigned to me as a body servant a man who had been a Greek wrestler, and who had been taken as a slave by Turkish pirates. He was prized because of his strength and intelligence, and he wore a fringe beard exactly like the beards worn by Greek warriors portrayed on ancient vases. During my very first hour in the Palace he threw away my old clothes (to be burned because of vermin, he said) and scrubbed my body till my skin smarted. Then he called the palace barber and had my wild long hair trimmed and combed in undulating waves. If the Greek was rough with me, it was, I suppose, because I was rough with him; to deal with me must have been rather like handling a young lion.

When my body was clean and my blond hair sleek and shining, I was clothed in a soft velvet tunic of aquamarine blue worked with pearls and gold thread, and long woolen hose of brilliant scarlet. My cap was yellow; its decoration was a curling ostrich feather. Once again my feet were shod in soft white leather with pointed tips, and my hands gloved in white leather embossed with gold and semiprecious stones. Around my neck was placed a heavy golden chain; upon my fingers, rings set with rubies, emeralds and amethysts; around my waist, an intricately worked Arabic sword belt, and scabbard holding a sword with hilt of inlaid gold. I was ready for my audience with Gualtiero di Palearia.

He came to me. He came wearing a black cassock with only a huge crucifix and bishop's ring to indicate his rank. He was a thin, unctuous, balding man with bad breath, and he constantly rubbed his hands with a rasping sound. On the instant, my dislike of him was thrice compounded, and I had to control my wild impulse to draw my sword against him in payment for some of the miseries I had suffered. Perhaps it would have been better for my future had I yielded to my impulse.

He bowed, welcomed me to the Norman Palace, and explained the "miracle" of his return. I had no recollection of having seen him before, though he assured me he had been a devoted servant of my mother's—and continuously at my side before the Germans' disastrous victory. As I had controlled my sword, it was now necessary to control the expression of my face, to avoid showing the skepticism that I felt. In his eyes, I must have been merely a simple boy of twelve, common of habit and of mind.

"My Lord," he said, rubbing his hands with intense self-satisfaction, "through the intercession of our most gracious Saviour we have the good fortune to come together once again. As it happened that your revered mother, the Queen, placed the Kingdom of Sicily in fief to the Church, the Holy Father has seen fit to nominate my unworthy self as Chancellor until the attainment of your majority. It is my most sincere hope that all your Majesty's wishes may be realized, but the Holy Father instructs me to say that in resuming his duly appointed guardianship over you, the ultimate decisions of government must remain in his hands—and therefore by deputation, mine—until the attainment of your majority. I thus report to you with the fullest affirmation of my loyalty and complete concern for your Majesty's interests; and you may rest assured that all will be done which needs to be done, with God's help, in behalf of your noble self and your ancient Realm."

In my reply I used for the first time in conversation the *pluralis majestatis*. "Until our majority," I said in a voice which was clear, firm, and cold, but revealed nothing of rancor, "our requirements will be simple to fulfill. Nor will we demand a detailed accounting of your stewardship, as we are sure that our guardian the Holy Father holds our welfare constantly in mind and remembers us in his prayers; so it is before him and before Christ that you, as Chancellor, bear responsibility. Our own direction of the Realm will be assumed in due time, as God wills. We are content to wait."

With a slow, dignified gesture I gave him my left hand to kiss (I preferred to keep my sword arm free) and waited. He was surprised, but without hesitation he breathed his fetid breath upon my hand, and backed away.

Thus I was transformed, quickly, from waif to king; but I was far from being the King. I held only the form and not the substance of power. Thus in my own eyes I was a mockery of myself.

9

TO THE Chancellor I had to appeal for whatever I wished done. Almost immediately I made arrangements for my friend al-Kaid to be assigned to the royal mosaic workshop; and for his sister Aïsha to be given a place with the royal spinners—the beginning of my "harem" (in Arabic, *harīm* means simply the "forbidden place," and therefore "women's quarters"). Of more significance, I appealed at once for the release from prison of my former tutor Guglielmo Franciscus, and an open pardon (for what crimes?) for the Archbishop Berardo. In answer to my pleas for Berardo I received nothing except evasions—and the assignment of an archpriest for confession. But Guglielmo was quickly located and brought to me.

I was shocked—no, horrified—at his appearance. All the old *gioia di vivere* had vanished. His skin was so pale that it almost assumed translucence. Dark, cadaverous circles ringed his eyes. Only the wild, black curls were the same. His face and body were so emaciated that his whole skeletal structure clearly showed. Always slight, now he seemed much smaller than I. He coughed, with a hollow rattle, from deep in his lungs. His prison had been a vault in the damp cellars of the Castellamare del Golfo, and he had seen the sun scarcely a score of times since he had been snatched from me. His mouth trembled and I cried, from mingled joy and dismay, as we flung ourselves into each other's arms.

" 'Lielmo!" I shouted.

His first answer was a cough, but he collected himself and pulled away from my arms. "My Lord," he said, bowing, "I might never have recognized you. You are not a child anymore. You've —you've grown!"

" 'Lielmo!" I cried again, pulling him back to me and kissing him in an ecstasy of welcome. "I would have known you anywhere," I said, lying, "even in the blackness of your dungeon. The real 'Lielmo hasn't changed at all! I can *feel* you. . . ."

My love for him was open and passionate, and surely helped him to endure. I kept him with me constantly, as much as he was able. He was to me father, mother, lover, all in one. His illness, curiously, had made him very erotic. We shared the same bed, alternating between bliss and the agony of his coughing spells, when I held him up like a child. When he could, he gave me scholarly instruction, and he seemed to have a feverish need to impart to me everything he had ever learned. It was Guglielmo who started my serious study of Aristotle; and it was well that he did—for in the months to come the Pope was to ban the reading of Aristotle and confiscate or burn all copies of his works. Happily, I studied with diligence. To all my other tutors I was a severe trial; to Guglielmo I was a model student.

I received instruction, too, from no less person than Gualtiero de Palearia himself. We dined at one communal meal each day—sometimes *merenda* in late morning, but usually *pranzo* in the evening. I, as nominal King, sat at the center of the main table upon a dais; Gualtiero, as Chancellor, sat upon my right—so close that I was always conscious of his wretched breath. One evening, as baskets full of fruit were being passed, he turned to me and said, "My Lord, with your permission I wish to speak a word on the subject of manners, as I have been charged by the Holy Father."

"Speak," I said, turning my head in avoidance.

"My Lord," he said in a gentle voice, "I am sure your guardian would be deeply grieved to see the way you bolt your food—as if perpetually hungry. And, in memory of your revered mother, take smaller bites and do not smear your face. A king should eat with delicacy."

My face flushed, my ears burned, I gulped down whole the segments of a *mandarino*. Of course he was right, but I took the admonition as ill-advised, simply because it came from him. For the young, no subtle distinctions exist; I could see in Gualtiero only evil, not even a little good. He was picking his teeth with a sharpened quill, as we all did, and in my vehemence I wished he might choke and die on the point.

Later, with mingled amusement and nostalgia I was to read a copy of a letter written by a palace informant to the Pope, describing me at this period of my life:

THE stature of the King is neither small nor taller than one would expect at his age. The Universal Author of nature has given him robust limbs and a strong body, with which his vigorous spirit can achieve whatever it undertakes. He is never idle, but passes the whole day in some occupation or other; and so that his vigor may increase with practice, he fortifies his agile body with every kind of exercise and practice of arms. Drawing his short-sword, in the use of which he is expert, he makes play of defending himself from attack. He often practices archery and is a good shot with the bow. He loves fast thoroughbred horses, and no one knows better than he how to curb them with the bridle and then set them at full gallop. This is how he spends his day from morning to eve, and then begins afresh the following day.

To his attitude of royal majesty are added a kindly and gracious air, a serene brow, brilliant eyes, an expressive face, a burning spirit, and a ready wit. Nevertheless, his actions are sometimes odd and vulgar, though this is not due to his nature but to contact with rough company . . .

He is intolerant of admonitions, and judges himself capable of acting according to his own free will, considering it shameful for himself to be subject to a guardian and regarded as a boy—which leads to his not obeying his tutors' commands. He talks with all and argues in a manner which diminishes the veneration of his majesty.

However, he has virtue in advance of his age, and though not adult, he has the gift of wisdom. In him, then, the number of years do not count, nor is there need to await maturity, because as a man he is full of knowledge, and as a ruler of majesty.

One point the Pope's informant neglected to note: my nights I spent chiefly in omnivorous reading of Roman history. Polybius, Livy, Julius Caesar, Pliny, Cicero, Dio Cassius, Aurelius Victor, Procopius—I read them all. And I was very much conscious of the fact that at the height of Rome's glory no Pope existed in Rome—that the Emperor himself was *Pontifex Maximus*.

In an effort to compensate for the gaps in my Catholic education, I was sent to Holy Mass every morning in the Palace Chapel, and every evening to Vespers. The Chapel was a magnificent golden hall of glittering Arab-Norman-Byzantine mosaics. In contrast, the archpriest was a melancholy baldheaded man with a beak, a true blackbird, who had been selected personally by the Pope. The blackbird instructed me with curt directives not only in the Rosary, with Pater Nosters and Ave Marias, but in such subjects as the mystical body of Christ, the Holy Trinity, divine grace, and the Holy Sacraments as a way to salvation. Of them all, I was most troubled by the Holy Ghost itself, for I could not rid my mind of a fearsome specter.

During confession, I unwarily admitted under prodding that I had, sometimes, a physical relationship with Guglielmo, and brought down on my head such a lecture on carnal acts that I have not forgotten to this day. "In the unmarried," said my father confessor, "even the slightest amount of deliberate sexual activity, whether it is sought, or accepted when it has arisen, is a grievous sin!"

"But Father," I protested, "I have hot blood in my veins; because I am a king, I am not less a man!"

"You are a soul!" he answered.

Shortly thereafter the Chancellor received a letter from the Pope, stating that he did not find either suitable or desirable the wholly male atmosphere in which I was growing up. Steps, the Pope implied, must soon be taken. A betrothal . . .

"But the Pope himself lives in a wholly male atmosphere!" I railed to Guglielmo.

"Perhaps that is the source of the worry," Guglielmo replied. "The vows of celibacy are no stronger than the men who take them."

I considered telling my confessor the story of my relations with Aïsha—how I visited her regularly and joyfully in a remote room in a tower (for her sake I did not wish to bring her publicly to my apartments just then). I refrained—for surely he would have labeled this sin as far worse than grievous, as she was not only woman but Mohammedan as well. Though my actions had seemed to me reasonable and natural, perhaps in reality I had sinned. If so, prayers for forgiveness were in order—not the mechanical prayers of the priest, but my own prayers. I therefore petitioned Jehovah, Allah, and Jesus—to show impartiality and be on the safe side. I did not include the Madonna, because I thought this was strictly a matter for men.

I had something else to worry about: I was a soul. What did that mean? Could a soul conceive other souls, or was the soul something mysteriously acquired immediately after birth? Why did the Church (through the mouth of my confessor) say that animals had no souls, when I myself had observed that animals behave in ways astonishingly similar to human beings? How big was a soul? How many souls could stand on the head of a pin?—as I paraphrased the great ecclesiastical debate about the number of angels who could perform likewise. These questions led me in later years to careful medical experiments in an effort to determine objectively the location of the soul in the human body—or, indeed, to determine if it could be found at all.

But I was also a king—a state of being which could be claimed by few human beings and no animals, however great the element of natural superiority. My own superiority was derived from birth and from divine sanction, as proclaimed by the Church, and carried with it an enormous responsibility for the welfare of my subjects. Already I was conscious of this weight, and was determined to become a man big enough to be a king, and a king big enough to be a ruler.

Sometimes during the long afternoons when the priests slept, I slipped into the empty Royal Chapel for a private rehearsal of my own. As I had been instructed, I dipped my fingers in the font of holy water, crossed myself, genuflected in the direction of the altar—then with dignity and full majesty I mounted the five steps to the great marble-and-mosaic royal throne. It was difficult to sit on the throne with dignity, however, as it was wide enough for five or six of me—obviously designed for a king and consort in full regalia. Also the throne was empty of seat or cushions, and I had to choose between standing or sitting on the hard marble with my knees hunched up. I chose to stand in the exact center, between the two mosaic lions rampant above me, and survey the whole glittering scene with the thoughtful, contemplative expression I considered most appropriate to a king.

The entire chapel was richly worked in mosaics, the walls chiefly in gold, the floor in red and green geometric patterns set in white marble. An Arabic inscription ran around the top, below the roof, and the vaulting was a mass of intricately carved wood, like stalactites, in Arabic geometric designs. The columns, I observed, matched neither in types of marble nor in size, so I concluded they had been removed from ancient buildings, probably Roman temples. The walls were completely covered with portraits of saints and episodes from the Old and New Testaments, all in multicolored mosaics. Bearded San Pietro and bald

San Paolo dominated the emaciated, pious saints. As for the Bible stories, I got no farther than Adam and Eve above my head on the left, for in all the world no man or woman was ever born with body so grotesque as theirs, and to say they were created thus was a libel on the image of God. Eve's breasts hung like flat sacks, and poor Adam bore not the slightest sign of genitals. With disgust I turned away from the sight, perturbed by the thought that probably I would be forced to observe these creatures for many years to come. It did me no good to know that the vaulting above was covered with paintings of oriental dancing girls and the like; carefully, they had been made invisible.

But another sight was far more disturbing than the emasculated Adam. Dominating the apse, above the altar and crucifix and six great flickering tapers, above the Holy Virgin, was a colossal head and shoulders of the Christ. In His left hand he held the Gospels and with His right He gave the episcopal sign of blessing. If the bearded face was serene, the eyes were not: baleful, severe, they shifted with the eyes of the beholder. I wondered if this Hebrew Jesus, so simple and pure in heart, felt displeasure at the pompous magnificance of the chapel erected in His honor. I wondered if He understood the Latin chants of the choir, became bored at the unchanging rituals, smelled the incense, admired the costly vestments, approved of the golden chalice and jeweled aspergillum, or recognized the wood in the reliquary as a splinter of the cross on which He died.

And then I realized that He had been placed in the apse as a king. A king more than a counterbalance to the throne, for His representation was far greater and grander than the physical presence of any living king. At one end of the chapel, the earthly king's throne; at the other, the heavenly king's altar. The two rulers of men. It was clear, abundantly clear in this Royal Chapel, that the Church meant to make itself supreme. The Church . . . the Pope . . .

I must have appeared very small and lonely, standing there on the throne, standing so silent, so burdened with thoughts. A boy still, my only assets my title and the blood which ran in my veins. Yet something more: my mind and my will.

Slowly I walked down the steps from my throne. This time I did not pause to genuflect toward the altar as I passed.

10

On my fourteenth birthday, the day after Christmas, I mounted the five steps to the throne in the Palace Chapel, wearing, this time, a crown and royal robes of state and carrying in my right hand a gold and ivory scepter. Under Sicilian law I had come into my majority, and the Pope's guardianship was at an end. I was truly a man. I was truly the King. My heart swelled with the solemn but joyous notes of the organ and choir; graciously I acknowledged the homage of all, regretting only that my mother had not lived to see this day, and that Guglielmo was too ill to attend. On this day I also began to shave; though my beard was light, I had a barber come every morning as a ritual.

The celebrations and feasting lasted until the new year. I caused lanterns and candles to be lighted as at a religious *festa;* and my emblem I emblazoned everywhere—an eagle with wings half-spread, rising to flight. I appeared in the streets of Palermo, riding horseback without armor, wearing a crown, waving to all and distributing bread, wine, and alms. To the shepherds who came down from the hills with bagpipes (as always at *Natale*), I gave special gifts—for they were celebrating both the Christ child's natal day and mine. I released from the prisons all persons convicted of petty crimes, and promised immediate review of all cases remaining. I made a point of passing through the Muslim quarters, for the followers of Mohammed had been ill-used under the Council of Bishops, and I wished to demonstrate that I was king of the Muslims as well as king of the Christians. I was anxious that all should forget my German forebears and think of me chiefly as the grandson of Ruggero the Great. In a single hour I spoke to the people in five tongues; they cheered me wildly and showered me with petals torn from thousands of giant geraniums and roses. That same afternoon, an almond tree burst into full blossom; it was considered a good omen.

At midnight of the first day, though my aides were exhausted, I felt no fatigue, and I summoned Gualtiero to my apartments. I had moved into the small suite of my grandfather Ruggero, with its Gothic arches and rich mosaics of birds and beasts, overlooking, on one side, the domes of San Giovanni degli Eremiti, with its so delicious memories. The Chancellor came at once, and I received him in the outer audience chamber.

It was evident he was disturbed and disgruntled at being called at such an hour. Or perhaps he was abashed at the speed with which I had seized the spiritual mantle of my grandfather; but he dissembled and managed an obsequious smile.

"Our noble Chancellor," I said, "from you, as from a genie, we have three wishes. The first is a complete accounting from the treasury. The second is a record of the disposition of our hereditary royal lands. The third is the immediate recall of our most beloved friend and archbishop, Berardo."

I could see, even by the dim and flickering light of ancient oil lamps, that he paled markedly. He offered no opposition, promising instead an immediate response, though I knew very well he would do nothing without communicating with Rome. Thus the quarrel with the Pope was officially joined. The Archbishopric of Palermo had fallen vacant, and the first test of power was at hand.

Meanwhile the Pope had been, as he wrote, most active in my behalf: he had found me a *fidanzata*. Her name was Costanza, daughter of the King of Aragon. She was ten years older than I, was the widow of the King of Hungary, and had borne one child. It was not her age which bothered me, as I knew very well from experience the infatuation of older women for boys much younger than themselves; but I felt that to follow another king to her bed added nothing to my dignity. Yet Aragon was powerful, and the promise of five hundred fully armed and mounted knights, as part of Princess Costanza's dowry, decided me. After a demurral as a matter of policy, I gave my consent to the Pope; and while I was yet thirteen Costanza and I were pledged by proxy in the cathedral at Saragossa in Spain. Now I was most anxious for her arrival in Palermo—or, rather, for the arrival of the knights. Five hundred knights! *Hòi* . . . !

I had much house cleaning to do before the appearance of my bride; but there was little to rearrange in the cupboards. The Chancellor's report on the treasury showed it practically empty, and my hereditary demesne had been whittled away by German seizures and by gifts of land to Sicilian barons. I found the relatives and friends of the Council of Bishops all well-provided, all well-ensconced behind castle walls.

As I was a king without money or treasure, and a king without land, I was also a king without arms. At my disposal were only a handful of knights loyal to the Norman tradition, a double-handful of soldiers, and a few leaky old galleys. My oars were cracked and splintered, my lances and swords rusty, my flags and banners tattered and faded. Fortifications were crumbling, stores and provisions nonexistent, armories empty. The whole country was in a state of decay. The burdensome taxes were stolen by collectors; monks, nuns and priests fattened on the land; inland Muslims were in rebellion; roads were unsafe from bandits; pirates infested the coasts; murder and robbery were rife in the towns; commerce was at a standstill; hunger was everywhere; the word justice was laughed at as a joke.

For a long time Sicily had been a kingdom without a king. Now I was a king with but the shadow of a kingdom.

I was a king, at fourteen, without a single state adviser I could trust. I was alone. Hence my memories of Berardo were almost of a divine father. In my dreams he mingled confusingly with Zeus, Jupiter, Jehovah, Allah, and my two famous grandfathers. Though publicly I betrayed no emotion, inwardly I was desperate for his return to me. To all observers my self-confidence was impermeable, but in actual fact I sorely needed Berardo's steadying hand. I waited patiently a fortnight; then I acted.

"Why have we seen nothing of the person of the Archbishop Berardo?" I demanded of the Chancellor.

He cringed. "My Lord, three of the five members of the Cathedral Chapter have refused to vote according to your Majesty's designation, and have appealed directly to His Holiness the Pope."

The old fury bounded back into my heart, the fury I had known when Markward's sweaty soldiers had laid hands on my royal body. I was perfectly aware of the rules of this new game, perfectly aware that the three dissenters had voted according to the Pope's orders.

"Banish them!" I cried. "If they have no respect for the wishes of their King, they have no right to live in the Kingdom. Let them board ship by sundown, or forfeit their lives!" I paused and calmed myself. "And you, good Chancellor, find and restore Berardo to his rightful post—or forfeit your own." With a truly malevolent pleasure I noted that he had ceased to rub his hands; he had begun to twitch instead.

I had cut to the core of the matter, to the core of Innocent III's ever-growing empire. It was Innocent's purpose to control completely the election of bishops in all countries, without recourse to the temporal ruler. With absolute power to appoint, transfer, dismiss, Innocent thus dominated a clerical state within a temporal state—exacting loyalty to the Pope rather than to the temporal ruler. With the Church's vast ownership of lands and treasure, the power of the clerical state might easily outweigh the power of the temporal state. Here was a new and subtler Trojan Horse within the Kingdom's gates, a horse filled with priests and friars, true—but whose lust for conquest was no less fierce than if they came with naked sword instead of crucifix. Already Innocent III had become known by the ominous title of *Verus Imperator* of all Christendom.

Other moves had been equally designed to enhance Innocent's position as ruler of a clerical superstate. It was he who elevated the doctrine of transubstantiation to the level of dogma—the belief that, in the Eucharist, the bread and wine are changed outright into the body and blood of Christ. It was Innocent who ordered that henceforth the priest should complete the mysteries facing the altar, with his back toward the congregation—the priest as the representative of the Pope, the Pope as the representative of Christ Himself. All power is derived from God. But, said Innocent, the Pope is "mediator between God and man; nearer than God, farther than man; less than God, but more than man." Nor did Innocent stop without making the logical deduction in his own favor: "God is honored in us when we are honored, and in us is God despised when we are despised." Who, then, would be astonished at the Church's conclusion that submission to the Pope is essential to every man for the salvation of his soul? *Every* man—including kings and emperors. . . .

Within the hour, I sat down and wrote to the Pope about my act of banishment. I told him that my leniency in the matter was due solely to the respect and gratitude I bore him as my erstwhile guardian, and to the respect and devotion I felt for Holy Church. I sent the letter by special messenger, by the fastest small vessel I could find in Palermo harbor.

I had not long to wait for an answer.

The Pope's letter in reply was heavy with ribbons and sealing wax, and evidently the words were weighty as well. As I unfolded the sheets, my hands shook with a tremor of repressed violence, as though my adversary actually had entered my presence. It was a curious letter, for it was written in a tone of pained surprise, taking the position that surely I had not known the import of my action and had been misled by unwise, hotheaded advisers. The language was admonitory, paternal.

"It would have beseemed you to reflect," the Pope wrote, "and to have been warned thereby, how the evildoing of your forefathers—in seeking to arrogate unto themselves spiritual authority—plunged your kingdom into chaos and confusion." So the real trouble was caused, I was told to believe, by the encroachment of the temporal power upon the spiritual; and never again, I was warned, must I be guilty of so grave a breach. Further, my most revered mother, the Queen, had signed a concordat with the Church, assigning to the King only the right of consent in episcopal elections. No electee could function unless he was *persona grata* to the Pope. I had no right whatever to banish the members of the Cathedral Council with whom I felt displeasure; they must be recalled at once. At once!

Again I was not master in my own house, not King in my Kingdom. I had no choice but to obey. So high a price my mother had paid, besides gold, for my guardianship! On all fronts, in the very first weeks of my reign, I was reduced to impotence.

Burdened with gloom and anxiety, I sought surcease in nature, riding out to hunt with falcons—the hunt eventually to become my favorite sport. But on this occasion I felt displeasure with the chief falconer, and nothing improved my mood. I noted that the birds were restless, and ordered a water spray to quiet them. The falconer, however, failed to clean his mouth properly before spraying, and the birds seemed more restless than before. I disliked, too, the clumsy seeling of the eyes of several birds in training; I thought the sewing of eyelids a cruel device as well as dangerous. It is my opinion that the eyes of birds see more than the eyes of men; how can we dare to tamper with organs so wondrous and so delicate?

From a group which included a gerfalcon, a saker, a peregrine, and a goshawk, I chose the peregrine—with a certain wry amusement at its ecclesiastical name. This "pilgrim" was a strong, older bird, and according to the chief falconer, well-trained. As we rode to the hunt I carried her on my heavily gloved left hand, holding the jess—the short thong—in tight. She was a magnificent specimen, and I was eager to see her in flight. I was glad to release her into the clear infinite Sicilian sky.

She circled on powerful wings above a gorge cut between the mountains, and then dived. In moments she rose again, her prey dangling from her claws—two black specks fused into one against the blue. Then, as the lure was spun, obediently she returned to us.

The prey that she brought was a young eagle.

Among the falconers were bursts of surprise and dismay when she landed; in my heart, a chill. So terrible an omen! I drew my short-sword, and with a whistling sound, severed at one stroke the offending peregrine neck.

II

IN THE months succeeding my defeat at the hands of the Pope, I had occupied myself with frenetic energy. When I was busy I was less conscious of the sting of humiliation. Besides my studies, which now included (voluntarily) Church history and the writings of such early Fathers as Irenaeus and Tertullian, I concentrated on the training of dogs, Arab horses, and armed men.

Perhaps I kept a pack of dogs about me so constantly as an antidote to loneliness; but the horses I wished to make surefooted and steady under the most adverse conditions of road and battle. As for the men, I wanted a picked group for both vanguard action and for the protection of my person. I chose, for maximum reliability, young Saracens of the type I had known when I lived in the streets. As Mohammedans, they were insensitive to threats of the priests or intrigues of the Pope; as horsemen, bowmen and lancers, they were unequaled; and as physical specimens they were superb, capable of enduring the most intense strain. I favored high mobility over heavy armor, and I equipped my men with light chain mail and Roman-style breastplates, with the peaked steel helmets called *bacinetti*, and with the thin but strong round arm-shields known as *bracchieri*.

Such a group, in the beginning very small, I tested with various excursions to trouble spots: here and there a band of robbers, a civil disturbance, a pirate raid. In most cases, a show of force and authority was enough to achieve desired results; but once or twice we fought pitched battles in which I found myself in the role of general waging a miniature war. One such expedition brought me to Segesta, and I saw my first Greek temple. Though I was impressed with its age, I was then too young to appreciate fully its pure, clean beauty.

Another expedition took place when pirates were troubling

Cefalù. For several reasons I was more than glad to defend this particular town. My grandfather Ruggero had built a massive cathedral here, in fulfillment of a vow when he was saved from shipwreck; and my grandfather, my mother and my father were buried here. I went at once to the cathedral, to bring flowers and pay my respect to the dead. I found them separately entombed in heavy sarcophagi, designed by my grandfather and carved under his direction from red Egyptian porphyry. To my astonishment, I found another sarcophagus quite empty. I resolved on the spot to appropriate the empty one for myself, for I rather liked its curious design. It was a triangular pediment set above a half-circle as a base, supported by four male lions, and marked with mysterious ancient pagan symbols. I ordered that all the sarcophagi be transported to the cathedral in Palermo: the resting place for dead kings and queens should be their capital. Musingly I touched the cold polished surface of the stone, remembering the words of the Psalm: "Their sepulchers will be their homes forever. . . ." Silent and reflective, I left the crypt.

In the scorching heat of midsummer, I took up an impregnable position on the great yellow-gray rock which dominates the town of Cefalù and dwarfs even the lofty steepled towers of the Norman cathedral. For my private headquarters I chose, primarily from a sense of the past, the ruins of the temple of Diana—which must surely have been built a thousand years before Christ was born. From the great rock we had a commanding expanse of both the land and the sea. It was my theory that accurate observation of an enemy's movements was half of any battle, and I—who fretted under the disadvantage of mild near-sightedness—had chosen for my elite guard only men who could see with ease the tiny star above the bend in the handle of the Big Dipper. Further, we kept perpetual watch in all directions. Thus was spotted a small group of travelers approaching by horse along the winding, rocky Messina road; and, at almost the same moment, the glint of a triangular lateen sail along the coast. Pirates! As we watched, it appeared that the pirates were preparing to land in a distant cove where the road passed close to the sea—a natural ambush. By immediate action, with our fast horses, we had a chance to surprise the pirates from the rear and save the travelers.

I was about to give the command to mount when a breathless scout arrived to report the results of an advance sortie. An important personage was en route, the scout gasped, but the travelers had no armed escort. The figures we took for armed retainers were in fact but monks, and the personage was dressed in the long dark robes and wide-brimmed low-crowned hat of a high ecclesiastic. The scout could not make out the family arms, but the other insignia were clearly of an archbishop. On hearing this, I was tempted to let the pirates have their way, for an archbishop would be a juicy prize (as one day I myself was to learn when I captured a covey of them). But on second thought, I guessed, with rage, that the Pope was sending me, unelected and unannounced, a new archbishop—almost a physical slap in the face. What a delight to snatch a papal morsel out of pirate jaws!

"*Avanti!*" I shouted. "*Avanti. . . !*"

The ride over the potholed rock-strewn road was more dangerous than the armed engagement, for our coming was wholly unexpected. At the sound of our hoofbeats the pirates attempted flight back to their vessel, and in their disarray we pulverized them. In the actual fighting, I took no part, as these opponents were unworthy of a king. Minutes later, around a sudden bend, the travelers came upon the scene. They halted in consternation on sight of the hacked and bloody pirate bodies. I myself stood astride the road, my white horse prancing, my shield up but my lance at rest.

The figure in the long dark robes, riding a mottled horse, slowly advanced. His robes and beard were streaked with the dust of the journey, as though he had been painted with smudges of gray. His face was dripping with sweat. He stared at me with fixed eyes, as at an apparition.

"Your Highness has saved my life," he said in a clear voice. "Now I may doubly celebrate your Majesty's wedding, as God, with your assistance, has clearly willed that I should do so!" He took off his wide-brimmed hat, doffing it toward me, and for the first time I saw his face without shadow. Inexplicably, he winked.

Deep memories suddenly stirred within me. "Berardo!" I cried. "At last, Berardo!"

I dropped my lance and maneuvered my horse to his side. In a single motion we were clasped in each other's arms; and as we kissed, the tears from my eyes mingled with the sweat on his cheeks.

"My son," he said, "my son—"

12

JOYFULLY we rode toward Palermo, banners flying, with Berardo on my right hand. Like any peasant, he munched on salted watermelon seeds, in spite of the heat of the road. We talked incessantly, covering the events of the years since our last meeting.

Berardo was strangely vague as to just what pressures had been applied to effect his return. He must have had some very degrading information about some very private matters in Rome. Such a victory was unthinkable for reasons less realistic. In any case, he was abruptly informed one day by a messenger-friar from the Curia that no obstacles would be raised to the resumption of his post in Palermo. After his flight from Markward, he had hidden himself as a simple monk in a monastery in Capua. He was not recognized. For a long time he had been ill—bedridden in fact; but his delight at the good news accomplished his recovery.

Each of us marveled that the other had survived, and what I ascribed to destiny Berardo ascribed to the will of God. Why, Berardo said, should men who worked evil be permitted the exclusive claim that God favored them? The ways of Satan were not the will of God. But I said, if my survival, and his, had been the will of God, why then had Guglielmo suffered so in my behalf? Was it the will of God that a young person innocent of all crime, except helping me, should approach the throes of death after so long-drawn-out an agony? Ah, mysterious are the ways of God, said Berardo; life is a mystery, death is a mystery. Then he added hastily: life should be spent not in the gloomy contemplation of death, but in the fullest use of life itself. True salvation lies in good works, not in the number of beads told, prayers said, candles lighted. And this, of course, is what set him apart from clergy and Church, made him a doctrinal heretic, and gave me the closest rapport I have ever had with any professional representative of any faith. For, to reverse the Pope's formula, Berardo was more than a priest: he was a wise and good man, the best that is human. Such is faith in Man—not of my time, but perhaps in the future.

Barely had we sighted the bulk of Monte Pellegrino, an azure haze in the distance, when we were met by a messenger riding full gallop from the Palace. Guglielmo had taken a turn for the worse, spitting quantities of blood, and begged me to come to him at once. My mood of joy was changed to foreboding, and we completed our journey in silence.

Guglielmo was surrounded, as always, by doctors dressed in their flowing red gowns and red caps. The caps were tied to their heads with white bands about their throats. I had given orders that he should have the best of attention, but over the months I had watched with increasing unease the doctors' ministrations. I was about to come to the conclusion that though they mouthed the names of Galen and Hippocrates and Avicenna and Rhazes, in point of fact they knew little or nothing of medicine, either Greek or Arabic. As the common people said derisively, they "understood only ass's piss."

For reasons best known to themselves, they had brought embalmed dogs, cats, and birds to the sickroom. They burned candles which gave off an acrid, loathsome stench, and were said to have been made from wax droppings before holy altars at Easter. Each day they took a specimen of Guglielmo's urine in a thick glass and held it up to the sunlight, in a gesture which seemed to me more like divination than analysis. From the urine they diagnosed Guglielmo's illness as having a particular temperament: a hot-dry humour. The cure, therefore, must be of a contrary temperament: a cold-wet humour. The therapy consisted of applying to Guglielmo's chest the cold-wet leaves of plants born of dragons, serpents, and scorpions. Indicated, too, they said, was a brew made of the dried skin of a toad mixed with goat urine. Many times had I seen him gag and vomit on drinking this. Lastly, they bled him; and at the end of each treatment he seemed weaker than before.

When we arrived in Guglielmo's room he was able to greet me only with his eyes. One doctor was taking his pulse. Another held under his nose the *spongia somnifera*—a sponge soaked in an elixir made from the marvelous mandragora, the plant with a root in human form. To extract this magical plant from the soil required a black dog, a sword, and a horn: the dog to pull up the root, the sword to kill the dog, and the horn to drown the howls of the mandragora as it died. So efficacious was the mandragora—the doctors said—that when it failed, all else failed, and hope was lost. And now the doctors were shaking their heads. . . .

I stood in a kind of paralysis, hearing nothing but the resonant buzz of multitudes of flies, feeling only the heaviness in my heart, thinking but of Guglielmo's soul. Would I see it leave his body? Would I recognize it if I saw it? Would this other part of Guglielmo know me, and remember the love I bore him? I would have pleaded with the soul not to leave him, but I sensed that already neither Guglielmo nor his soul could hear me. Even so, I was not resigned to Guglielmo's death. I resented it . . . bitterly . . . bitterly.

With a sudden, jerky movement he sat up, pushing the doctors away so that the magical mandragora was dropped to the floor. He gasped, coughed. Blood spurted from his mouth, covered his body, soaked the bed. He fell back, twitching. The doctors fluttered like scarlet birds taking flight, crossed themselves and sighed in unison.

From the background two hooded monks advanced, their eyes but slits; I thought of black-plumaged vultures closing in on prey. But since it was the body, not the soul, they wanted, they had to wait a little. Precedence was taken by a priest, whose expressionless face I did not recognize. He was holding a ciborium containing the Blessed Sacrament. Behind him a pale-cheeked acolyte tinkled a silver bell with one hand and with the other held aloft a long, lighted taper—like a beacon to Guglielmo's flickering soul.

In a gesture of authority, Berardo brushed priest and acolyte aside. "You are too late," he said.

So Berardo, my Berardo, administered last rites to Guglielmo, my Guglielmo—symbolically hearing a confession of sin, symbolically touching the wafer to stiffening lips. Absolution and the Holy Sacrament . . . so tenderly, so gently, as though Berardo held in his own hand not Guglielmo's hand, but his soul. So tenderly, so gently, Berardo closed Guglielmo's eyes.

"It is written: 'The Lord giveth, the Lord taketh away,'" he said. "Blessed is the name of the Lord."

As for me, I shed not a tear. It was in that moment that I firmly resolved to found—someday—an academy of medicine whose science would be based on the living body of man.

13

I WAS hard put to avoid looking like a pauper in the eyes of my betrothed. Though her arrival from Spain had been planned originally for March, she was delayed until August—so the royal garments which had been prepared for the springtime were not suitable for the late summer heat, and had to be prepared anew. Costs were therefore doubled—except, of course, for the plate, the jewels, the crown. I had decided, in the interests of economy, to present to my Queen some of the jewels I myself had worn at my coronation as a child—the six Byzantine enamels portraying various saints, the six golden eagles with wings of lapis lazuli. But her crown was to be newly fabricated, and I spared no expense.

The form I chose was a round bronze cap, hammered thin, banded in gold set with pearls at intervals. Above the golden band were patterns worked in seed pearls, and a ribbon of pearls which both circled the crown and formed a cross with its center at the top. Everywhere were encrusted giant pearls of rare beauty, polished rubies, topaz, sapphires, amethysts. From the sides, like enormous earrings, hung long triangular pendants of golden chain bearing crossbars and dangling squares of gold set with jewels. As a finishing touch, in the center of the crown above the forehead was mounted a huge ruby with the name *Costanza* engraved in Arabic. The whole effect was splendid and impressive, Byzantine, oriental, indeed almost barbaric. The workmanship, as compared with the few jeweled objects left from antiquity, was crude; but the craftsmen were the best I could find. At my court, I resolved to revive arts and crafts, that such skills might not fall completely into decadence. But just then I was unable to pay for the crown, much less able to subsidize a school for goldsmiths.

So anxious was I for funds that I decided, in spite of Berardo's advice to the contrary, to extort money from Jews. This was a prevailing practice of Christian princes, and took the form of tricking Jews into either renouncing their own religion or denying the divinity of Christ. This latter was a dangerous matter: for blasphemy, in Catholic lands, severe penalties were applied—and hapless Jews were forced to buy themselves out of difficulty.

I therefore called before me the richest Jew in the Kingdom, a graybeard quadruple my age, a merchant and moneylender, a man of much guile and worldly experience. To him, after compliments on his reputation and wisdom, I posed the question: "Which is the one true religion—Judaism, Christianity, Mohammedanism?"

He begged my permission to reply with a parable, and I assented. Thus he began: "Once there lived an old man who owned a precious ring of rare and beautiful craftsmanship, a ring reputed to insure divine aid to its owner. Now the old man also had three sons, and each of the sons coveted the ring, each feeling that someday the father's most beloved son would inherit the ring. The old man was greatly troubled by the attitude of his sons, and was loath to die, for he was sure they would fall to quarreling and fighting among themselves. One day he hit upon the idea of making two additional rings, so like his own that he himself could tell no difference between them. Thereupon he died in peace, leaving a ring to each of his sons. And the sons, instead of quarreling over the rings, were perfectly content: for each son was certain that he alone possessed the original."

In my delight at the old Jew's answer I laughed aloud. "You are a man after our own heart," I said.

At once I named him to a royal post as financial adviser—much to the disgust of Gualtiero di Palearia, who (in deference to the power of the Pope) still held the office of Chancellor. Eventually I trusted so in the old Jew's judgment that he became one of my most frequent counselors. He offered me a very large loan without interest, which in due course I repaid in full. He also helped me to work out the details of a head tax which I applied to Jews and Muslims—not so heavy as to encourage conversion to Christianity, but heavy enough to make them feel their faith had value. It was I, however, not he, who insisted on graduating the tax in accord with ability to pay—thereby increasing the content of my coffers manyfold.

Despite all this, many of the wedding festivities had to be

arranged on credit, in anticipation of the arrival of bags of gold as part of my betrothed's dowry. I sensed the reluctance in some quarters to lay out large sums in my behalf, and my pride was stung at having to go begging, crown in hand, so to speak. I made up my mind that I would set the finances of the kingdom so to rights that others should come to me as suppliants, not I to them. But to rescue a country from chaos takes time.

At long last my lookout atop Monte Pellegrino announced that the Spanish galleys had been sighted, and I gave the word which turned the whole marina into a carnival. As the ships docked they were welcomed with waving banners and music from trumpets, then saluted with volleys of flowers. I myself did not go to the *molo* to greet my betrothed, but sent Gualtiero as my deputy—after all, it was his master the Pope who had arranged this marriage. But chiefly I felt a sense of royal dignity in reverse proportion to my years: my bride must come to me.

I was, in fact, far more anxious to see the five hundred fully armed knights than my wife-to-be. I ordered that they should escort Costanza through the center of the city to the Norman Palace, two by two and spaced at a horse's length apart. I thus hoped to impress on all and sundry the extent of the military aid I had received—with all its implications. I was sure that the news of the knights' arrival would spread with the speed of bird flight, and give some of the troublesome barons a cautious thought or two. As I saw the cavalcade winding up the road to the palace gate, lances and banners aloft, drums throbbing, armor gleaming, I was exultant with delight.

At once their leader, Count Alfonso of Provence, Costanza's brother, came to me and offered homage. He bowed with a graceful Spanish flourish, and I wondered if Costanza was as pleasant to look upon as he. I raised him with my hand:

"As we become brothers-in-law," I said, "so shall we also become brothers-in-arms." And his sun-bronzed face lighted at the prospect of fighting.

I did not see the Princess Costanza until that evening when I called upon her with the Archbishop Berardo to pay my respects. I found her being fanned by dwarfs, for the night was hot; and to amuse her, a pet Gibraltar monkey on a golden chain was doing tricks. She was attended by her brother, the Count Alfonso, and by her ladies-in-waiting. She was veiled as when she had passed through the streets. She was tall, taller than I, as

I realized when she stood; and of her features I could see nothing except two dark unsmiling eyes. I kissed her hand, and expressed my joy at her arrival.

As a gift I had decided to bring no necklaces, rings, or bracelets, as these were part of her regalia and she would see them on the morrow, but to bring her the supreme present—the crown. This was of course unusual. I was pleased at the general gasp of astonishment when I clapped my hands and two Nubian slaves entered bearing a purple silk cushion, on which rested the crown. I wanted above all to study her face as she examined the great jewels, for in the reflected light of the torches the jewels glowed and pulsated like living things.

"Madonna," I said, "tomorrow at high noon this symbol of majesty shall be yours. We bring it now as a humble offering for your pleasure, as it was designed by us and each single stone selected with thoughts of love."

No change could be detected in the expression of her deep dark eyes, and I felt rebuffed. With the rebuff came a sense of anger. Because she is so old, I thought, and has known a man already, she sees me as a boy and not a grown king. Immediately I regretted a marriage which had not yet finally taken place. I wished most especially that her name were not like my mother's: *Costanza*. . . .

"My gratitude is infinite," this Costanza replied in Latin with an accent foreign to my ears. "With the help of Heaven, I shall try to be a worthy consort for your Highness, as God has willed our union." The tone was calm, but with a note of resignation which I did not miss. If she did not like men, she would nevertheless submit to a king as part of the Christian duty of a queen.

Her personal gifts to me were a black crucifix, carved from the wood of Christ's cradle; a reliquary of silver, containing a tooth of John the Baptist; and a reliquary of gold, containing a shred of the tablecloth used by the Saviour at the Last Supper. Though all were relics of the utmost importance, entirely suitable for veneration by the multitudes, I should have been forewarned that Costanza was herself a religious fanatic. As I learned later, she subscribed in private to the practices of the Flagellants—though only once in the thirteen years of our marriage did I see her collection of leather thongs and whips, tipped at the ends with beads of lead and tiny barbs of iron. Thus she atoned for her sins, whatever they were, and assured herself entry into Heaven free of spiritual blemish.

Next day we were married in the cathedral by the Archbishop Berardo. It was stiflingly humid, with *scirocco*, the hot wind from Africa. And though we all dripped with sweat under our magnificient robes and armor, we deviated not a hair's breadth from the prescribed pomp of our ceremony. Trumpets blew, choirs sang, hallelujahs were lifted to God. We exchanged rings and the pledges of holy matrimony. With my own hands I crowned Costanza Queen. The spectacle was exalting; but my heart was heavy as a block of Greek-quarried stone. Then the feasting and drinking began, to stupefaction.

That night in the royal bedchamber the ceremony was completed. I had selected Berardo and the Chamberlain Riccardo as witnesses; the massive four-poster canopied bed was hung with curtains of transparent silk, so that their vision might not be impaired. Berardo reminded me that the Church considered as mortal sin any coital position other than man-above-woman; and that he, as Archbishop-witness, did not wish to be forced to report to Rome than an heir of mine had been conceived in mortal sin. He therefore hoped that the heat of passion would not cause me to forget his words. I reminded him, in reply, that Ovid in *The Art of Love* had written: "from your own bodies fix your methods—one fashion does not suit all alike." Nevertheless, to avoid embarrassing him officially, I would pay heed to his words. I caught a bemused glint in his eyes, as acolytes marched about the bed swinging censers and he blessed the nuptial chamber.

My wife came to bed veiled, wearing an ivory silk nightgown embroidered in gold with the initials FR—*Fridericus Rex.* When the veils were removed by her ladies and the gown opened, by the light of the great candles I saw for the first time her face and body. The face was long, sad, cadaverous, Spanish; the body was perfect, except that it was pitted with masses of tiny scars (in my innocence I supposed she had been scourged by the pox). Though she had luxuriant fair hair, which I called beautiful, my admiration of this natural asset availed me nothing. With me she was stiff and unyielding, and I thought of the warm supple flesh of Aïsha. Thus I played with illusion.

And at dawn, the witnesses were able to report to the waiting crowds that the royal marriage had been consummated—thirteen times. I had hoped to score fourteen, in honor of my years, but that last was beyond me. . . .

However, everyone was well satisfied, including the Queen.

14

I did not spend the traditional eight days of seclusion with my bride, but moved at once, amid some grumbling, to organize my military force. I had no time to waste in gluttonizing, as I wished to undertake a campaign against the barons before the coming autumn rains.

Not for a moment had the encroachments against my hereditary demesne ceased, and it almost seemed as though the haughty but greedy nobles were testing me to the breaking point. I had the feeling now that my worst enemies were not the remnants of the Germans, but the greatest landowners, who sought continual aggrandizement for themselves. Of these, the most offensive by far were in Calabria. Their peasants literally groaned under the yoke, and my rule was scorned. It seemed to me good strategy to strike the strongest first—though to do so meant a long hot march from one end of Sicily to the other, over mountains and through dry river beds which might at any minute become roaring torrents, then across the treacherous Strait of Messina (the ancient Scylla and Charybdis) to the mainland and a difficult landing. But first I made a legal move.

As was my right, I issued a royal edict ordering all landowners to submit their title deeds to the crown for reëxamination. The edict was read aloud and posted in every market center. The Calabrian reaction rose like a strong sudden wind at sea. I was defied. I gathered my Saracen guard close about me, for I knew that once again my life was in danger, and prepared to chastise those nobles who wilfully created disorder in the Realm.

The ringleader of the Calabrian malcontents was the fat, middle-aged, loud-mouthed Anfuso di Roto, Count of Tropea. He it was who had appealed to me sometime before for two castles which were situated in the midst of traditionally royal lands; and in addition, he—who could scarcely distinguish the prow from the stern of a galley—wanted the title of Admiral. I refused, as was certainly proper, and he became so choleric that I thought he would, like *il diavolo,* go up in a puff of smoke. As he left my presence he shouted this incoherent threat:

"I will not be treated as a commoner—else I'll show you my strength!"

For the time being I chose to overlook his behavior, though my own rage was as icy as his was hot. It was as if he had called me a *cretino*. I could have killed him on the spot; but I had no wish to provoke a civil war. Despite my restraint, however, his indiscretions continued. He returned to Calabria, and went about braying that he owed no fealty to me. The noise he made was so loud that very little time was needed for it to reach my ears.

"I will be equal to the King!" he cried. "Here in Calabria I will be equal to the King!"

By now my Aragonese knights were surfeited with tournaments, wine and lovemaking, and were anxious to do battle with anyone I declared my enemy. They were so cohesive a fighting force, and so well armed, that they felt themselves invincible. The time had come to put them to the test; so I ordered them, under the command of Costanza's brother, to break camp and take the long coast road to Messina. I felt sure that, once they had crossed the straits to Calabrian soil, the braggart Count of Tropea would flee from the weight of their armor. Or, if he stood still to fight, he faced the danger of a peasant rising in his rear—as he was far-famed by his nickname, the "Hangman."

Alas, my knights and their squires never reached Messina. At about the halfway point, they were seized by sudden and violent loss of control of their bowels—a difficult thing for men in armor. As described to me afterward, they felt oppressed by enormous weights, sharp pains stabbed them in their abdomens, and they vomited as though poisoned. Then they began to die. With early and extreme rigor mortis, they lay about one another stiffened in grotesque and horrifying positions. Hardly fifty of the whole group survived, and Costanza's luckless brother was among the casualties.

At first I suspected poison, though never for a moment did I believe the rumor that the knights had been bewitched. Nor did I give much credence to Gualtiero's statement that he had known all along the expedition was doomed to failure because of the conjunction of Saturn and Mars under the sign of the Balance—though from someone else I might have believed the stars had brought me bad fortune.

On investigation, I discovered that two or three days before the onset of the malady, almost the whole company had paused to drink water from a famous shrine to the Virgin. In an adjoining house several persons had died mysterious deaths, allegedly by witchcraft. I caused the house to be inspected, and found nothing except that offal was dumped in such a way that it polluted the water. Perhaps the excrement of the dying had spread the malady, I reasoned; and all this I remembered, some years later, when I came to decree health regulations for the cities.

But what little I had learned of water pollution was no compensation for the loss of my knights. The loss could be described only by one word: disaster. Not a major disaster, true; but at that moment a very serious setback for me. The Queen and I went into mourning for her brother, and withdrew from all social and festive gatherings. Though it seemed evident to everyone that I was in no position to enforce my rule on the Kingdom, nevertheless I decided secretly on a bold move. Secretly, that is, except for discussion with Berardo.

One day I had heralds announce that the King was going on a journey. He planned to hunt boar in the forests near Piazza Armerina, and birds in the marshes near Catania. The Queen would accompany the King. How could the slightest military intent exist in such travels? Certainly none! Only the Archbishop Berardo was left behind to keep an eye on the capital.

Actually I was stopping at Piazza Armerina because I was genuinely interested in the ruins of a vast Imperial Roman hunting lodge, a villa called *Platia*. And I chose Catania not only because the falconing was good, but because it was close to Calabria—yet not close enought to be obvious (as would have been the case had I chosen Messina on the straits). If I took a larger Saracen guard than usual, plus all the knights available, everyone was sure to think I did so because of dangers on the road. The greedy barons clearly were to be left in peace—what had they now to fear from me?

We traveled slowly and with some pomp, as I wished to make as great an impression as possible on the countryside—particularly on the Muslims who had migrated in great numbers to the interior. Everywhere I found myself greeted with cool reserve, having stimulated neither fear nor admiration. Perhaps, instead, I was something of a curiosity—a boy king married to a mature widow, the great Ruggero's grandson who was nonetheless impoverished and ineffectual. Sensing all this, I chewed inwardly on rage while outwardly I was all placidity and smiles.

I was delighted with our stay in Piazza Armerina, and in the ruins of the imposing villa I found much to interest me—so much that I had no time for the chase at all. It appeared that the huge edifice, or rather collection of edifices, had been inhabited more or less up to the time of the Arab conquest, had been partially restored under the Normans, and finally destroyed in an insane rage by my mother's much older half-brother called Guglielmo *il Cattivo*—and for this single act of vandalism he fully deserves for all posterity his title of "the Bad."

In spite of the ruin, I was able to delineate four groups of halls, each complete with galleries, peristyles, courts, and baths. Some of the superb mosaic floors were visible, and others I ordered to be uncovered of the dirt and sand which had drifted across them. I particularly admired the scenes of hunting in Africa. Depicted were lions, tigers, camels, antelopes, crocodiles, huge river beasts with great nostrils, and huge land beasts with horns on the snout (certainly the prototype of the "unicorn" whose bones al-Kaid and I had found). For some animals, the Romans hunted with nets, just as we do. I liked also the scene with Diomedes; the stag and Theseus; the labors of Hercules; the circus with chariots drawn by peacocks. When we came to the ten maidens playing ball, all nude except for narrow cloths about their hips and breasts, the Queen turned aside; and at the erotic scenes she covered her eyes with her veils—blushing, I am sure. Without the Queen's presence, I inspected some of the nude statuary which had been excavated, and I was struck by the extreme beauty of the bodies, both male and female. Nowhere in evidence were any of the diabolical gargoyles which among us passes for sculpture. Even the Roman angels, though well equipped with wings, were naked, and revealed quite unashamedly their genitals; about the sex of Christian angels I had often wondered.

Of all the items of interest, I found most fascinating the system of aqueducts, lavatories, and baths. Not only was the constant music of running fountains to be heard, but clear clean water flowed continuously through the lavatories and latrines, washing away excrement and filth. The baths themselves must have been a delight. The *tepidarium* was a room heated by warm air circulated through double walls, causing the bather to sweat. In the *caldarium* a hot bath was taken in a basin, and in the *frigidarium* a final refreshing cold bath. Also provided were facilities for massages, and rubdowns with olive oil. Seats were available for visitors. Mosaics, statuary, and bas-reliefs provided adornment. Everyone bathed—noble, plebeian, slave. Apparently the Romans bathed not only for health's sake but for pleasure, making a bath—since nudity was accepted as a normal state—a kind of social occasion. Alas, we Christians hardly ever bathe. We are not much interested in the body, but chiefly in the soul. On the spot I decided to overlook my Christian origins and to bathe every day—rain or shine, hot or cold. And when I build my castles of the future I shall provide chapels for the body and leave the churches for the soul.

But I could not tarry forever, indulging in the sport of antiquarianism, for the present world was too demanding. If I could not restore the Imperial villa, I could restore the prestige of an Imperial descendant—as indeed I was.

Ahead of me was a delicate and dangerous task; I would use a hunting net, like the Romans. But my net would be invisible.

15

WE LEFT the mountains and crossed the flat fertile plain toward Catania, marveling at the black, hardened rivers of lava which now and again obstructed our path. On our left loomed snow-capped Etna, massive, gigantic beyond belief. Mushroom-shaped clouds occasionally puffed heavenward from the crater, with an ominous rumble like indigested thunder. At night the whole summit glowed with bursts of fire and incandescent stones—an awesome, terrifying sight. Was Etna truly, as the ancients believed, the forge of Vulcan; or were these the fires of Hell, as the priests now said, licking upward from beneath the earth as a warning to ever-sinful man?

Truly frightening are the priestly descriptions of Hell: an inverted cone of many layers, each ridge reserved for sinners of its special category, each ridge with its special torments, ending finally in a frozen pit. Great putrid whirlwinds blow across the ridges, scattering offal and decaying filth over the naked bodies of those condemned to eternal torture. Rivers of blood and of boiling pitch are filled with drowning victims. Men rave in madness from the scorching thirst. Souls wander cleft from chin to crotch, all internal organs dangling. Giant insects sting, winged demons torment with sharpened forks. Worms writhe in living flesh. Harpies with bird beaks tear bodies limb from limb and feed on the bloody parts. Men's genitals are eaten by huge scaly turtles, women are raped by the fanged heads of huge poisonous snakes. Slimy green demons rake open children's bellies with long curved claws. Bodies are frozen in ice with only heads protruding. Satan himself stands at the frozen center, buffeted by gales of smoke and flame, exhaling the stench of death. He is a monster figure with furry legs and cloven hoofs, bat wings, horns and a tail. He has three heads—one red, one black, one green—in mockery of the Holy Trinity. His clawlike hands stuff bloody human flesh between his sharpened teeth. He is waiting . . . waiting . . . for all sinners, all heretics, all unbelievers. Thus are we threatened with Hell from birth to death.

Now, as our horses jogged along at so great a distance from Etna and Hell that we were safe, I wondered (as I watched) if the smoke and flame might not be as natural a manifestation as water, earth, and air. I must find time, I thought, to ascend the volcano as high as man might go, and judge for myself the characteristics of its behavior. And at the thought, I felt afraid—but more curious than afraid. In the days to come, as I hunted in the lakes and marshes, Etna became a constant companion—so much a part of the landscape that a mountain which burned seemed normal. I was afraid no longer.

My hunts, which included, always, observation of nature, were part of the plan against the barons—a plan of pretense not unlike the innocent sightseeing of Justinian's wily general, Belisarius, in this self-same area. Each day I returned from the hunt with two or three fewer men—not lost in the marshes, but dispatched in disguise to Calabria. In this way, the spies of the Count of Tropea had nothing to report, and the Count and his cronies were lulled to sleep. On the advantages of their carelessness and my surprise, I held great expectations.

All went well. My Saracens, disguised as monks, merchants or Arabians newly arrived—or even, a few, as women—crossed the straits, arousing no suspicion. Their arms were smuggled across at night; and the horses were shipped in batches by bogus traders going to fairs. At last all was in readiness. The appointed day arrived—a festa.

At the strategic hour, when the drinking and merrymaking were at their height, my Saracens struck. The Count Paolo of Geraci they took as he stumbled from the village piazza into the darkness to piss on a wall; the Count Ruggero they took as he dawdled to relight a candle in the procession of a local saint; the Count of Tropea they took, flustered and amazed, just as he was about to exercise his feudal right of *jus primae noctis* with the pretty young bride of one of his peasants. Others they took, also —the brashest, the meanest, the most dangerous. With their prey they converged at Reggio, where I had vessels awaiting them, and set sail, with a fair wind, for Catania. At one blow, I had wiped out my most implacable opponents. Such was my good fortune.

How the news spread! To make sure that all men were convinced of the truth that I had arrested my enemies, I marched them in chains through the streets of Catania, wearing rich clothes and coronets as marks of their rank. As for the Count of Tropea, he humbled himself and bowed low. When I saw his fat buttocks, I laughed and said:

"Well, I never raised a pig—but this one I shall be happy to relieve of its bacon!" Some of the courtiers joined me in laughter, but some thought the remark too crude.

Straightway I addressed a circular letter throughout the Kingdom, to all nobles and prelates of importance, explaining my actions and implying that others who defied me would meet the same fate. I was precise and clear. I was determined to treat my captives in a manner both stern and merciful, and though I intended to imprison them until their tempers had cooled and their fraudulently acquired lands were reorganized, I denied this group none of the luxuries to which they had been accustomed. My father would have drawn and quartered—or at the least, beheaded—them all; but I had made up my mind to adopt a policy of violence only as a last resort. I hoped to become so powerful that I could afford this luxury for myself, though of all my advisers only Berardo supported my point of view.

The Queen, incidentally, suggested that the prisoners be stripped naked and flogged through the streets with lashes of spiked steel. (Privately I thanked heaven that this Costanza was not a man and not my enemy.) As she was then suffering from pregnancy, I took care to placate her by suggesting that her remedy be used some other time on captives who were not Christian—and who therefore had forfeited the right to brotherly love. In this spirit we celebrated Christmas.

Well satisfied with my hunt and the game I had bagged, I thought of hanging up their coronets like stags' antlers, as trophies. But this of course was only a momentary fancy. Quite unawares, I was faced with a new situation which made the revolt of the nobles seem like playing a game of knucklebones with children. In January, after a rousing New Year, we mounted horses for the return to Palermo—without the slightest intimation of the danger awaiting. I had not even the echo of a whisper to prepare me for the fact that my good friend and protector, that honest and faithful Bishop-Chancellor, Gualtiero di Palearia, had again betrayed me. For his own devious purposes he had chosen to withhold from me certain critical information received from the Pope.

My career as King was threatened with termination; and, indeed, my life itself was at stake. Unknowing, and lulled by my first major success as a monarch, I rode on through rough winter winds toward threatening disaster.

My crown rested safely, I thought, in my saddlebags.

16

I HAD BECOME the last of the male Hohenstaufens. My Uncle Philipp had been murdered in Bamberg, one day in the early summer of the year I ascended the throne. Of this event, of course, I had been informed. I knew, also, that the murderer was a disappointed suitor for the hand of my cousin Beatrice, who had passed only recently her eleventh birthday—but who was nevertheless eminently desirable as a wife because of her Hohenstaufen blood. At this point the Pope, who never seemed to tire of his activities as matchmaker, conceived the plan of marrying Beatrice to Otto—her unfortunate father's mortal enemy.

Thus the Pope provided Otto with a legitimate claim to the Empire, nullified my claims, and isolated Sicily for himself as a papal fief. Otto, who was no more than a hulking German gladiator with the physique of a giant and the culture of a pygmy, was to be crowned Emperor by the Pope. These favors, naturally, had a price. Otto promised, among other things, a completely free hand to the Pope in German episcopal elections; and also renounced all claims of the Empire to the Kingdom of Sicily. Of these details I was informed in bits and pieces; but only with Berardo's help was I able eventually to put together the picture puzzle.

At about the time of my own wedding, the delicate Beatrice (how she must have trembled at the sight of Otto!) was betrothed to the Emperor-elect. While I was amusing myself with the mosaics of seminude maidens playing ball, Otto was crowned in Rome. I was not invited to the party—no doubt being thought much too young for such complicated political games. Then the Pope relaxed from his labors, for at last he seemed to have consummate success as the maker of kings and emperors.

Alas for him, he relaxed too soon. When Otto looked in the

Roman mirrors, he saw not poor Otto the Welf, but the Holy Roman Emperor Otto IV. Suddenly he became conscious of his size and might. It was not long before the Pope had publicly to admit: ". . . the sword we fashioned for ourselves deals us dire blows." But, as always with the Pope, there were ways and means of blunting the sword and weakening the blows.

The Curia of the Church not only admitted, but openly boasted, that in its service it had "the ears and eyes of many." Otto was quickly to learn (and I also in due course) that the boast was far from idle. Hardly had Otto formulated his plans before their details were known to the Pope. Hardly had the first of Otto's invading soldiers set foot upon Church lands before Otto's excommunication was read aloud in the churches. All his vassals were released from their oaths of fealty, all who aided him were excommunicated and damned. And suddenly the Pope remembered that his former ward was also a Hohenstaufen, who even as a child had been elected King of the Germans. A new phase in the relationship of guardian and ward had begun.

Of all this, the ward was duly informed through his Bishop-Chancellor, whose ears and eyes were no doubt part of the Curia's system of hearing and seeing. But where the ears and eyes functioned, the tongue failed. This was the vital information Gualtiero chose to suppress: *my subject German barons of Apulia had leagued themselves secretly with Otto, and had promised collaboration in the seizure of my Kingdom.*

It was Berardo, not Gualtiero, who brought me the news that the Germans, led by one of Markward's successors, had infiltrated the whole of my mainland nobility with treason. At last the showdown with my Janus-faced Bishop-Chancellor had come: he would have one face or the other, but not both.

I called him to me privately, once again in my grandfather Ruggero's little salon of the golden mosaics. He bowed, but I had other plans.

"The knees—" I said curtly, "—the knees, and so remain."

"As you command, your Majesty," he said, visibly trembling.

"Honored Chancellor," I said in soft tones, "have you had word of late from Diepold von Schweinspeunt, that Count of Acerra whom not long ago you recommended so highly for the post of Lord Chief Justice of Apulia—and whom we therefore appointed? Any word at all—good word, that we may rejoice? Or bad word, that we may give thought to the protection of our Realm against our enemies?"

"No word at all, my Lord," he said, even on his knees rubbing his hands to scrub away the taint of money. Then his voice thickened—"that is, no word worth troubling the serenity of your Majesty. Rumors, or course, many many rumors—but of facts . . ." He ceased rubbing his hands and shrugged his shoulders. His composure had returned.

"And have you checked the rumors to ascertain the facts?"

"My Lord!" he said, blustering. "The rumors run thick as thieves—no man could separate the true from the false!"

"Alas that you are but one man," I said, "for the rumor that Diepold is true to us, appears false; and the rumor that you are false to us, appears true. What say you, our Bishop-Chancellor?"

He paled, and came near to groveling on his belly. "Surely your Revered Person would not believe—"

"Stand up!" I ordered, tiring of this comedy. "Since you are but one man, it is better that you hold but one office. Henceforth you are no longer Chancellor, even though you retain the title. Confine your activities solely to the functions of Bishop; put on your miter and return to your own See in Catania. Let us not behold either of your two faces again in the capital, or you will have no face to be seen! Go! Go! At once!" Strongly I had to control my feet, resisting the impulse to kick him.

But however much my own emotions were satisfied by the temporary dismissal (by Sicilian law a Chancellor held life tenure in office) of this professional mischief-maker, the danger from Otto's steady advance was not lessened, nor my relationship to the Pope improved. Indeed, my reacquired benefactor, the Pope, was infuriated. He wrote me a hasty letter of admonition:

> As you are now past the age of childhood, you should put away childish things. . . . The Bishop of Catania, the Chancellor of the Realm, has been your guardian hitherto and has undergone many toils and sorrows on your behalf. But now, forgetful of his services, you take no notice of him. . . . Recall the Chancellor forthwith and take his advice forthwith; let no one assail him, or we shall take it as an outrage done to ourselves.

I chose to let the outrage stand: I refused.

It so happened that the Pope had more need of me, at the

moment, than need of his Bishop—so the point was pressed no further. In fact, so strange had our positions become with respect to one another, that the Pope's only hope of salvation lay in me—and mine, in him. For after Otto's excommunication, only a Hohenstaufen could successfully lay counterclaim to the loyalty of the German princes beyond the Alps—and only the machinations of the Pope could activate that loyalty. Neither he nor I had the arms or the men to oppose Otto.

Without the least opposition, Otto by-passed Rome and marched rapidly into the south. Everywhere he was *heiled* by the German nobles as their new leader, and the Sicilian nobility marched with them. In Apulia, one town after another fell before Otto's armies—first Barletta, then Bari, then Brindisi. The whole provinces of Basilicata and Calabria surrendered. Suddenly Otto was astride the Strait of Messina. Humbly the Pope offered to give up the lands of the Church (already occupied by Otto) if Otto would renounce all claims to the papal fief of Sicily. And I? I bitterly, bitterly offered to renounce all claims to my hereditary lands in Swabia (which I had just verified in Swabian monastery records) if Otto would not cross the straits into the island of Sicily.

Otto's answer was that he "spat upon" us both.

We had been playing for time, and we seemed to have failed. At night, from Messina, the number of fires in Otto's camp could be seen steadily increasing. He was waiting only for additional ships, said the spies.

This was the grim moment Costanza chose to fall into labor, and present to the Kingdom an heir. At the birth of our child there was little rejoicing; though I, boy that I was, felt more than a man's pride at having sired a son. We named him Enrico to remind the Germans that my father Heinrich had been their last legitimate Emperor; and that I, his heir, was Friedrich—like Barbarossa. But the christening was a doleful affair. So great was Costanza's tension that in the cathedral she fainted, and the baby was almost dropped to the floor. An evil omen, whispered the soothsayers: the boy, at his end, would die in a fall.

Rumors spread; alarm increased. Scarcely two years had passed since I set out to discipline the rebellious nobles, and now all was worse than before. In Palermo harbor, a fully manned galley rode at anchor—secretly ready to speed me and the Queen and our first-born to safety in Africa. But to keep a secret from

Sicilians is impossible. To stifle panic and restore public confidence, I chose to emblazon sun and moon—symbols of universal sovereignty—on the royal seal of Sicily. Never, it seemed, could a king with a collapsing kingdom have picked a more inauspicious hour to behave like an emperor. . . .

Now indeed it appeared that the stars had turned against me!

17

YET THIS was the very time that the slow poison prepared for Otto by the Pope's intrigues began to take effect. The ingredients were marvelously subtle and complicated, blended with the skill of a master magician. The effect produced a gradual strangulation, and finally, from fear, an ague. Such are the uses of diplomacy in the hands of an expert. Even had I been Otto, I would have been compelled to admiration; but he was said by some to have a hollow head.

The Pope's game had begun months before with a letter to the German bishops, strongly hinting of the excommunication to come. The bishops were not slow to take the hint. They diligently set to work, contacting all Otto's enemies (which were legion) and organizing an opposition party. Meanwhile Innocent had written to the King of France, Philip II, telling tales out of school. Otto had been overheard to remark, said the Pope, that he could not sleep at night so long as the King of France held lands rightly belonging to his (Otto's) beloved uncle, King John of England. The Pope added slyly that he regretted not having been so quick as the wise French king at seeing through the gluttonous and warlike intentions of the German, Otto, who seemed insatiable. The King of France was as quick to understand as the bishops, and French gold flowed straightway to Otto's enemies. Then the Pope cautiously made contact with the opposition German princes, reminding them that in Sicily existed a last survivor of the noble line of Hohenstaufen. As the crisis deepened, the Pope's exhortations and threats became more violent, and a steady stream of couriers sped to the north.

Then, suddenly, the tide reversed, and a steady stream of couriers sped to the south. They arrived in Otto's camp and reported that all Germany was in revolt. They reported that the Archbishop of Mainz, the Prelates of Trier and Magdeburg, the Landgrave of Thuringia, the Dukes of Austria and Bavaria, the King of Bohemia—all had gathered in Nürnberg and declared Otto deposed. They urged Otto to return to Germany at once to defend his Imperium. (How did the Pope's agents manage so bald a declaration, when it was obvious even to a child that Otto needed but to cross the straits and all Sicily would be his, with the Pope outflanked?)

But Otto listened, and one night he dreamed a dream: a young bear clambered into his bed, growing larger and larger with every breath until it occupied the whole space and pushed him crashing to the floor. Next morning he arose "shaken to the marrow," he told his aides, only to be greeted by messengers who informed him that I had been elected Emperor in his stead. In panic, he broke camp, fled with all the haste in his long legs toward the Alps. His flight some deemed miraculous, and I concurred, as the miracle was the work of the Pope.

A year passed, a year of impatient waiting, and an ambassador arrived in Palermo, both from Germany and from Rome. The ambassador, the noble Anselm von Justingen, bore with him the manifesto of the German princes, which had received the Pope's approval on certain conditions, and now lacked only my own acquiescence.

At once Berardo raised grave questions about the Pope's demands. He requested that we walk together in the palace garden, not to be overheard, and his voice was heavy with warning.

"My son," he said (the phrase, as always, was particularized for me), "I am well aware that you do not lack experience in dealing with the Pope. Even so, you know only his words and not the man behind them. I am sorry you have not seen, in person, the sinew of his mind. He seems now to be offering you your heart's desire. Have you thought that perhaps he is offering *his* heart's desire? That to be the Pope's vassal is not the same as his ward—a different matter altogether? That once you have sworn complete subjection, you belong to him? All else is secondary. The implications, my son, the implications!"

I plucked a single *margherita* from its bush, where it was blooming out of season, and pulled off the petals one by one. At the last I exclaimed, "I win! Dear Berardo, you must wait and watch me match deeds to the Pope's words. . . ."

He shrugged, and laughed. "Next time, let me pull the petals off the *margherita*."

As I was eager for the manifesto's public proclamation without delay, I arranged for a reading in the cathedral, attended by pomp and ceremony. The Queen and I were borne to the cathedral in a canopied litter, that we might be seen by the crowds which lined the route. We were cheered with enthusiasm, for the threat of Otto and another German occupation was not a pleasing prospect to the masses. For their deliverance they gave me more credit than the Pope; and, under the circumstance, I was hardly inclined to correct their impression (does everyone give the Devil his due?).

At my insistence, the Queen was heavily veiled—though not so completely as a Muslim woman; I thought thus to propitiate both major religious elements among my subjects, or at least offend nobody. As we approached the cathedral she turned toward me and pulled aside a portion of her veil, that she might speak clearly.

"My Lord," she said, and her voice was low, but strident, "my Lord, you have not consulted me or asked my advice, so I cannot know your decision. Nevertheless I wish to express my feelings. I am frightened at the prospect that you may become Emperor. It is not only the passage to Germany which alarms me—difficult and dangerous as it must be. The future—I am disturbed about the future. What will be the effect on our Enrico, in coming years? And what of the Germans themselves? My Lord, can Germans be trusted? When I was in Hungary—" She broke off abruptly; this was her only allusion to her former status. "I fear Germans, my Lord; I fear them greatly—and I fear for you among them!"

Her words stirred deep memories, for they echoed that other Costanza, my mother. I felt an emotion closer to tenderness than at any time since our marriage. My regard for Costanza my wife had been steadily growing since the birth of our son; with babe in arms, her character had undergone a great softening. (Her other child, by the King of Hungary, was long since dead.) She seemed more content, almost happy; nor did she seem to distrust me, or need to rely on the violent emotional outlet, the lash, which was her way of atonement. Her long, sad face had become mellow—nearly, in a sense, beautiful. Now I was touched by her concern.

"Madonna," I said, "you must not be disturbed. We have thought of all these things. You have forgotten that Federico to the Germans is Friedrich. To them we would seem a German among Germans, the scion of Germans. They cannot deny fealty to one of their own. . . ."

She sighed, replaced the veil, and crossed herself.

And at that moment I looked up, to the dizzy heights of the cathedral towers, remembering. . . . Now to the youthful emperor they seemed less awesome than to the child king, but dizzy heights they remained.

To measured trumpet blasts we walked slowly toward the throne. We were seated with grace and majesty, while the organ intoned in triumph. We wore our crowns and robes of state, though I had chosen to reserve my grandfather Ruggero's mantle for an even grander occasion. Berardo stood beside me, on my right hand, in the richest vestments of an archbishop. The vast nave was filled to overflowing with my courtiers and officials and their wives, and the colors of their clothing were brighter than a tropic flower garden. The organ ceased. A bell sounded. The silence of expectation descended.

The noble Anselm coughed, and unwound his scroll. I watched him carefully, but in his open face was no hint of treachery to come—a plot to be conceived with my own first-born son. Slowly, very slowly he began, as a man unused to reading. The Latin words of the Manifesto boomed out of his deep chest with a German accent, rumbling through his beard, echoing and reëchoing through the vault:

> "God Almighty, seeing by Adam's fall that mankind would abuse free will and would become involved in the nets of contention, set up the Holy Roman Empire that its Lord, like a God upon earth, might rule kings and nations and maintain peace and justice. After the Greek Emperors ceased to do their duty, Holy Mother Church and the Roman Senate and People, recalling the said Empire, transplanted its root into mighty Germany, that this dominion might be sustained by our stately princes, our vigorous knights, and our bravest warriors. The Empire without a head is like a ship in a storm without a master pilot. Heresies are springing up and the universal Church is being harassed. Bees are scattered when they lose their queen; so kingdoms, if unrestrained by a bit, go to ruin. The sun is eclipsed; the world

needs an Emperor to check disorders. The nations have cried aloud to God, who has awoke from sleep and bethought Him of the Empire. He has inspired us, the Princes of Germany who have the right of election, to draw nigh to the throne and to meet together in one place, as is our duty. We have been each of us examined as to his will; we have invoked the Holy Ghost and gone through all the customary rites; we have all in common turned our eyes to the illustrious Lord, the King of Germany and Sicily, the Duke of Swabia, as being worthy of the honor. Though young in years, he is old in character; though his person is not full grown, his mind has been by Nature wonderfully endowed; he exceeds the common measure of his equals; he is blessed with virtues before his day, as becomes one of the true blood of that august stock, the Kaisers of Germany, who have been unsparing of their treasures and persons, in order to increase the honor and might of the Empire and the happiness of their loyal subjects."

The cathedral resounded with cheers of approbation—the music of a secular choir winging northward in my honor; and then a mighty chant of the cathedral choir itself—a clerical Te Deum mounting heavenward in my honor. I looked outward over the eager and excited faces of my subjects. I felt the Queen stir beside me in a gesture suddenly restless and troubled. I scanned the bearded countenance of the Archbishop Berardo, strangely impassive as a mask. All about me I sensed shadows of the past: my Sicilian mother, my German father . . . my grandfather Ruggero the Great, my grandfather Barbarossa the Emperor. . . . They whispered and beckoned, gestured and grimaced, threatened and demanded, appeared and disappeared in the shafts of moted sunlight . . . but of them all, the Red Beard loomed largest . . . dominant.

I raised my hand, and the silence was that following a thunder clap—which seemed to me to have come from my heart.

"We will accept—" I began.

I was convinced that Divine Providence had been manifested through me, against all the probabilities or hopes of men.

I was seventeen. The very stars were mine.

II

PUER APULIAE

I

NOT UNTIL springtime could I leave Sicily for Rome, the first lap of the long and perilous journey to the mysterious German lands beyond the Alps. For purposes of state, I rode from Palermo to Messina to take ship, and the island of Sicily never before had seemed so compelling. The road was one long parade of dazzling blossoms, exotic odors, imposing mountains, sun-baked rocks, sparkling beaches, cooling forests, terraced vineyards, silver-green olive groves, and rippling fields of grain.

This was my land, and I loved it. I was attracted by its beauty, repulsed by its chaos. My strength was derived from its strength, and my weakness from its weakness. The weakness I resolved to convert into strength, for if good was God-given, then evil was man-made and could be corrected. Already I dismissed the Devil and his works as phantasy based on phantasy: the cloven-hoofed and goat-horned Pan who allegedly once roamed this land. I savored the sense of power for good which is the divine right of a king. Everywhere I was cheered: artisans lined the streets of the towns, and peasants lifted their sickles or hoes in salute. Joyously I ordered that every filthy, long-nailed, scraggly-haired beggar we met should be bathed and trimmed and combed and clothed anew, that he might know the Emperor-elect, his Lord and King had passed.

In Palermo, opposition to my acceptance of the German princes' call had subsided. The Queen, however, became more and more virulent on the subject. I was forced roughly to command her silence. It was clear that basically she was afraid of once more becoming a widow; for my youthful vigor in bed had succeeded in making her very fond of me. Though Berardo continued to be dubious, he did not harass me with doubts or dire forebodings, once the decision was made; on the contrary, he flung himself with fullest energy into the preparations for my departure. "All will go well," he said, but added an old Italian proverb: "*Se il Diavolo non ci mette la coda.*" (If the Devil doesn't put his tail into it.)

Much had to be done—not the least of which was a rapid refreshment of the German language I had learned as a small child. What fragmentary words and phrases I recalled were hardly adequate for the vocabulary of an Emperor in Germany itself, and I was afraid that the German use of Latin was no more facile than my use of their guttural tongue. I kept a tutor with me day and night, and forced myself to think only in German. *Mut und Kraft!*

The other problems concerned Sicily itself and the demands of the Pope, for he was anything but content to acquiesce freely in my election. He made certain to hobble me in the very moment of bidding me Godspeed, and I groaned with the familiarity of his procedures. Was he not satisfied, I thought, with the chaos he had induced in the Realm while I was his ward; did he think that now as King I would always submit humbly to the intransigence of his overlordship? Yet I had no choice but to accede if I wished to protect Sicily from new invasions from new *Führers*, and to acquire the eventual strength needed to restore order and progress throughout the land.

From me the Pope extracted a reaffirmation of the concordat signed by my poor mother under duress. With me, he went even further in extending his own authority to appoint ecclesiastical officials without the advice or consent of the crown—thus building ever stronger his clerical state within the temporal state, adding kindling for future flames. He extracted, too, a yearly tribute in gold—no small sum—which was not then available to me, and actually would not be until I became Emperor. The best I could do was a promissory note, and he had to be content. But the real joker in the arrangement was that I must cease to be King of Sicily altogether, divesting myself of both title and administration. He was satisfied with nothing less than the crowning of my infant son Enrico as King, the appointment of Queen Costanza (my Pope-picked wife!) as Regent, the recall of Gualtiero di Palearia (my Pope-picked friend!) as Chancellor.

On this last I gagged almost to the point of physical retching, and chose to bargain a little. I would approve the first two items, I said, without hesitation; but the third—that precious bishop (everyone assured me he was exceptionally kind to his children) —only if in exchange His Holiness would name Berardo as papal legate plenipotentiary to accompany me on my journey. This *quid pro quo* the Pope accepted, and I had the satisfaction of knowing that at least one trustworthy person would be at my side. So my son Enrico became King almost before my own brow had become adjusted to the crown, and the Kingdom itself seemed to have slipped between my fingers like hourglass sand. Finally, as Berardo had so feared, from me Innocent extracted the last dram of submission: I must swear, in person, fealty to him as his vassal. I must bend the knee before him in Rome. Then, and only then, might I have his blessing—and the Imperium.

I chose to bend.

As it would have been most impolitic to go to the Pope surrounded by a Saracen guard, I was hard put to assemble a group of men on whom I could rely. I decided that it was better to travel with a few whom I could trust than with many of whom I was unsure, for no danger is greater than betrayal from within. I therefore selected a few of the older Norman knights who had remained loyal throughout all adversity, added their sons for sinew, and leavened the crowd by the addition of Count Alaman da Costa—a Genovese of far-reaching influence. He was a jolly and witty little man with commercial interests in Siracusa, and possessed an endless supply of jokes about traveling merchants and innkeepers' daughters. We had become friends when I was hunting *baroni* in the marshes around Catania. I made him officially a member of the Royal Council, and, with my bearded patriarch, Berardo, we were complete.

No, not quite complete. I wanted body servants who would be incorruptible, either as spies or purveyors of poison. I chose, therefore, two young Saracen slaves, Harun and Abu, who were lovers. I chose lovers because they would be content with one another during the long journey, and thus avoid the danger of incidents with Christian girls. For additional safety, I had Harun and Abu shave the thin Saracen beards which ringed their mouths, dressed them in the doublets and tights of ordinary servants, and wryly renamed (or, better, christened) them Pietro and Paolo. For submitting to these indignities I promised freedom when we returned to Sicily. Of their faithfulness I had no doubt.

With a certain amount of relief I said good-by to the Queen, though I was careful not to show my emotion as I consoled her, sobbing, in my arms. But at leaving my son Enrico, hardly two years old, I felt a real regret. I had discovered, during his infancy, that I liked babies, and almost every day I played with him. As he grew, I taught him to throw a ball, to climb, and to somersault. I rode him with me on Zinki—my white Arab stallion—letting him hold the reins to the hackamore. He loved this activity above all, and I had high hopes that he would become a first-rate horseman. But, as the time of departure drew near, all this had to be put aside. For a last farewell I fondled and kissed him; he wriggled and chortled with delight. I noticed then, suddenly, how much he had come to resemble his mother, and I wondered if the resemblance would increase over the years. I was informed later that he moped many days after my departure, demanding constantly to know my whereabouts. He felt abandoned, and perhaps he never forgave me—a basic cause of the estrangement which later came between us? I bade him farewell as King of Sicily, but I gave orders that he should be taught the German language. (Yes, it was I.) Already my head was bursting with long-range plans.

At sea, once we were out of sight of land, I had plenty of time to think. As we passed near the Aeolian Islands, where Ulysses sought the aid of the god of the winds, I wanted to stop briefly and see the ancient Lipari workshops in which sharp obsidian blades were made from the black volcanic glass—long, long before the discovery of bronze. I wanted to stop at Stromboli and climb the volcano which still lived, treating us to spectacular bursts of fire as we sailed past. But there was not time. In addition, I, though Emperor-elect, was only a passenger on this galley, which was owned by a Greek and plied a regular run. The captain, a wizened man, was a Liparesi himself, and he counseled me with the most common word of islanders: "*Pazienza*, your Majesty," he said, "*pazienza*."

I could hardly have been more impatient. I was impatient to have a ship—no, a fleet—of my own; I was impatient to stop when and where I wished; I was impatient of poverty; I was impatient for power. At night I could hardly sleep in my cabin, from impatience; and by day I blew on the sails like Aeolus and urged the rowers to ply the red and white striped oars with greater effort. But the captain only shrugged his shoulders and squinted at dolphins swimming faster than the ship. The water lapped against the hull with the same monotonous sound Ulysses heard, and I longed for the goatskin of strong winds, the magic speed. To calm myself I sketched gulls in flight, and tried to fathom the secrets of the air-borne. I discovered, incidentally, that I am not a bad draftsman. In the evenings, for recreation, we played cards—Berardo and I, Count Alaman and the captain —a game called *scopone*. I found, after a few games, that Berardo and the Count were cheating outrageously; and in the privacy of my cabin I challenged Berardo with my discovery. He blushed, and admitted the truth—but said the cheating was necessary to offset the Count's advantage. With a laugh, I agreed; but in fact I think that Berardo enjoyed the luxury of sinning a little.

All went well as we bore northward. The weather held. No pirates showed. No illness developed. Capri, then Ischia, we sighted. We put into Napoli for water and provisions. I had no wish to leave the ship, except to visit the tomb of Vergil, but I had work to do. I held court in the Castle of the Egg, towering from its oval island near the shore. It was called the *Castel del' Uova* not only because of its shape, but because Vergil was reputed—with the aid of magic—here to have inserted an egg through the narrow neck of a carafe without breaking either egg or bottle. I received many lords who wished to meet me in person and pay me homage, and secretly I was angry when I noted their amazement at my youth. Their dignity, I thought, should certainly equal mine. I was not yet aware of the extent of the legend which was growing about my name, the legend of the fair-haired boy king who triumphed over all enemies, a second David, invincible.

In fact, I felt not only invincible, but immortal—that is, not so much contemptuous, as unaware of the existence of death. Of course for other people—but not for me. Arrows might be fired at me, but they would not pierce. Swords would not cut, lances scathe, fire burn. I might drown? No, impossible. When, a day out of Napoli, we were warned by friendly passing fishermen that galleys of the Pisan fleet lay ahead, waiting to ram, board, burn our vessel—to extinguish once and for all the bone-flesh-and-blood existence of Friedrich von Hohenstaufen, my reaction was merely to laugh. So Otto had paid them to attack and destroy the German part of me; but I had other parts—I was Federico the Sicilian, I was a genie who lived in a lamp, I was a flame of life which was inextinguishable. They could not touch me.

But they could touch others. I posted an archer by each oarsman, and a soldier to shield both. Wise precautions, Berardo said. Then dear Berardo, scratching his beard in most unsaintly fashion, persuaded me that it was unfair to providence to tempt her unduly; and besides, he said, had I thought how interesting to ride to Rome (in triumph) along the Via Appia Antica? I would approach the city as had the Caesars, and trumpeters would precede me. At this idea I was enchanted, and agreed to land at Gaeta, where the Via Appia touches the sea. Thus the enemy galleys were thwarted. Under towering mushroom pines and cypresses, I rode content along the road built (so Berardo informed me) by Appius Claudius, Censor in the year 312 B.C. And as we passed, I marveled at the skill of the bridge builders, whose work had remained intact for exactly fifteen hundred years, and at a roadbed so solid that at certain points the Roman wagons, braking, had worn deep ruts in the stone. Thus I would build, I thought, when someday I had the money and the masons. And every Roman edifice we passed, I observed with care the method of its construction.

We came at length to a great aqueduct leading into Rome from the mountains, but it no longer carried water. In the fifth century it had been cut by the barbarians, flooding the coastal marshes which had been drained by the Romans, and giving rise to multitudes of insects and the night-vapor fever which had depopulated the land. And in the city itself, Berardo said, the fountains had ceased to play and the people drank the unclean water of the Tiber, for the Christians were more interested in a future life than in the repair of an aqueduct. "And to this day it is not repaired," he added, "so if in your present life you are concerned with normal bowels and a quiet gut, drink wine, my son, not water when you enter the city of Rome!" I laughed, but I understood that he had issued a warning. My guts, I thought, were iron; but I remembered how my father had died, and the mysterious massacre of my five hundred Aragon knights. I would drink wine.

We passed, as we neared Rome, more and more tombs and noble monuments (for the Roman law forbade burial within the city). The most noble of all was the tomb of Cecilia Metella, which had been seized by the Caetani family and now served as a fortress; its great round tower dominated the road and threatened all who passed. At the tower we paused, tethering our horses, and were welcomed by the keep, who had been forewarned of our coming. At once I sent messengers to the Pope, to advise him of my arrival and inform him that I would await his bidding.

With Berardo I climbed the tower. On the parapet, flies buzzed, no air stirred. Berardo, who many times had come to Rome, munched philosophically on his salted watermelon seeds, and watched my face. Limned before us, in the yellow-brilliant sun of a hot April morning, were the distant mushroom pines and lofty cypresses, the domes and triumphal arches of the Eternal City, enclosed and slumbering behind the Aurelian Walls. Roma . . . dreaming, it seemed to me, of a new age . . . a rebirth of its ancient glory. . . .

I was so moved that I could not speak; tears hazed the landscape before my eyes.

2

We were lodged in clerical apartments close to the Basilica of San Pietro, built by Constantine, where once had stood the Circus of Nero—a change of structures which symbolized the triumph of Christianity, as Berardo explained. The area was called the *Vaticano*, Berardo said, because of the *vaticinia*, or predictions, issued there by pagan priests in ancient times. Now it was Lent, and black-robed Christian priests scurried about, intent on preparations for the Easter festival of blood, death and regeneration.

"Rome always has been a city of priests," Berardo said, "but now the robes are different. In Roman days, during the Lupercalia, certain priests wore no robes at all; each carried a phallus made of goat-hide, and ran naked about the streets striking women with the phallus—a spring fertility rite. Shocking . . . shocking. . . ."

I laughed. "That's Carnevale—only the name has changed!"

We washed ourselves with muddy water in marble basins, and changed to fresh clothing. So poor had I become that my Saracens Pietro and Paolo were hard put to find for me hose without patches, a tunic without raveled sleeves, or a cloak without tatters. Already Berardo had heard the rumors flying about Rome that I had arrived in rags, a suppliant for papal charity. My ears burned when he told me, and I swallowed my humiliation. The rumors were all too close to the truth. But for the dignity of my bearing, no observer would have guessed that this plain-clad, unarmed youth was a king, an emperor-to-be. I resolved to approach the Pope as if I wore a cloak of gold embossed with pearls, and by my regal attitude make all beholders forget the actual clothes upon my back.

Almost at once the Pope sent word that he was prepared to see us, at the Laterano, and my heart quickened at the thought of meeting at last the man who served as a living link between me and my mother. We were led by a priest through what seemed an endless maze of chambers to a huge waiting room, where Berardo and I were left alone for an hour. In the emotion of the moment I had been almost ready to fling myself into the Holy Father's arms like a prodigal son, but irritation grew in proportion to my impatience at the long wait. It is hard for any healthy young animal to keep still, even harder for the young human male, and hardest of all for a virile young king who is used to authority and freedom. I examined the view from all the mullioned windows—nothing but gardens. I counted the number of crucifixes to be seen—seventeen. I counted the number of priests and monks who passed—sixty-nine.

"An hour of precious life wasted!" finally I exclaimed.

"*Pazienza*," was Berardo's complacent reply, scratching his beard.

I scowled, and jokingly made the sign of the evil eye, while he crossed himself.

With a scraping sound, inner doors opened and a young priest with ink-stained fingers appeared. In a beautiful, resonant voice, enunciating very slowly, he said, "His Holiness wishes to see the young King alone."

I turned to Berardo, winked, and said, "*Pazienza*!" Then obediently I followed the priest.

I found the Pope surrounded by retainers, seated upon a throne elaborately carved and surmounted by a purple canopy. He wore a richly embroidered vestment about his shoulders and a miter upon his head. His hands were clasped in an attitude of prayer, and his head was bent forward so that his lips touched the tips of his fingers. He was not praying, however, for his eyes were active with thought, and my entrance seemed momentarily to startle him. Slowly he lowered his hands into his lap and raised his head.

"Eh—*puer Apuliae*," he said, "our son of the Church!"

Why he called me a boy of Apulia instead of Sicily I did not know, but the designation clung to me for years and proved to be prophetic. I looked steadily into his face, evaluating as best I could the long dominating nose, the pursed hard-set mouth, the purple density of the varicose veins in the clean-shaven cheeks, and above all the remote calculating eyes. He was now past the age of fifty, and the power of his personality was cumulative with his years. Here indeed was a strong man, a man determined to dominate the world. I had the feeling that in his mind he had been playing chess, himself omnipotent and manipulating both sides at once, planning moves with bishops, knights and queens to checkmate kings both white and red and give himself a double victory. I stood before him now, not his ward, not a boy of flesh and blood, but an ivory king to play against that other king who had proved so troublesome—and therefore, in fact, I thought, nothing but a pawn. This was my guardian, Pope Innocent III.

I bowed, and he extended his gloved hand for me to kiss. I made a genuflection and kissed his ring.

"Welcome in the name of Christ our Lord and Redeemer, and His blessed mother Maria," he said formally. "How good is God's will that brings you to us safely—this meeting has been much too long delayed!"

"Most Holy Father," I replied, "we come to you as both ward and vassal, in prompt obedience to your commands. Our breast is filled with gratitude at the aid and succor your Holiness so graciously extended to us in the hour of our greatest need. Our Kingdom was saved from rapacious hands, to the greater glory of Christ and Holy Church and the most exalted Pontiff himself. Nor have we forgotten the assistance extended by your Holiness to our revered mother the Queen Costanza during the time of her distress. Ever in our prayers have we remembered the beneficence of your Holiness, and sought the blessing of Heaven upon your exalted name."

He was a little taken aback, I think, that I spoke with such dignity—more like an old cardinal than a boy. And I suspect, too, that the emphasis I put upon the royal *we* grated just a trifle in his ears. But he betrayed no signs of irritation, and his eyes retained the inner concentration and remoteness of the chess player deep in the game.

"Come now," he said, wheezing a little as he hoisted himself from the throne, "let us walk together in the garden that we may talk as ward and guardian, and not as King and Pope."

So we walked together, but not for one moment did he forget the game. The words were kindly, even familiar; but the substance was strictly political. I must do liege homage to him in public, for all the world to see. For this I would receive the funds I needed for the trip to Germany. And without the slightest hesitation, I agreed.

It was not until I was leaving his apartment that he remembered he had a gift for me. He summoned the ink-stained priest, who produced a yellowed sheet of paper, its watermark a fool's cap. It was Guglielmo's letter. As I read it then, for the first time, my heart was pierced by fresh pain.

> WHEN it appeared clear to him that he was at last the prey of his enemies, he—who had only recently passed the age when he was rocked to sleep by maternal lullabies—defended himself by arms and by tears, without losing nobility. As a mouse, afraid of being caught by a ferocious animal, leaps at its attacker, he tried by every possible means to stop the arm of the one who dared to lay hands on the sacred body of God's anointed. Then, filled with a mighty rage, he tore his own clothing off, and scratched with sharp nails his own tender flesh.

I wondered if the Pope recalled its contents. Evidently he did, for he remarked in tones of mild remonstrance: "As a boy, you often reacted in a foolish, hot-headed way to authority; but now, thanks be to Heaven, you have learned admirably how to bridle your impulses to folly." Then he patted my head as warmly as if I were a favorite nephew.

3

THE POPE had selected Easter Sunday as the date for my act of obeisance, and advised that I fill the intervening time by visits to holy relics and scenes of martyrdom of saints. My mind was full of ancient Rome, however, of which I had read descriptions in the *Mirabilia Urbis Romae*, written in my mother's time—and while Berardo was busy with ecclesiastical affairs I crammed in every possible moment of sightseeing. I was accompanied only by my two young Saracens. Without the slightest fanfare, I wandered about the streets, picking my way between patches of refuse, horse dung, and human feces, seeking every remainder of the city's ancient glory.

I was astonished to find that in a capital once so filled with countless statues and *colossi*, of marble, bronze, silver and gold, hardly a handful remained. I admired especially two muscular nude males standing beside horses, in marble, said to be by Phidias and Praxiteles, but now badly chipped and broken; and, in the forum of Mars, a marble of the god, beautifully and impressively carved. Of bronzes, only one gilded equestrian statue still exists, said to be of the Christian Emperor Constantine; but the quality of the workmanship was so fine that it must surely date from an earlier period, before Christianity raised its hand against the pagan arts. It is, incidentally, so easy to distinguish between the stone-and-brick work of the ancient Romans, precise and fastidious, and the crude and careless handiwork of masons in the recent past, patched here and there with broken bits of fine antique marble. I observed particularly at the Arch of Constantine a great disparity between the earlier sculptures (evidently taken from other monuments) and the sculptures of Constantine's own time, concluding that by the fourth century decadence had already set in. But now matters are far worse, for both the Arch and the great Colosseum itself have been incorporated into fortifications built by the

Frangipani family—their handiwork cluttering like barnacles the once noble lines of the ancient architecture. This, alas, is true all over Rome; warring families have fortified, each against the other, ancient structures which once (like the baths) were the common property of all.

Notable is the metamorphosis of the Mausoleum of Hadrian—once a receptacle for the ashes of the cultivated Emperor, and now a hodgepodge of bastions and towers called the Castel Sant' Angelo and intended for defense of the living body of the Pope. Its priceless statues have been despoiled and broken; even the great bronze pine cone, which once adorned it, has been carried away to the private gardens of the Pope. Today the ashes of Hadrian and the memory of his good works, are but shadows. Yet Hadrian's good works are not totally lost, for the stupendous Pantheon for the Gods of Olympus still exists much as he—an atheist—rebuilt it. Had it not been transformed early into a Christian church, probably it too would have been razed to the ground—even so the gilded bronze tiles of its roof were plundered, and its statues broken or carried away. I stood, a dwarf, among the cluster of gray and pink granite columns at the entrance, staring at the massive bronze door placed by Hadrian. A door for giants, men as well as gods. And within, all is enclosed in the perfection of a circle, illuminated solely by a circular opening at the very peak of a vast, breathlessly ascending dome. The light rays fall like miraculous rays from heaven, and a sunbeam seems a personal intercession from the god of gods himself. As Hadrian had meant that I should, I stood in silent awe, not daring the sound of a whisper in the Olympian edifice. Oh me, I thought—to have at my command the architect, the engineers, the resources to build another such!

On Easter morning, I rose an hour before dawn, not only for the Mass, but because I wished to stand on Capitoline Hill, alone with my thoughts, and watch the sunrise. I brought with me a two-candle lantern, though I had no fear of the pagan demons reputed by Christians to inhabit this spot. I climbed the ascent as the gray light was first turning pink, and I could pick my way among the scattered stones. A double tier of arcades survives atop the Capitoline, and I could read the corroded inscription that Q. Lutatius, Q.F., and Q. Catulus, the consuls, were responsible for building the substructure and the *Tabularium*. They had built well, I thought; could they have foreseen how ferociously barbarians, Christians, and nature itself would undo their handiwork? So I stood where consuls and Caesars and captive kings had stood, and looked out as they had looked at the panorama of the Roman Forum in the dawn light. I saw what they had never dreamed would be seen here by the eyes of man: a waste land. A few shattered walls, an arch or two, lonely columns by threes or fours, the portion of a pediment, a font of running water long since stilled, a fallen, legless, armless, headless statue—all suddenly touched, now, with an aura of gold, but quickly fading under the full light of day. Vines cover the benches of senators, weeds grow where marble bloomed, pigs root and goats graze among the dung and filth where once was the center of the world. Again and again I cried to myself, How, oh how could all this have happened? Are men so insensate that they destroy, without caring, the very best of themselves?

Heavy with the sense of desolation, I turned to leave. As I did so, I kicked aside a bit of broken stone and my eye caught a golden glint reflecting the sun. I stooped, scratched a moment in the earth, and stared wonderingly at the coin I held in my hand. It was of gold, and showed the profile of an Emperor wearing toga and laurel wreath. Inscribed were the words CAESAR AVGVSTVS.

Augustus—"consecrated by augury"—surely this meant me. These moments had been my consecration to the destiny of a Caesar. It was then that I felt, as later I said publicly, the august spirit of the Caesars take possession of me. I resolved that when the power should come to me, I would restore and reglorify this city which had been the wonder of the world. What matter if a thousand years had passed? Soon, soon, I too would become an Emperor of the Romans! No longer did I regret the immediate task in hand, this mockery of a Caesar, the pledging of feudal homage to my liege lord the Pope. This was but one more step along the path to that summit I would achieve. Then might I mock the mockery! But now, obedience—for the present is necessary to the future.

I followed the service of the Easter Mass; and, on signal, I approached the throne of His Holiness the Pope, and bowed my uncrowned head before the head which wears the tiara. Then, on my knees, humbly, I placed my hands in his, and swore in a loud clear voice fidelity to him and his successors. At last he seemed well satisfied, and smiled.

But my face was a blank, expressionless as any chessman king.

4

My purse filled with the Pope's gold, I was ready at last for the journey to Germany, and thence I would have flown if I could. I barely listened to the Pope's blessing, given to his "son of the Church," and I paid no attention whatever to the scornful designation of my detractors, the "Priestling-Emperor." I was too busy outfitting myself with elegant clothing to heed much else. And also I floated with such buoyant excitement that I failed to sense the importance of two seemingly unimportant events.

I have yet to understand how the events in a man's life fall into sequence prophetic with meaning, though astrologers lay the causation in the stars. Astrologers! If the stars cannot lie, astrologers can! Though frequently I consult astrologers, and frequently use their predictions to my own ends, I cannot believe that the stars determine a man's destiny—else all men born under the same sign would have the same destiny. I am inclined to agree with Sant' Agostino's refutation of astrology. It is so easy to observe that persons born under my own sign, *Capricorno*, even born at the same moment, are not the same as I. But then, the astrologers say, I am a king, and therefore I have the destiny of a king. Destiny? Ah, indeed!

I was destined by Providence to touch, peripherally, within days of one another, the lives of the two individuals (aside from Berardo) who were to have the most significance in my own life —and yet foresee nothing of significance. It is hard to recall that two names now so impacted with meaning then meant nothing at all. *Pier della Vigna* and *Bianca Lancia:* names, merely names to shrug off like any others.

It was the evening before our departure from Rome, when Berardo came to me with a letter uncurled in his hand. He carried it as I might have carried a prize falcon—with a certain exultance at its touch.

"Now what?" I said, made curious by his manner.

"My Lord," he answered, "I bear a most extraordinary document, written in Latin in a style so elevated and beautiful that I am tempted to believe some unknown but great Roman poet has been suddenly returned to this life!"

"*Hòi*," I said, "he has written a new *Aeneid*?"

"Oh no, my Lord—only a letter asking for work in your chancery."

The enthusiasm I had caught from Berardo abruptly evaporated. "A hunter of patronage," I said. "They are legion, and not poets!"

"This one is different, my Lord. He is a boy of seventeen—"

"A boy!" I said, scowling. "My own age. Good Berardo, I had hoped better of you! Surely by now you think me a man—"

"I think of you as my son," he said, smiling in his beard with a kind of divine patience. "And this other one I know intimately. This boy brought me bread, cheese and wine when I was hiding in Capua. He is handsome and brilliant—but impoverished. His name is Pier della Vigna, but he has not a vineyard to his name—"

I laughed at the pun. "His father, then, was neither lord nor satyr?"

For the space of half a breath, it seemed to me, Berardo hesitated. "His father was a notary, an intelligent man but poor."

I scowled again, and I knew why. What if this *Piero* was in fact the natural son of *my* Berardo? I felt a pang of mingled jealousy and anger. "How comes it that the son of a poor notary writes a Latin so sublime?" I said, trying the hide the telltale sharpness in my voice.

"He was taught by a priest I know," Berardo answered calmly. "He showed great aptitude—so great that he has been in Bologna for a year, at the university. Now, tardily, he comes to Rome—"

"Why does he want to work in my chancery?" I said, finally covering the sharpness, "—why not back to Bologna for a scarlet gown and the furry cap of a doctor?"

"He has not the money to return to the university, my Lord. And he admires you tremendously—"

Mollified a little, I said, "Let him return to Bologna. Then we'll put him to work in a year or two, when we return from Germania." I removed a small bag of gold from my belt, and tossed it to Berardo with the nonchalance of Midas himself. "Give your Piero this—the education of the people should be the responsibility of the State."

This idea I tossed off as I had tossed the bag of gold. But it remained in my head; I thought it over carefully, and in due time gave it practical implementation. But how curious that my original motive was born in a reaction of jealous anger!

Berardo weighed the bag thoughtfully, as if balancing it against the letter in his other hand. "My Lord, it would be best if you yourself gave this to Piero. He would be overwhelmed. Certainly he will arrive in the morning—"

"We depart at the first cock's crow," I said sternly. "Leave the gold and a message. Surely you would not have me wait for a fledgling student, when an Empire calls?"

How seriously the very young take themselves! Thus it was that I rode out of Rome by the Via Aurelia as *Piero* rode in by the Via Flaminia. Had we met on the road, had I looked but once into the inner depths of his eyes, I would certainly have kept him with me from that moment forward. But years were to pass —many more than I had anticipated.

So, all unaware of what I had missed, we pressed on to Civitavecchia, to board a Genovese galley provided by my Genovese merchant-friend, Count Alaman da Costa. In the excitement of embarking I forgot completely the name of *Pier* della Vigna. But soon I would encounter that other name: Bianca Lancia.

The Genovese had been informed by spies of the probable movements of the Pisan fleet, so we had no difficulty in evading danger. With a strong wind we made good time to Genova, and we found the entire harbor decorated with flowers and banners in my honor. I warmed at once to the Genovese, though I saw not a single white half-domed house, lofty palm, or giant ficus tree as in my beloved Sicilia. The houses were pink, blue, yellow, gray, with peaked roofs of tile, and had windows underscored by little balconies. Count Alaman pointed out one of the largest structures, overlooking the harbor from a hill.

"That is where you are to stay, your Majesty," the Count said. "It is the palazzo of Niccolo Doria, a man to be trusted."

True were his words, as I discovered in future years when Genova became a papal stronghold, and the house of Doria held fast to the Ghibelline standard. Now I became an honored guest, anxious to be gone, but unable to leave because the way was blocked by supporters of Otto the Welf. For two months I was dined and feted. After I had made commercial concessions to the Genovese "valid for the day I become Emperor," they replenished my gold and added more. But the two months were truly notable because of that other name: Bianca.

She, like myself, was a guest. Her brother, Manfredo, a pale, intelligent youth, was visiting his friend, Percivalle Doria, who sang exquisitely with the lute. Manfredo, Percivalle and I were all about the same age, but Bianca was only twelve or thirteen. Though in the future all three were to play their destined roles in my life—Manfredo as a trusted administrator, Percivalle as one of my vicar-generals and a leading poet at my court—it was Bianca who captivated me.

The Lancia were a Piemonte family, once wealthy but now in difficulties because the father had been dead for a year or two. He had been a remarkable man, a poet, and noted for his advanced views. Though at the time I thought Bianca had been betrothed to Percivalle, it was not so—her father had said she was to marry only a man of her own choice. But then she was much too young to think of marriage, for she was slow to develop—and besides, she had no dowry. I had been in the Palazzo Doria a week before I had any time to myself, and it was then that I first noticed her.

Late one quiet, blue-shadowed afternoon, while most of the household still rested, I walked alone in the garden. By a bronze dolphin fountain, I came upon a slender young girl sitting with a book. So intent was her reading that she remained entirely unaware of my presence. For long minutes I watched her, enchanted. Though she sat in a shaded spot, under wisteria in bloom, about her she had an astonishing aura of sunlight. Her hair was golden, her skin had a golden paleness, her eyes a sky-vault blue. Without jewels of any kind, she wore a blue silk dress, with tight sleeves and tight bodice, embroidered with a golden pattern of four circles tangent to a square. Her breasts as yet were hardly visible. On her head was a small round cap, a net of small twisted ropes of blue and gold, from which her loosely plaited hair descended halfway down her back. From the hem of her dress escaped the pointed tips of red leather shoes. The fingers which held the book were slim and sensitive, and the delicate features of her face were cleanly formed. As she read she sometimes smiled, or frowned and bit her lower lip in agitation. At times she seemed to experience anguish, for she breathed heavily, and the air passing through her too thin nostrils made a soft whistling noise. Then suddenly she looked up and straight into my eyes. For a moment only she betrayed confusion.

She leaped to her feet and bowed the awkward curtsy of adolescence. "Your Majesty!" she cried.

"Who are you?" I said gently.

"Bianca Lancia, my Lord," she answered, and she did not turn away or drop her glance in shyness. A hint of color touched her cheeks. "I am the only sister of the noble Manfredo—"

"He has mentioned you—but he did not say that you could read." I was surprised to hear in my own voice a teasing, playful note. "You might be profitably engaged in embroidery, or fitting soles to hose. Or do you plan to become a nun?"

Now she truly blushed. "Why should not a woman learn to read and write?" she said defiantly. "My father stated more than once that women equal men in intelligence, if not in physical strength!"

"Your father was wise in many things, and fortunate in many others—not the least in you," I said, to placate her. "Please, tell me what you are reading?"

"The exploits of the son of Anchises and Venus," she said.

"Aeneas!" I exclaimed, not hiding my delight. "And what episodes?"

At last this bold and gifted girl looked aside from directly into my face. "Queen Dido and Aeneas—" she said, and sighed.

I took Bianca by the hand and we sat together on the marble bench; a charming impromptu throne, I thought. "Come," I said, "let us read the tale aloud, first one of us and then the other. You shall begin—"

"Oh no, my Lord, please—you."

My eyes scanned where her finger indicated, and I saw that Aeneas in the underworld was confronted by the shade of Dido, after she had killed herself with a sword for love of him. With the trickle of the fountain an obbligato to my voice, I read slowly:

" 'It was not of my own will, Dido, I left your land.
Heaven's commands, which now force me to traverse the
  shades,
This sour and derelict region, this pit of darkness, drove me
Imperiously from your side. I did not, could not imagine
My going would ever bring such terrible agony on you.
Don't move away! Oh, let me see you a little longer!

To fly from me, when this is the last word fate allows us!'
—Thus did Aeneas speak, trying to soften the wild-eyed,
Passionate-hearted ghost, and brought the tears to his own
eyes."

Suddenly, spontaneously, I put my arm around the girl who sat beside me. I could not bear that she should suffer quite so much for Dido.

In the days following, I did not take her to bed, though I longed to do so. Some inner restraint, some compelling intuition forbade this liaison. She was not too young, I told myself; but she was too young. She was not quite ready yet for the transformation of the spirit into flesh.

For almost two months I saw her constantly, and we talked of everything. Sometimes I kissed her, and sometimes I did not. She was a little afraid—yet she had no fear. Never anywhere had I seen a girl or woman like her; she was, I thought, the sensitive female counterpart to the male in me—and thus I was the male counterpart to her inner self. Had she been male, I would have wanted her to be like me; had I been female, I would have wanted to be like her. So we were in love with ourselves in each other, and each other in ourselves: a perfect balance. And, had she been a little older, I would have completed that fusion which brings true perfection. I found consolation in telling myself that soon I would return from Germany, in a springtime when flowers would be in full bloom. . . . I had forgotten my wife completely.

On the evening before my departure, a performance was given in my honor by Percivalle Doria. Accompanying himself on the lute, he sang one of his poems:

"*Amore m'à priso*
e misso m'à 'n balia
d' altro amore salvaggio . . ."

I watched Bianca's face. Never for a moment did she acknowledge the existence of any man save me. . . .

5

THE LAST lap of my trip to Germany began with an ominous incident. Though we left at dawn, a crowd had gathered about the gate of the Palazzo Doria, as if some extraordinary event was expected. At my appearance I was greeted not with the usual cheers but a suspenseful silence. As the crowd parted before our horses, a ragged old woman, blind in one eye and gray hair flying, stepped directly into my path. Abruptly I reined in. My horse reared and flailed the air with his forehoofs, and only by the narrowest of margins did I avoid trampling the filthy half-human creature.

"Behold the priestling-King," the woman shrilled, "—he who will never live to reach his goal!"

"Beware the hag, my Lord!" cried Percivalle, crossing himself, "no doubt she is a *strega*!"

"A thousand thanks for your prophecy, Monna Madre," I called derisively in a loud voice, "but I fear no witchcraft paid for by Otto's agents. I too will pay—exactly what the prophecy is worth!" And from Percivalle I took a copper coin and flung it at the woman's feet.

The crowd hooted and shrieked, "Burn her—burn her!"

"No, no!" I shouted. "Leave her for the flames of Hell!"

We rode on. I was undisturbed; who ever lives to reach his final goal? And if the witch meant merely Germany—I had faith in more than my sword. I could not fail, for destiny was with me. But it took me an hour to restore the normal spirits of my companions. Even Berardo appeared depressed.

The direct route, via the Simplon Pass, was closed to me, as Milano had declared itself my enemy. I therefore chose a circuitous way which led me first to Pavia. I was greeted there as if already I had been crowned Emperor—knights, clergy, and townsfolk marching with me and carrying a canopy over my head. My Genovese escort left me, and I pushed onward with men of Pavia, who had arranged a rendezvous to deliver me safely to men of Cremona. One Saturday, just as the evening bells rang out for Vespers, we left Pavia and, to avoid interception by the Milanese, rode all night.

The meeting place was to be on the banks of the river Lambro. We arrived before dawn, found no signs of the Cremonese, so our grooms unsaddled and tethered our horses and we settled down to wait.

The lush meadows of Lombardia, with their faintly stirring poplars, were very different from my Sicilia. The earth was black loam, rich and odorous where it had been turned by the wooden plows drawn by white oxen. The land itself was crisscrossed with canals dating back to Roman times. The midsummer night was filled with whirring and buzzing insects—beetles, mosquitoes, fireflies, and we were forced to wrap our cloaks about us. I thought of Bianca, and marveled that she could be so much a child in body and so much an adult in intellect. But who could better understand this phenomenon than I—I, the boy-man? Then nightingales began to sing, and dawn was upon us.

But not only dawn. We were surprised by a splatter of arrows, some of which found marks in men and horses, and the song of the nightingale was mingled with wild neighs and screams of pain. The Milanese had knowledge of our meeting place, and fell upon us with the first light. Simultaneously we heard the shouts of our allies from Cremona, who had reached the opposite bank.

Then began one of those frenetic bits of activity with which I was all too familiar in my childhood—instant response to a violent situation which threatened death, everything happening so fast that afterward all real events seem to have been exaggerated into dream. With apparent calm I called to the captain of the Pavese to hold the ford for my companions—that I myself would ford alone, as I must not permit the capture of my person by the Milanese. I myself untethered my horse and with the agility of an acrobat vaulted upon his bare back. I drew my sword, covered myself with my shield, and spurred the horse across the pebbly shores and into the treacherous shoals of the river.

I swam him as if he were a steed of Poseidon, and, totally winded, he reached the opposite bank. The Cremonese greeted me with shouts of joy, but I had no time for rejoicing. Berardo, my knights, and my Saracens Pietro and Paolo remained to be rescued, and I sent the Cremonese to bring them. In minutes, though it seemed hours, we were all together again, all dripping wet; and, guarded in the rear by the Cremonese commander, we rode at full speed for Cremona. The Milanese were thwarted, but I chalked up a mark against them which I was never to forget. And afterward I tried to make amends to Pavia, for my escort was almost wholly massacred.

The word of my escape sped on the wind. Everywhere people said that I had forded the river by a miracle; angels had lent wings to my horse because it was the will of Christ that the Milanese should not take me. So I was greeted everywhere with new curiosity, respect, and fear—and the legend of invincibility began to grow and grow. I began to be called "the Angel of the Lord." But I did not let this aura of holiness deter me from paying my obeisance to the birthplace of Vergil as we passed through Mantova, and Catullus when we reached Verona. In Verona, I visited, too, the great Roman amphitheater, second only to the Colosseum, and sighed upon its ruins.

Gazing upon the distant Alps, I seemed almost in sight of my goal, and I felt undeterred by the mountains. What was this barrier but a mass of rock, and how many times in history had it been crossed by hordes of Germans? Now I would reverse the tide, and cross as the Romans had crossed, bringing Roman law and Greek culture into barbarian lands from Italy.

My adherents from Verona took me up the valley of the Adige as far as Trento, and there they left me. Farther than this along the Brenner I could not go, for the Duke of Bavaria was partisan to Otto's cause. I had no alternative but to turn westward, to cross the forbidding wall of the great Alps, into the Engadine. And thence, I hoped, down the valley of the Rhine.

Now for my company I had only my own little band. We paused and bent back our heads to gaze at the swirling mists and frozen glaciers high upon the towering peaks. Then every man of us, including my Saracens, made the sign of the cross.

6

THE CROSS followed us—or perhaps it would be more accurate to say we followed the cross, for we seemed to travel from one to the other along the trail and at every intersection. The shrines were of wood, sheltering crucifixes carved of wood—with each crucifixion more graphic and grotesque than the preceding. The features of the Christ became more distorted, the wounds deeper, the blood more copious. It was obvious that religion was serious and painful to the inhabitants of this land, and I could not help contrasting these shrines with the shrines to the Virgin in Italy—shrines in warm and glowing colors, with portraits of a beautiful young woman lovingly holding a babe. These people who enjoyed such agony in the Christ would not be an easy people to govern, I thought, for they would be rigorous in everything.

As we traversed the passes our horses trod belly deep in melting snow, which froze at night and caused us great discomfort. Sometimes we heard the rumble of snowslides, and sometimes we picked our way along the edge of precipices so alarming that we dared not look over to see the bottom of the gorge. We passed above the line of the lofty, dark fir trees, where all was bleak and empty, an emptiness filled only by the mists of clouds and the moan of lonely winds. And then at last we began to descend.

At first we had traveled through a region where the people spoke a strange kind of Latin, called Romansh; then gradually this language gave way to a German dialect very difficult to understand. As we entered the valleys we found them guarded by small castles, of very crude design and construction, as if men unskilled in the working of stone had built haphazardly one room and then another. Almost the only art or decoration was simple stencils on the walls, and the latrines were often only holes to one side of the central hall. As we progressed toward Germany the castles became larger and more imposing, but their quality did not change. The peasants' houses were notable for mountains of cow manure and great piles of wood all neatly stacked.

Toward the middle of September we finally reached Chur, a town in the valley where flow the headwaters of the river Rhine. I was astonished at the timbered houses with their gabled roofs, often made of gray slate, and at the smallness of the windows, guarded by wooden shutters painted with yellow stripes or red zigzag designs. Houses overhung the streets, and shops were marked by signs of wrought iron with crudely painted pictures. The streets swarmed with people who had come out to see the boy King from the mysterious Sicilia. I was greeted by the Bishop of Chur and a considerable company of ecclesiastics, who (in accordance with the Pope's orders) acclaimed me with all honor. To this day I remember not the Bishop's face, but the pungent odor of horse dung, steaming on that crisp September morning, as both our horses chose the moment of salutation to let loose.

I was greeted, too, by a band of sixty German knights, who had heard about my coming, and had ridden to Chur to join my retinue. While waiting, they amused themselves, I found, by such common sports as bear baiting and wagers on a pig. In this latter, three men and three pigs were placed in a pen. Each man wielded a club, and struck at the pigs as they ran about squealing and grunting, madly trying to escape. The sport, it seems, was to pick the pig which would survive the longest. The knights were gravely disappointed when they learned I bore no treasure; but I promised them a double reward, in due course, and much adventure—and after our talk they joined me with enthusiasm. So sorely did I need to implement my band that I would have welcomed suits of armor stuffed with straw, if they could but ride with me and make a showing.

The Bishop of Chur, not averse to a little adventure himself, rode to St. Gallen. The Abbot of that great monastery received me not only with honor, but with three hundred horsemen whom he added to my train. For this I thanked him as much as for his blessing, and we all rode on apace toward Konstanz, for rumors were afloat that Otto was about to cross the lake.

Now again a few hours played a decisive role in my life, for had I delayed but the space of three, Konstanz would have been lost, and with it, probably, Germany. With joy we reached the heights above the lake and glimpsed its pale blue water. Among the trees rose the ramparts of the town of Konstanz, ringed by autumn foliage more spectacular than any I had ever seen. All flags were flying.

"A good sign, your Majesty," said the Abbot of St. Gallen, a sallow man who bounced heavily on his trotting horse. "Evidently the Bishop has received inspiration from Heaven, and your Majesty's coming is anticipated."

I took the words with ill grace, for I had discovered too late that the Abbot had not sent ahead a messenger on a swift horse, as was customary. He had been too long withdrawn from the world, I thought, and needed shaking up a little.

"Let us hope the inspiration comes from Heaven and not from Otto," I answered sharply. "We should not like to ride all unsuspecting into a trap—else your three hundred horsemen will find themselves in Heaven!"

Chastened, he proposed that the royal party hold back while he rode ahead to the city gates to ascertain the situation. This we did, grouping the knights about us in battle formation. Then from a hilltop Berardo and I watched his progress—a toy ecclesiastic riding up to the drawbridge of a toy gate to a toy town. And as he approached, the drawbridge was raised in his face. . . . The nervous rustle of consternation among my knights rose like an undulating wave. The Emperor-elect was rejected! The horses sensed our emotions, and restlessly pawed the ground as we waited.

At length the Abbot returned, shrunken, I thought, several sizes, and bouncing pathetically on his horse. Though I was glacier-cold with fury, I was completely self-composed. "And what" said I, "was the inspiration received from Heaven?"

"Your Majesty," said the Abbot, literally squealing, "the Bishop of Konstanz spoke with me from the parapet. He is most gravely confused, for the town is prepared to receive Otto. The flags fly for Otto. His servants have already arrived, and even now the cooks prepare dinner for Kaiser Otto's appearance tonight. . . ."

"*Kaiser* Otto?" I said. "Fortunate, Abbot, that the Holy Father did not hear that slip of your tongue. But in remembrance of your services to our person, we will forgive. Come now, and lead us to the bishop—just you, and the Archbishop Berardo, and ourself."

Slowly, without the slightest hint of urgency we wound our

way down the road almost to the edge of the moat. Only for a moment did we stare at the figures clustered on the walls.

The Abbot made the sign of the cross, and intoned, "Hark ye! hark ye! In the name of the Father, Son and Holy Ghost!"

Then Berardo raised both hands above his head, bearded and vengeful like a prophet of old, and cried out: "I am the Archbishop Berardo, Papal Nuncio Plenipotentiary. Forget not the excommunication of Otto the Welf! I call upon you to receive in your midst and do homage to Friedrich, son of the Emperor Heinrich VI, grandson of the Emperor Friedrich I, anointed of God and of His Holiness the Pope, and duly elected King of the Germans!"

I took off my helmet, and three times I passed before their eyes, riding my horse like a wild stallion, brandishing my lance aloft, and allowing the sunlight full play on my long golden curls. Then abruptly I reined in my horse at the edge of the moat.

"Lower the bridge!" I called. Then I shifted from Latin to German: "It is the command of *Kaiser Friedrich der Zweite!*"

Creaking and groaning, the windlasses began to turn. Haltingly the rusty chains lowered the bridge into place, and the great riveted gate began to open. The sound of my horse's hoofs echoed triumphantly upon the wooden planks.

7

OTTO'S DINNER was one of the most savored meals of my life. Even the *Sauerkraut* I found a tasty dish, and did not disdain a second helping—though the belches of my companions should have offered sufficient warning. We quaffed stein after stein of beer, which I did not much like, recalling that jingle written in the fourth century by the Emperor Julian the Apostate:

How came this goat-reek? Wine is nectar-scented.
The Celt from barley-tops, so We suppose,
For want of grapes and nose,
This brew invented.

I was on the verge of quoting, but stopped myself in time. Which would have been more insulting to my German clerical hosts: quoting a pagan or not liking beer? I resolved on the spot never to murmur about the food or drink or climate of this stern and rigorous land, but to sup and drink without complaint and wrap myself in furs. It was the least I could do to bear with my subjects, for indeed they offered me the best that they had.

It was while we were eating that Otto arrived before the gates. To find them closed in his face must have been one of the most jarring surprises of his life. He raged and swore at the guards, shouting and bellowing like a veritable bull, stamping back and forth on his long legs as though his armor had no weight, and waving a torch with such force that I thought he himself might try to fire the town. He was reputed to have enormous strength in his fists. I watched from a concealed position on the ramparts, not deigning to speak with him or let him know of my presence. Even in the wavering shadows of the torchlight I could measure his power. He was very tall and muscular—not merely bulky, as had been reported to me in Sicily. But, despite the fact that he had grown up at the court of his uncle Richard Coeur de Lion in

England, he was uncultured, brutish, lacking in wit. Had I met him in combat, I am sure that, even though so much smaller, I would have won. I would have pitted my suppleness of mind and body against his massiveness—and I would have led him to self-destruction. And in the end, I did, though we never once met face to face.

A special score I had against him was his recent marriage to my cousin Beatrice—at age fourteen—to whom he had been betrothed by the Pope three years before, when all was well between them. As a last desperate hope of maintaining his claim to the Empire, Otto forced the wedding while I was picking my way across the Alps. Poor Beatrice could find no escape; she was led to the altar, pale as death. Thus was her end foreshadowed, for she perished a few days afterward, "under mysterious circumstances" —her own hand. For Otto, a terrible omen; and watching him rant before the gates, I sensed his desperation, and felt for him (a moment only) a touch of compassion. But I remarked to Berardo that I thought it would require a pickax to beat any sense into his head.

Enraged and frustrated, finally he withdrew, shouting again and again his curses: "*Verflucht sei diese Stunde!*" He had not with him sufficient forces to lay siege to the town, and I had not sufficient forces to sally forth against him. The humiliation of camping at the gate while I plucked the meat from his suckling pigs and capons and guzzled his beer was too much for any man to bear. And the story, of course, grew mightily with every telling; it was more valuable to me than a victory won over heaps of corpses. Otto retreated, howling like a dog, far down the Rhine.

My victory became a miracle. It was recounted as an act of God. It was said that I was appointed by Christ to save the Germans the agony of their endless civil wars between the nobles, and to alleviate the suffering of the people. I was hailed at once as hero and savior. Daily, hourly, new adherents arrived to align themselves with my standard. *Prinz*, *Herzog*, *Graf*, *Baron*, *Markgraf*, and *Landgraf*, all came trooping to render homage, many wearing armor with helmets like grotesque faces with snouts, horns, or tusks—an assembly, I thought fleetingly, of living gargoyles.

When, a week later, I rode to Basel to hold my first court, I was accompanied by a retinue of abbots and bishops and nobles in a triumphant procession. Pleased that the laity as well as the clergy recognized me as Sovereign, I invited Count Ulrich of Kiburg to ride on my left and Count Rudolf of Hapsburg on my right. In my honor, all along the river, castles and churches were illuminated at night with thousands of flickering oil lamps. And in Basel I found waiting five hundred soldiers sent me by the Bishop of Strasbourg, and a petition from the King of Bohemia that I confirm his crown.

I had crossed the Alps, and I had won. I was indeed: *Kaiser Friedrich der Zweite*.

But my victory yet required consolidation. I was, after all, in the heart of my ancestral lands, the Duchy of Swabia, the oldest of the Roman colonies in Germany. Germany, the rest of Germany—Franks, Saxons, Thuringians, Bavarians, as they thought of themselves—was another problem. I had first to deal with the relationship of the clergy to the nobility. The Church had come to own more than half of the land of Germany, and in the Rhineland archbishops ranked above the laity as princes, just below the King. I was deeply indebted to the Pope for my successes—but also I was not unaware of the anti-Papal sentiments rising in Germany. It was Berardo who quoted to me verses of the famed minnesinger Walther von der Vogelweide, beginning with the lines, "Ahi, how Christianlike the Pope laughs at our wrongs, when he recites his triumphs to the Romish throngs," and ending, "Eat pullets down, ye priests, and drink your wine; and leave the foolish German laymen—fasting."

I found, at first to my astonishment and discomfort, that the barons had the right both to sit and wear their hats in the presence of the Emperor—and this was not disrespect, but an outgrowth of the elective principle which vested so much power in the hands of the nobles. The nobles themselves were quarrelsome and greedy, contending among themselves for land and privileges, and the better-educated clergy outdid them all by assuming positions of administration and buttressing themselves not only with arms, but with Holy Mother Church and the Word of God Himself. The peasants moaned and groaned, taxes were high, warfare and devastation frequent, and everywhere ignorance reigned supreme.

As for my own situation in Swabia, my Uncle Philipp had tried to buy success against Otto by mortgaging much land and releasing tax and toll rights to those nobles who backed his cause. Thus Philipp's death found him destitute; and my inheritance, as had been the case in Sicily, was a debit. But the name of Hohenstaufen, the blood of Barbarossa, was an asset of far greater value than land or gold (as in Sicilia I had the asset of the blood of Ruggero). I was of the *stirps regia*—important because Otto had begun to circulate tales that my birth was illegitimate. I was one of their own, come home to assume my duty toward my people. But more than this I was "the magic child" from the magical South, and already the minnesingers were weaving legends about my name:

> Now comes the Pulian Child along—
> The Kaiser's sword is twice as strong . . .

For a while, events moved very rapidly, and I found myself with little time to ponder basic problems. Otto had invested my grandfather Barbarossa's great castle at Hagenau in Alsace, and he had to be repulsed. This was done by my cousin, the Duke of Lorraine, one of the first really powerful nobles to declare his support for me. In return, I wished to reward him with three thousand silver marks—but to do so I had to make a loan, as in my first days as King of Sicily, and one of my creditors was that selfsame Anselm von Justingen who had brought the call of the German princes to Palermo.

Late autumn was setting in, misty and damp. I decided to move at once into the castle at Hagenau, as it was one of the most massive and imposing of all the castles north of the Alps. Its walls were thick and well arranged for defense. Within I found, to my delight, a splendid library. The state rooms were paved with red marble—in this climate, a floor of ice. The chapel had been built by my grandfather especially to display the crown jewels of the Empire, and I was much distressed at its emptiness—for not only the jewels but all the regalia remained in Otto's hands. This was more serious for the symbolical than the actual value—for people believed in the sacred character of the regalia as consecrated by the Pope and derived from Heaven. So long as Otto held the regalia, he remained legal representative of Christ, retained a certain title to the Empire, and many people continued to call him Kaiser. But for the moment my distress could not be resolved, as Otto continued steadily to retreat.

Nevertheless, I took from him one of his most valuable possessions—his Chancellor, Konrad von Scharfenburg. At first I felt a sense of distrust, because Konrad was also Bishop of Speyer and

Metz. In my own Bishop-Chancellor, Gualtiero di Palearia, I had already suffered quite enough from this heavenly-earthly combination, and I wanted no more of it. However, it was easy to read from Konrad's fleshy, avaricious lips and ambitious eyes that he belonged entirely to the victor, just as he had written that he was completely at my disposal. I thought it wise to build a court with men who had defected from Otto's cause.

I formed another policy, too: liberality. Otto was noteworthy for his stinginess. He took all and gave nothing. The news of my gift to the Duke of Lorraine carried with it the pleasing ring of silver, and I quickly found an astonishing number of nobles eager and ready to serve me. As part of the Pope's arrangements with the King of France, ambassadors arrived bearing considerable sums of money, and the Chancellor inquired where I wished the coins to be stored.

"Nowhere at all," I replied. "Neither this nor any other money is to be kept: it is to be distributed among the princes."

These words were greeted far and wide with jubilation. Only Berardo wondered if I should not hold funds in reserve. "Why," he said, "such excessive generosity?"

"Wisdom counseled it," I answered. "It gives us an advantage in men's minds over our foe—who acts quite otherwise, and thus brings down on his own head the hatred of men and the displeasure of Heaven."

For the French gold I had to pay—by signing an alliance with France. In November, shaking and shivering from cold such as I had never before experienced, I set out for Vaucouleurs to meet the son of the French King—a man as cold and repellent as the weather. I was warmed, however, by the agility with which I dodged daggers thrown at me by Otto's hirelings. Since mutual interest overrides mutual dislike, Philip Augustus and I reached an agreement satisfactory to us both.

In December, under slate-gray skies and driving snow, I made my way to Frankfurt—so homesick for Sicily as I had never been before and never since. I understood at last the constant Teutonic invasions of the south—surely only to escape the cold! On the fifth, I was acclaimed Emperor by a great gathering of the German princes, who attested their fealty and homage to me and renunciation of Otto. I had no doubt of their enthusiasm, as I had distributed among my followers the vast sum of twenty thousand silver marks. After four days, I moved on to Mainz for my coronation—a mock affair, as Otto held both the true regalia and Aachen, or Aix-la-Chapelle, where Charlemagne lies interred.

At last I was Emperor—but not yet was my throne secure. In the eyes of the faithful, I had yet to be crowned not only in Aix—but in Rome. And this latter, my old guardian, friend and protector, Pope Innocent III, was in no hurry to accomplish.

8

Time in Germany was slow-moving. The eight years I spent there, before returning to Italy, seem in retrospect like twenty. They blur into boar hunts in the dark forests, into hawking on soft blue mornings in late springtime, into many a *Walpurgisnacht*, into ancient heathen Maypole dances, into eternally falling snow, into great Christmas celebrations before huge fireplaces filled with blazing logs, into brimming platters of roast goose, into thousands of steins of beer, into endless sausages, into countless concessions to the Church. I thought rarely of Bianca, who seemed now only a charming child I had met on my travels; often I thought of my wife and my son Enrico, for my head already was filled with plans for his future.

Quickly I was forced to give away to the Church in Germany almost every advantage I had reserved for the State in Sicily. To oppose the Church I needed behind me the strength of an hereditary kingdom, or solid support from a united body of lay princes. I had neither. Like the princes of the Church, the lay princes were interested only in their own aggrandizement. My objective became, therefore, the strengthening of the concept of Empire as a *Roman* Empire; and I deliberately chose to cultivate the backing of the clergy, whose world outlook was less provincial. But my price for favors, when finally revealed, was high.

The Germans themselves, in comparison with the facile Italians, to me seemed big-boned, heavy, and awkward. They prized more highly the mighty fist than the witty tongue. As grace of movement was not important to men in armor, the huge German knights made a most impressive sight—though when they wore tubolar helmets I could not help regarding them with a certain amount of distaste, recalling the image of Markward and the murder of Guglielmo's beloved grandfather. I was much too practical, however, to allow such emotional nuances to interfere with my present responsibilities as King of the Germans—nor for one moment did I forget my German inheritance and my debt to the German princes.

From time to time I was beset by the petty rebellions of nobles—sometimes not so petty. My cousin the Duke of Lorraine died, and was succeeded by a proud and comely son, Thibault, of about my own age. Immediately Thibault announced that he would not pay homage to a boy. He seemed intent on doing the opposite of his father on every policy—for his father was said to have ruled him with a heavy hand. It would be foolish, I thought, to permit this boy to develop a bitter and perhaps costly feud: so one night I had him captured while he was fornicating in a brothel. He was brought at once to me, and I found him furious with humiliation. I liked him. He had a light in his eye, was sharp of wit, and good to look upon. I did not cast him into prison, as he expected, but every night had him come and dine with me—permitting the presence of his squire to hold his cloak and sword, as if he were an honored guest. I challenged him on many issues, and stung his intellect. We bickered—I allowed him to say whatever came into his head. In the end we formed a lasting friendship.

As a counterbalance to the power of the princes, I did what I could to increase commerce and therefore the importance of the Imperial towns—the free cities and the princely towns I could not touch. I foresaw that someday burgher and guildsman might want a more active role in the conduct of affairs. I improved roads and communications; I guaranteed safe conduct to merchants; I cleansed trade routes of robbers; I encouraged fairs and the exchange of every type of goods.

I traveled about Germany a great deal: to Speyer and Worms, to Augsburg and Ulm, to Nürnberg and Würzburg—my *Wanderjahre*. I was impressed by the sinuous beauty of the Rhine valley and the excellence of its wines. I lingered there whenever I could. On these journeys I used the Arabian stallions my little party had brought from Sicily. The German horses, for riding or plowing, were heavy, like the people. My Arabians seemed like sinewy ponies in comparison. I found that when I rode with knights in armor, I too must mount a German horse or be dwarfed by the giants who surrounded me.

During this period, also, I became intensely interested in

agriculture. I became conscious of the inefficiencies of the serf system, for I saw with my own eyes the difference in yields when the land was worked by the Cistercian monks. I admired this Order, whose members lived by tilling the soil—being forbidden to take rents—and whose methods of cultivation were astonishingly effective. But in Germany I could not even bend—much less break—the rigid bonds of feudal tenure. The best I could do was to be received myself into the Cistercian Order, which I chose to call "the shady grove of Christ." For the "gray monks," who lived in the utmost simplicity by the labor of their own hands, I had the utmost respect and reverence. In them was kept alive, I thought, a truly Christian spirit.

Otto, meanwhile, remained a thorn in the flesh which I seemed unable to pluck out. I wished to diminish, not increase, the extent of civil war—and since I had the Church, most of the princes, and most of the populace on my side, I felt that the time must come when Otto would stand wholly alone. He would fall victim to himself. Nevertheless, I began slowly to accumulate arms and supplies, and to organize an army for use if necessary.

I had not anticipated the urgent need of my army because of an invasion by the English. Otto had leagued himself with King John to attack France, thinking that success of the English would gravely jeopardize my position as Emperor. But Otto seriously underestimated the strength and unity of the French, who were feeling their sinews as a nation, and seriously overestimated the capacity of the English to invade. He was beguiled by King John and his own wishful thinking. At Eastertime, hardly two years after I had come to Germany, I found myself in command of an army on the lower Rhine, with the intent of attacking Otto's flank and relieving pressure on the French. But before my army saw action, the French in July counterattacked and thoroughly smashed their opponents at the battle of Bouvines. Otto fled. Philip Augustus sent me Otto's tattered, bloodstained banners.

With my intact, unscathed army I marched on Aix-la-Chapelle. But force was no longer necessary. Otto's supporter and ally, the Duke of Brabant, capitulated and sent me a fledgling—his son—as hostage. Unfortunate Duke!—only three months earlier Otto had married Maria, the Duke's favorite daughter. I marched triumphant into the ancient town, proclaiming it to be "the capital and seat of the Kings of Germany . . . because in this town the Roman kings are crowned and sanctified, and it shines in glory only second to Rome herself."

Just then to be crowned and sanctified was out of the question. Others of Otto's supporters had escaped across the river Meuse and were regrouping. In a swift action I flung my army across the Meuse at a point where I was not expected, and with an enveloping movement scattered my enemies. The military action involved was hardly more than minor, as the opposing forces simply vanished—and once again Otto disappeared. I thought at first he had fled to England; but he had not. When a year later the news reached me of the "Magna Carta" (promptly but not effectively annulled by Pope Innocent), I understood from King John's troubles at Runnymede that Otto's Saxon-English coalition was finished.

In spite of the collapse of all his hopes, Otto declined to yield. He chose, instead, to hole up in the last town remaining to him: Köln. With his new wife he spent his days and nights playing dice. I deliberated flushing him, but decided to let the inexorable logic of history have its way. The citizens of Köln quickly tired of their indigent guests, and offered to pay Otto's debts and give him and his wife six hundred marks to be gone.

Disguised as pilgrims, the pair slipped away. My disgust knew no bounds.

9

MY NEXT task was to finish the business of coronation—though Otto, having abandoned all else, stubbornly refused to abandon the regalia. Nonetheless, he could no longer prevent me from sitting on the throne of Charlemagne. An entire year was consumed in preparation for my coronation; and so important did I consider the event, that I decided to date my reign from July, the year of our Lord 1215, the twenty-first year of my life.

I entered Aix accompanied by a huge throng of knights and nobles and clergy assembled from all Germany, a cavalcade of such brilliant colors as hardly ever seen before under the hazy northern sun. I had caused regalia to be made as closely similar to the original as possible, sparing nothing to increase their magnificence. A special ceremony had been planned to transfer the remains of Charlemagne to an impressive new reliquary, wrought in silver and bearing on its sides the images of the Apostles and the German Emperors. My image, too, was represented, and I felt that at last the ambition of my youth had come to fruition. I recalled the puppet paladins, in Palermo, and the great crusade of Charlemagne against the infidel, and indeed my heart swelled. Since the fall of Rome no other man had so dominated history, and I was humbled at my role as his successor—humbled, but proud—for all the great deeds of history were not yet done.

"Hic est Christi miles fortis,
Hic invictae dux cohortis . . ."

The chant of the choir, as I entered the cathedral, rang in my ears like echoes of the past. I was overcome by the desire to see with my own eyes the body of Charlemagne. As we approached the shrine I flung off my heavy robe, and, to the astonishment of bishops, nobles, and artisans, nimbly leaped upon the scaffold. With my own hands I opened the lid and gazed down at the shriveled remains which had lain thus for four hundred years. Might not in another time some other ruler thus see me? Might not my own sarcophagus of porphyry become a shrine? I seized a hammer from a workman and with my own hands drove the silver nails which fixed the lid in place. I had paid homage to Charlemagne from my heart. . . .

But at the coronation I did another thing which caused astonishment, and which had a profound effect on the direction of my life. I had repeated the ancient formula as required of me—the prayers, the anointing and the return of sword and scepter, the coronation oath. Then the Papal Legate, Sigfrid, Archbishop of Mainz, placed the silver diadem which is the crown of the Germans upon my head, and I ascended the throne of Charlemagne. I was sharply conscious of the crude stones which formed the steps, of the small boxlike armchair, of the wide stone stripes which decorated the arches above me. But most of all I was conscious of the hush in the cathedral; for none could deny that this was another moment of history.

Suddenly, before the bewildered eyes of the Archbishop, I seized the Cross. In a clear, loud voice which echoed in the vaults, I cut each word from the other: "We, the King of the Romans, to the honor and glory of Christ, vow before the Father, Son, and Holy Ghost, to lead a Crusade to free the Holy Places of Jerusalem from the infidel!"

Wild cheers and shouts were the response: "*Heil dem Tag! Heil der Stunde!*"

I sought the face of Berardo. Of all that throng, he was, I think, the only one who understood what I was doing; but from his lips came not a sound.

I was King of the Romans, King of the Germans—but I was not yet *Romanorum Imperator et Semper Augustus*. Only the crown of Charlemagne, set upon my head by the Pope himself, would give me the right to that full title. The crown of Charlemagne was hidden away in some secret cache on the estate of Otto's brother, the Duke of Saxony. And the Pope was sure to be furious at the vow I had just made before all Christendom—for in effect I had snatched the Cross, and the leadership of the Crusade, from the Pope's own hands.

10

At once I made plans to bring my wife and son to Germany. As for Costanza, I felt little or no interest in seeing her again, but I needed an Empress as consort. As for Enrico, I thought Sicily could well spare its five-year-old King, for I had conceived another role for him. Yet without the consent of Pope Innocent, every move I wished to make was blocked. Then the Pope, all unwittingly, expedited my schemes—though many months were consumed in the doing.

Innocent called a Council to meet in the Laterano in Rome, in November, and I dispatched Berardo to represent me as Ambassador. So persuasive was Berardo's tongue that the Pope, despite his deep anger against me, himself picked a man to send to Sicily. Or perhaps his own plan, in the absence of Enrico, was to take full possession of Sicily as a Papal fief. But my plan was destined to fruition, and his to failure, for—as the Pope would have said—God chose to intervene.

The Laterano Council (the Fourth) was the pinnacle of Innocent's career, the climax of all his dreams, for it proclaimed willingly every cherished doctrine which had elevated him above the world and halfway into Heaven. Over two thousand delegates were in attendance—the greatest number in the history of the Church—and among them all hardly a voice was raised in any dissent. Formally presented was the theory of transubstantiation, with its vast grants of new powers to the priesthood. When Berardo returned to Germany, he described everything to me —including the senseless death of the Archbishop of Amalfi, who was blindly trampled under the feet of the ecclesiastical throng.

> The Pope is the visible representative on earth of God invisible: he is infallible in matters of faith and omnipotent in things of faith. . . .

Every deviation of thought or of faith from that which the Church teaches is an opposition to her will, a repudiation of her, a heresy, a rebellion, a crime against God. . . .

Temporal society is derived from the spiritual and falls under its law. . . .

Such were samples of the official doctrine. The universal dominion of the Church had become the universal dominion of the Pope. With holy water Innocent had quenched his thirst for power; but the fonts were to be refilled from the springs of conflict. Thus Innocent made inevitable a mighty struggle, in which eventually I was to become a leading instrument.

As for my taking the Cross, Innocent said not a word. He preached to the multitude, promising remission of sins for all who served the Crucified One by joining the Crusade. He set the date at one year hence. He called upon kings, dukes, princes, and all other nobles to take part or send substitutes. He decreed a tax of the twentieth portion of "all ecclesiastical profits" for three years. But he did not so much as whisper that I—with all my new resources—had volunteered.

In due course the Council confirmed me as Holy Roman Emperor. One voice, a Milanese, was raised in opposition. The Pope did not defend me; he said nothing. In rebuke to the opposition he arose, gathered his robes, and walked out. Before I was confirmed, Otto was deposed. And the deposition of a Roman Emperor by a Church Council—however much in my favor—carried an ominous ring to my ears.

Within the year came the abrupt intervention of God. Innocent fell ill and quickly died. Though the substance of the man was gone, the lengthened shadow of his power remained. Even so, when I sighed at the death of my old guardian, my sighs were mixed with relief. The new substance was not the same.

The new Pope assumed the name of Honorius III. He knew me, but I hardly knew him. My wardship to a Pope seemed never to end: as Cardinal Cencio Savelli, the new Pope was the man who had been Legate to that amorphous Council of Bishops which allegedly guided my destiny in childhood. For me his face was vaguer than his name; but such was his character—vague. Now he was old and ailing. He was neither eager to add to the power bequeathed him by Innocent, nor willing to relinquish a single prerogative. He was a jurist and finance administrator, and was famed as editor of the "*liber censuum,*" the tax book of the

Church. Though he loved the accumulation of money and was strangely stingy, his chief concern as Pope became the liberation of the Holy Sanctuaries. For this he was willing to open both the coffers of the Church and the veins of all Christians. As Christ shed his blood for the redemption of men, so must men shed their blood for the redemption of places holy to Christ.

Curiously, this dictum did not seem to apply to me. The new Pope seemed totally unaware that I had taken the Cross. Without the slightest consultation or even communication, he postponed the date of the Crusade two years, and proceeded with preparations entirely on his own. Somewhat piqued, in writing to him I ceased using my customary signature, "King by Grace of God and of the Pope." Certainly Honorius had nothing to do with the matter.

At about the time of Innocent's death, Costanza and Enrico arrived in Germany. Their journey had been difficult and hazardous, as I learned with much concern, for in my absence from Sicily all the old turbulence was being revived by the nobles. I realized how urgently my own firm authority was needed once again—but now I was captive not only of my own ambition, but of my agreements with Pope Innocent. The dead hand, with almost the equivalent of life force, continued to restrain me from the grave.

In one matter, however, I proved the immediate victor. Hermann von Salza, whom Innocent had dispatched to Sicily to fetch my Queen and son, returned not to the Papal court but remained at mine—though for the rest of his life he was torn intermittently between these two loyalties. He was a Thuringian, and not long since had become Grand Master of the Order of Teutonic Knights—the newest of the military Orders, a bitter rival to the Knights of San Giovanni and the Knights Templar. Von Salza had gone as delegate to the Pope's great Council after seven or eight years' military service in the Near East, and was well acquainted with all the problems confronting a Crusade. To my delight, I discovered that he spoke a little Arabic, though he had no sympathy whatever for the Muslim point of view. He was a serious man, sincere, straightforward—wholly devoted to the strengthening of his Order. I sensed in him at once a man valuable to my cause: where he led, many another German would follow.

Before receiving my wife and son, I invited von Salza to

dine with me, privately, to hear the full report of his journey from Sicily. Only Berardo was present, but in this I made a mistake. They were both in their late forties, some twenty-five years older than I—and instantly I divined the undercurrent of jealously between them. (Later I tried to reassure Berardo by saying that I sought in von Salza not an intimate, but a trustworthy intermediary to the Germans—a role which Berardo could not fill.) As individuals, they were astonishingly different; yet each, with passing time, proved equally steadfast.

Von Salza was as solid as his big-boned body—no subtlety at all. He was not ill-educated, but he was not well-educated. His manners were not offensive, but certainly had no polish. He flopped himself into the leather chair I indicated, stroked his pink clean-shaven face, munched on his fingers as though they were sausages, belched after gulping down beer, and heaved sigh after sigh.

"My Lord," he exclaimed in the blunt voice of a field military commander, "it's a long road from Sicily, a long, long road. As His Holiness the Pope commanded, I have brought safely to you the Queen and the young King Heinrich. But *mein Gott*—how my feet hurt!"

I discovered afterward that his feet always hurt, and on many a march I was to see him soaking them in stream or helmet. They were the bane of his life, and the single most persistent subject in his conversation. But in his first words to me he had used the very phrase which was uppermost in my own mind: young *King Heinrich*.

No longer did I think of him as Enrico, King of Sicily. . . .

II

I RECEIVED the Queen and the young King, formally, in the throne room of the Castle of Hagenau. The month was December, and to take the edge off the frigid air, I had ordered logs to be burned all night in the huge fireplaces. In addition I had caused many stags' antlers to be removed from the walls so that tapestries could be hung over the bare gray stones. The red marble pavement had been polished and scores of sheepskins strewn about the floor (some covering trap doors which opened to grisly dungeons). Candles were lighted in hundreds of black iron candelabra. The minnesinger Walther von der Vogelweide I had called to court, and he prepared songs of welcome. Yet nothing I could do either effectively relieved the cold or dissipated the pervasive atmosphere of barbarity which suffused the room.

I thought, as an Italian, that a thousand years of contact with the Roman culture had not been enough to civilize the Germans. And as a German I envied and longed for the culture and climate which could never be mine. Yet I, *Federico-Friedrich,* was both, knew both . . . was responsible to both, and could escape from neither.

It was easy to see from Costanza's face, as she was escorted to me by her ladies-in-waiting, how she felt about this trip to Germany. I wondered if her opinion was equally obvious to all the courtiers present. Her frown was persistent, her eyes sullen and brooding, and from time to time her teeth chattered from chill. Now she was thirty-two, and I was astonished at how much she had aged in the few years since I had left her. Though her hair was still fair and shining, the darkness had come again into her face. And no doubt she had resumed the expiation of sin by the use of her whips.

The boy walked beside her; already, at the age of six, he was haughty and reserved, like his mother. He was a little copy of her; in no feature or characteristic did he seem to resemble me. He stared straight at me with a touch of arrogance, and in his eyes was no sign of recognition. I felt a flash of regret for the hours not spent with him, the training and love I might have given him. Nor could I ever restore the relationship which had been lost. We struck no sparks from one another.

Costanza bowed. "My Lord, we are arrived. We greet your Imperial Majesty with great joy," she said in Latin.

I arose from the throne, kissed her hand. "The absence has been too long," I said. "We welcome our Empress to Germany and to the august throne of the Romans."

I gave my hand to my son to kiss. He knelt mechanically, and recited the words he had been taught:

> *"O dank dir, Gott, für diese Lust!*
> *Mein Vater schliesst mich an seine Brust!"*

I took him in my arms. I was impressed at his facility with German, yet brushed by sadness that he had not spoken to me in the Italian tongue I so loved. I kissed him and, with the Empress beside me, sat him at my feet.

Then presents were publicly exchanged, rich and impressive—though but one made an impression on me. This was the gift of the Teutonic Order to the young Heinrich. Master Salza had sent ahead the child's measurements for a suit of German armor (not chain mail, but solid steel), and before our eyes the boy was completely arrayed: greave and solleret, cuisse and tasse, breastplate and pauldron, gorget and gauntlet, and finally, helmet—a tubolar helm with horns.

My son, the product of my own loins, stood before me as a warrior German. I winced in momentary distaste. But, alas, to this omen I paid no heed. Within a month, in formal court assembled, before the greatest princes of the land, I named him Duke of Swabia, and the course I had elected was irrevocable.

But fortune, as though understanding what I did not—that I had lost a son—chose to compensate me. For some time I had dallied with the widow of a German nobleman. The unlucky man had been killed by a bear, and left his young bride locked in a chastity belt, languishing. I unlocked the belt. She was beautiful: fresh-cheeked, blond of eyebrow and hair, slim, firm of flesh, vigorous in bed. But in a few years, as with all the other matrons, blue spots would pit the lard encasing her legs, her breasts and belly would bulge like cabbages, and her breath would stink from too much beer and *Wienerschnitzel.* She was not stupid, but wholly uneducated in all the things which truly mattered to me. On the day of our parting I would have forgotten her name (was it Frieda? or Freia?), had she not presented me with a bastard son. I named him Enzo. He was to become very dear to me.

Nor was fortune content with this gift (the first of many bastards to come); at almost the same moment Otto was removed from the scene. Hermann von Salza, wild with excitement, brought the news.

"My Lord, my Lord!" he boomed, as he entered my presence. "*O himmlisches Entzücken!* Your old enemy is finished! He fell sick at the Harzburg; and after he confessed to the Abbot, the priests chanted the Miserere and beat him to death with rods. . . . 'Lay on! Lay on!' he howled, to atone for his sins, 'harder, harder!' Then the poor devil died—he who was once an Emperor and now no more than a bloody pulp!"

"A miserable end for a brave man," I said, touched by compassion, "for whatever else he was, certainly Otto was no coward." But I was more than thankful; the way was now cleared for the final fulfillment of my plan.

I had but to negotiate with the princes and the bishops in secret; but to throw dust in the Pope's eyes; but to wait with that *pazienza* to which I was already so well accustomed.

And indeed it was not long before messengers arrived from Pope Honorius, bearing urgent summons to the Crusade. The letter was addressed to "the victorious king, before whose countenance the heathen fly" and continued: ". . . youth, power, fame, your vow, the example of your ancestors summon you to fulfill your glorious enterprise." I was not deceived: it was a call for help.

Now it was my turn to delay.

12

All was going badly for Honorius. His whole campaign against the infidel had been misconceived and mismanaged. The first objective of his crusaders was to conquer Egypt (a land rich in plunder), and after its fall, turn on Jerusalem. Francesco d'Assisi, now in the good graces of the Church, had been sent to preach Christianity to the famed Sultan, Malik al-Kamil. Nothing availed. Messages of despair were sent to the Pope: "Only the Emperor can save us!"

I now prepared to complete the game of chess I had begun with Innocent. I urged the Pope not to countenance any delay on the part of all who had taken the Cross: I myself proposed excommunication of the dilatory. I set the earliest possible date of departure, the Festa of San Giovanni. I requested the Pope to take the Empire under his protection while I was away crusading. And my coronation in Rome itself was imperative. The Pope agreed with eagerness to all my suggestions.

It then transpired, to my great regret and dismay, as I informed the Pope, that I could not leave as planned. My affairs, alas, were not in order. The Sicilian question remained a question. And how could I possibly leave Germany with the problem of my succession unresolved? The date of my departure was postponed to September, then to March of the following year, then to May, then left open altogether. The Pope was filled with rage and panic; the Curia, with indignation.

So many concessions had I given the German lay princes that they had become my firm supporters. With the bishops, however, I had to bargain like a fishwife: I promised them rights of coinage and customs duties in their lands, rights to a beer tax, disposal of their feudal fiefs as they liked, bestowal of their personal wealth by will or testament, and finally, I promised that the ban of

Empire would follow automatically ban of Church. In this last, what a weapon I put into their hands! They acquiesced. . . .

One more bit of bargaining I had to do. The Imperial regalia and crown of Charlemagne remained in the hands of Otto's stubborn brother. I arranged for the Pope to demand their surrender; but the Duke of Saxony proved as truculent as Otto himself. So I tried another tack: I sent Hermann von Salza with the offer of the post of Vicar-General of the Empire (largely honorary) in my absence. Shortly thereafter the insignia and the regalia were displayed before me. With the vestments I was sorely disappointed, so poor was their craftsmanship; and I resolved to substitute not only the coronation mantle of my grandfather Ruggero, but other garments as well—so much greater was their splendor.

Now I chose to inform the Pope that while I intended to adhere scrupulously to the agreements I had made, and not unite Sicily to the Empire; nevertheless, while I was in Italy I would act as Regent of the Realm in my son's name. The Pope's reaction was immediately to take the boy under his personal protection, but more than this he could not do.

Then I called a great farewell Diet in Frankfurt, to precede my springtime departure for Rome and the coronation. One day, when I had happily arranged to be elsewhere, the princes met and elected Heinrich King of the Germans. The princes were content with their Hohenstaufen; how could the Pope complain? I had won a great diplomatic victory over the Curia. I was free to leave Germany, where already I had remained much too long.

My private reservations were another matter. Heinrich, now a big boy of ten, was frivolous, an abysmally poor student, impatient of all guidance. His whims blew whither the winds listed. I saw danger ahead. But I placed him in the hands of a man I trusted, a man whose points of view were not too divergent from my own—the Archbishop Engelbert of Köln. It was my hope that Engelbert would prove to be another Berardo. Costanza was disconsolate at leaving. She wept in outright despair, day and night, night and day. She was convinced that she would never see her son again.

But despite these marring thoughts and this flood of tears, my heart was buoyant. I felt a happiness I had not known for all the German years. I was ready to leap the Alps at one single bound: I was going home again.

13

We came down from the Brenner Pass into vineyards loaded with ripening grapes. When I saw the towers and rooftops of Verona, all ashimmer in the golden September sunlight, I could not restrain tears of joy. I halted my cavalcade, a great company, and swung off my horse; with reverence I took up a handful of earth. Though we were far, far from Sicilia, this nevertheless was the land of Italy. I had left it, hunted like a hare; I returned —a lion. We camped by the crystalline waters of Lake Garda; for in the interest of unity, I had resolved to show no special favor to any town, camping outside of each. I reveled in the warm autumn air, swimming in the lake, and exposing my body to the sun (to the scandal of all except Berardo). I felt an enormous increase in vigor, as though I were thrice myself. And with my two-year-old son Enzo I played as if he were a lion cub.

Everywhere I was recognized as Emperor, even by the Milanese, and beset by scores of appellants for special rights and favors. I confirmed all the old rights of the towns, but granted no privileges with respect to trade or lands in Sicily. This, to the Genovese, was a bitter disappointment, for they were expecting fat commercial plums. With my old enemies, the Pisans, I dealt so generously that they became attached to my cause for life. Venezia I freed from customs dues within the Empire, and the Doge promised me a yearly tribute of money, pepper (I preferred saffron, but these canny merchants considered it too costly), and a sumptuous robe.

Many details of the coronation yet remained to be settled, so I sent Hermann von Salza ahead as my Ambassador to the Pope—while I myself marched leisurely southward. In Bologna I made an exception to my rule about the towns, and entered to visit the law school and attend a banquet. The banquet was held in the lofty red-brick Palazzo del Podestà, where I met the famed lawyer Roffredo da Benevento, a man of soft voice, and a face like a pelican. I urged him to accept a place at my court, and he agreed.

"But, Sire," he said, "I beg a special favor from your Majesty: may I also arrange for my assistant to join me?"

"As you like, good doctor," I said, thinking it strange that he should take my time with so trivial a matter.

"My assistant is an exceptional young man," Roffredo continued, unwilling to let the matter drop. "He came to the university here at your behest, my Lord. His name is Pier della Vigna . . ."

I frowned, searching for some troubled memory. "The name," I said, "is not unfamiliar." Then I saw the curious expression on Berardo's face—and remembered everything.

"By all means bring your assistant to court," I said stiffly to Roffredo. "We can assign him to work with the Archbishop Berardo!"

Roffredo next day joined my retinue, but his assistant was nowhere in evidence. Of this I was glad, for I regretted my assent, and felt a petty desire to spite Berardo in the matter.

We pressed on. How beautiful I found the gently rugged Apennines, the hazy blue valleys of Toscana, the soft rolling hills of Umbria. How restful to my gaze the purple grapes, the green-black cypresses, the olives silver-gray. The peasants stared with wondering eyes at the pomp and magnificence of our train, and from their behavior I knew that legends of my invincibility had gone before. I thought, however, they were a trifle disappointed at seeing the fabulous Emperor who looked so extremely young even at six-and-twenty. I responded to their cheers with a grave smile and called out, sometimes, my wish that they receive the grace of God.

Nearing Rome on the Via Flaminia, we were joined by Percivalle Doria and Manfredo Lancia, who had come together from Genova expressly for the coronation. At once I recognized them, and threw formality to the winds. They kissed not my hand, but I their cheeks—with the warmth of a long lost brother.

"How you both have matured!" I cried. "Not boys, but men!"

"And you, too, my Lord," Manfredo said. "The weighty affairs of state have added girth to your shoulders."

I sighed. "That is but the weight of German armor," I said. And then I remembered. "Your little sister—Bianca?" I asked politely, though for a moment I could hardly recall the name. "And how is she?"

"Not greatly changed, my Lord," Manfredo said. "She remains as shy of men as ever."

"A charming child," I said. "So charming—and a rare intelligence."

Then Percivalle sang for me his newest songs, and I decided that he, too, must come to my court in Sicily. Manfredo, whom I had sent on several missions while I was in Germany, I made an official of the Empire.

Next day—it was now the end of October—the Pope's ambassadors appeared, demanding fresh assurances that the Kingdom of Sicily would remain apart from the Empire. They were concerned with legal technicalities—that I use a separate seal, install no officials of the Empire, and such like. I cared not a fig for such details, and would have signed a basketful of similar agreements. I used both Berardo and von Salza in these negotiations, and I secured from the Pope von Salza's heart's desire: the right for the Teutonic Knights to wear a white mantle like the Templars, their hated rivals. As for the Pope, apparently he had resigned himself to the inevitable, and the date of coronation was fixed for the last Sunday before Advent, the twenty-second day of November, in the year 1220.

Another date was fixed, too: the date of my departure for the Holy Land, hardly ten months thereafter.

After doing penance for past delays, I wore over my armor the Holy Cross. Garbed thus, I rode on to Rome.

14

"OUR UNCONQUERABLE will became fused in the Imperial dignity," as I chose to phrase it, and man and office became identified as one. I was the Empire, the Empire was I. I wanted this coronation to be remembered for a hundred, a thousand, years. I spared no effort, no expense. I was determined, too, that no riots should take place, as at the coronation of Otto; nor would I, in any circumstances, be content to be crowned in secret—as was my grandfather Barbarossa. I loved the Romans; in response to this love, surely they would love me.

We pitched our tents outside of Rome on the Monte Malo, and began to groom and polish everything. Our thoroughbred horses, our saddles of velvet and gold, our bridles of silver and brass, our armor of steel, our tunics and capes of satin and wool, our banners of silk—everything shone and sparkled and gleamed. We had banished dirt, disorder, and corrosion. And, though it was November, I forced my entire company—amid much grumbling—to bathe. I told them their souls could not be purified unless their bodies first were clean. I was perfumed and rubbed with oil, and clad in the spotless white of a crusader, with red cross on breast.

Accompanied by the chant of monks, we rode slowly—the Empress on my right—into Rome by the Via Trionfale, on white Arabian horses. At thc Porta Collina, we received homage from the clergy of Rome. A solemn procession was formed. First went horsemen scattering from purses coins marked with my arms; then the monks, chanting once more; then followed clergy in rich vestments carrying censers and crucifixes; then a sword-bearer carrying point heavenward, the ceremonial sword with its emblem of a cross-potent and great rubies flashing in the sun. The crowds roared and cheered, greeting me with the wildest enthusiasm as one of their own.

We now drew near to the ancient Basilica of San Pietro, with its fountain of purification, its columns of marble and porphyry, its roof of bronze tiles (once showered with fire by my grandfather Barbarossa). The clergy gave way, and Roman Senators strode forward to lead my horse to the entrance. I dismounted, and slowly began to ascend the steps up which Charlemagne had crawled on hands and knees.

On the top step Pope Honorius waited, on his right the cardinals, bishop and priests—on his left the cardinal-deacons and lower clergy. Like a rare jewel in a colored kaleidoscope, he himself was wearing the tiara and a vestment of purple silk magnificently interwoven with gold. No doubt, as a boy, I had been in his presence, but I had no memory of having seen him before. Now he was ninety. His cheeks were luminously pale with the transparence of papyrus, and his sunken eyes seemed in contrast all the bigger and darker. He wore a scraggly gray beard, hardly more than a fringe to his face. About him was an atmosphere of exhaustion, an indefinable air of sadness, as though he could no longer cope with the hosts of sinners who roamed the world. But if he was pious and tired and weak, the Curia was realistic and strong and inexhaustible. Not for a moment was Honorius permitted to falter in carrying out the program of his predecessor. When he stretched out the gloved right hand with the pontifical ring on the third finger, the hand was indistinguishable from the hand of Innocent III.

But I was not allowed to kiss the hand. It had been demanded, and I agreed, that I kiss the Pope's feet. In all humility I kissed the satin slipper which protruded from under the hem of his robe. Then in token of the tribute I brought, I poured out a bagful of gold. I rose, and the Pope embraced me and kissed me on the forehead. Now began the ritual of litany and prayer, much resembling the consecration of a bishop. The Pope and I walked together to the Chapel of Santa Maria in Turribus, where I took an oath to defend the Church against all enemies in any moment of need. Then the Pope went to the altar to pray, while I was received into the Canons of San Pietro and robed for the coronation.

All of my vestments had been brought from Sicily, where they had been stored in the Royal Workshop in Palermo; all dated from the time of the Norman Kings, except the gloves and the shoes, which were made especially for me. I was dressed by acolytes. First they drew on hose of red silk with gold embroidery, with an Arabic inscription in green at the top. The shoes were also of red silk, with soles of neat's leather; rubies, pearls, amethysts and emeralds were worked with gold into a design of griffins and sirens. Next I was clad in a tunicella, an undergarment of deep purple silk, trimmed in scarlet silk and gold lace, and decorated with enameled gold plates and vermicular filigree work. After the tunicella came the alb, which I slipped over my head like a woman's gown. It was made of yellow taffeta on yellow silk; the chest and sleeves were worked with pearls and gold embroidery, and the bottom of the skirt was trimmed with gold lace and precious stones. On the orphrey were adverse lions on a white background and adverse griffins on purple. Two inscriptions, one in Latin and one in Arabic, stated that the alb was made in the Royal Workshop in the year 1181. Around the alb was placed the girdle, the *Cingulum Pontificale*—a belt of blue silk heavily studded with rubies, pearls, and tiny plaques in gold filigree. And lastly, the stole—a band of yellow silk decorated with pieces of gold, eagles embroidered in black and tassels of pearls—was placed around my neck and crossed above my breast. The gloves I drew on myself; they were fashioned of scarlet silk, adorned with gold enamel plaques, rubies, sapphires, and pearls, and on each palm was embroidered in gold an eagle with head turned left.

Now my robing was complete except for my grandfather Ruggero's great scarlet coronation mantle with its lions and camels embroidered in pearls. When at last I felt its heavy weight upon my shoulders, I laughed aloud. No longer was I the Sicilian Boy. I was, instead, a Man—a King—an Emperor. I was content. . . . There remained but the crown. . . .

Cardinals met me at the broad silver gate, and I entered the Basilica of San Pietro. I paused at his shrine to kiss the burnished big toe of his bronze statue, and proceeded to anointment at the hands of a cardinal. The air of the church was pungent with incense, and all about was a forest of flickering tapers. I moved on to the altar to make confession to the Pope. High above me I saw the brilliant blue-and-gold mosaic of Christ enthroned between the Virgin Mother, the Apostles, and the four symbols of the Evangelists. Fleetingly I recalled that other mosaic Christ with the accusing eyes, in the Royal Chapel in Palermo. There Christ sat above the King; here, with His representative the Pope, above the Emperor. The pattern had not changed. Even the Emperor must resign himself; the clergy reign supreme.

The Pope gave me the kiss of peace, and prayed for me—a special and particular intercession with Heaven in my behalf. Then he placed a miter for a symbolic moment upon my head, and with slow and deliberate gesture took up the Imperial Crown. The thick hammered gold of its eight linked plates gleamed in the candlelight; its multiple jewels flashed. The single arch of jewels, from front to back, was reminiscent of a Roman helmet—but a helmet surmounted in front by a cross. On the sides, from the temple-plates, pendants dangled; and at the top of the brow-plate was set the famous and magical "stone of wisdom." The crown was massive, crude, impressive. As it was set upon my head, an enormous excitement infused me; confirmed at last was my conviction that I stood above and beyond all ordinary men. I seemed an extension of man himself—divinely created and designed to undertake the omnipotence of man as a manifestation of man's destiny. Thus in the very moment of my consecration I harbored heretical thoughts; and had the Pope been able to sense my emotions and read my mind, he would have dropped the crown in horror.

I experienced another emotion, too, like the sensation of a lightning flash, or a momentary aberration in a dream. I saw myself not only from within but from without—as I must appear to the spectators of this solemn pageant. I projected myself to them and among them, standing with a taper in my hand, breathing the scented air, watching my own coronation. I stood beside Berardo—exactly as the acolyte now stood beside him. A dark young man my own age, black-robed with white lace; dark hair, combed and cut like mine; cleanshaven; an intense, sensitive, beautiful face. He was looking only at me, absorbed wholly by me. Then a pulling inside me, adding to my excitement a new tension. A demand from me to him: "Look *into* me!" as though I would blind him with my radiance. He looked, his eyes more brilliant than the greatest jewel in the Imperial Crown—his eyes luminous with love. I had caught him unawares. So we met and spoke to one another secretly with our eyes before either could reverse his role, for I was he . . . and he was I. I felt a surge of joy for him . . . for me. His face flushed. His eyes glazed. Overwhelmed by his own boldness, he turned his head aside, glanced downward unseeing into a void. The candle flickered, became extinguished. I was I. . . . He was he. . . .

The Pope was extending the ceremonial sword. I drew it from the scabbard, and brandished it, in symbolic defense of Holy Church. Then Scepter and Imperial Orb. I heard the echo of the choir, repeating the very same words heard by Charlemagne, the very same words heard by the Caesars of old: "*Friderico piissimo Augusto, a Deo coronato, magno, pacifico Imperatori, Vita et Victoria!*" And, once more I took the Cross, swearing to liberate from the infidel the Holy Places of Jerusalem. This time I received it from Cardinal Ugolino of Ostia, a gaunt, long-nosed, tight-mouthed man whose name I was never to forget.

There followed the coronation of Costanza, in robes almost as magnificent as mine. Then High Mass. I cast off crown and mantle, and served as subdeacon to the Pope. Finally the Empress and I were administered Communion by the Pope, and received his blessing. Withdrawing, we marched in procession to the entrance steps of San Pietro, where, as a final gesture of submission, I held the Pope's golden stirrup and led his horse a few paces forward. I mounted my own horse, and we rode together to the Church of Santa Maria in Transpontina, where we parted—he to his palace and I to a banquet given for the nobles of Rome.

On my mind was not food, but the extraordinary sentient eyes of the acolyte. I was determined to see them again.

15

WHAT, THEN, is the definition of love? Do we love, as we say, our dog, the sun, the sea, our grandfather, our home, wine, the Church, the Madonna, honor, God, truth, our first lover, our wife, our husband, our children, our closest friend . . . ? How can one word include all the subtle gradations of these emotions? Obviously, man is capable of more forms of love than one, each no less valid than the other. And how many loves can a man or a woman have in a lifetime? What, then, is being "in love"? Is this a wrenching violent emotion which begins like a blow to the heart, then gradually throbs away into a slow dull ache—where once was joyful pain? Or, is it only sex, or rapport, or both . . . ?

It would be absurd to say that I was "in love" with the young man I had seen holding the taper in the Basilica of San Pietro. But it would not be absurd to say that something about him I loved. Wherein lay his appeal? His likeness to myself? His unlikeness to myself? The intuitive need of a young man for another young man as a friend? The curious melancholy beauty of his face, which already haunted me? My inability to find, thus far, a woman with whom I could share more than a bed? Or was there at work some other magic of which I understood nothing, with misty origins in antiquity—known only to those satyrs and fauns who roamed woods and vineyards? Or was this a secret of sorcerers and alchemists, who brew love potions irrespective of sex? I thought: Perhaps I am bewitched . . . ?

Nor could I rid myself of this notion when I saw, at one of the lower tables in the banquet hall, my acolyte. He was engaged in animated conversation with the noted jurist Roffredo da Benevento and Berardo. I was astonished at the familiarity with which they talked. He was using, of course, many gestures, elegant gestures—for how can a true Italian speak without gestures?

I turned to the Cardinal Colonna, a man a few years older than I and of great power and influence in Rome. "Does your Eminence chance to know the richly dressed young man who speaks now with the Archbishop Berardo?" I said casually.

The Cardinal squinted and wiped the wine from his lips. "Your Majesty, never have I seen him before—though I would judge him to be a visiting prince." He squinted again. "Extraordinary face, half-spiritual and half-carnal—each struggling for ascendancy. . . ."

That face! It was even more youthful than my own. I have seen it so often on the statues of antiquity. One moment the slim face of a young faun emerging from the shadowy forest who has not yet discovered anything—and the next moment the face of a satyr, as cynical as Pan after the famous love affair with Hermaphrodite! Dark eyebrows, not so wide apart as mine, very large, very dark eyes, vivid with unspoken thoughts more expressive than language. A mobile mouth, now solemn yet suggestive of wry laughter—but the eyes above all were the apertures of his mind and heart, for they were kindled with the burning animation of life. Each time he turned his head so that I could not see his eyes, I felt deprived.

The banquet became more and more tedious—I thought it would never end. I felt no need of food. I was too highly keyed from the excitement of the coronation—and now the excitement of this new infatuation. I longed to run and dance, like some character in a satyr play, but of course I gave no outward sign. So there I sat with patience, while all about me men stuffed themselves with prosciutto, ravioli, macaroni and Parmesan cheese, scampi, gelatina, fish, pheasant, veal, venison and wild boar . . . vegetables and salad . . . wines . . . cheeses . . . all the fruits of autumn . . . and malvasia. I picked, drank little; sucking the wine-red juice of a pomegranate, I felt marvelously refreshed.

I conversed much; but all the while I was watching my acolyte. I must speak with him, I told myself, now, without more delay, for the night is waning . . . ! I whispered to one of my disguised Saracens who stood behind me (freedmen now), and in moments my acolyte-prince appeared before me, as a wish comes true in a dream.

Once again I was compelled to admire his beauty. With natural grace he rested the weight of his body on his left foot, and bowed. He wore long tights, his left leg wine-red and his right half-white, half-blue. His brief yellow tunic of velvet was worked with gold, and across his left shoulder was thrown a short yellow cape lined in blue. He carried no sword, but a small jeweled dagger dangling from a belt of woven gold. The form which had been hidden by the acolyte's robe was now revealed: I saw a body slender, strong, graceful, firm of buttock, codpiece full to bursting. On the little finger of his left hand was not a signet ring, but a ruby which glistened and flickered in the candlelight.

I looked straight into the lustrous but brooding eyes with that gaze so direct and probing that only those who were strongest and most self-possessed could bear it. Now another element, desire, was added; honored were those desired by an emperor. He did not seek to turn my stare aside, or flinch. His eyes, in their response, told me that he felt more than honored: he felt for me what I felt for him. He would go wherever I chose to lead. Then I smiled, and with the smile openly revealed my admiration.

He answered, though I had not spoken. "My Lord has want of me?"

"Not want—need," I said. "What is your name?"

"I owe you thanks for earlier generosity, my Lord—I am called Pier della Vigna."

I was staggered, and my face must have betrayed my amazement. Not noble! I thought. The clothes of a prince—but Pier della Vigna! I remembered Berardo's remarks about his origins.

"Does your Highness recall?" he said, responding defensively to my silence. "It has been a long time since I wrote my letter—"

"Too long," I said, "much too long. I recall very well. I wish only that I had met you earlier . . . now we must make up for lost time. Come with me!"

I rose, and the musicians stopped playing. I signaled for them to continue; such of the guests who could, rose to salute me. I did not tarry, but slipped away with my Pier della Vigna and the two Saracens bearing torches.

Outside the palazzo the torches were useless, for the moon at full illumined the city. "This night we will not sleep, you and I," I said to Piero. "We will make it a night never to forget . . . !"

Wrapped in long cloaks, and with only a guide and my Saracens for guards, we set out for the ruins of Hadrian's villa, pushing our horses to their limit. There was yet time to reach it before sunrise, and so we did. Among towering cypresses the great complex of crumbling buildings lay hidden—theaters, libraries, academies, palaces, ponds and fountains—a sprawling wounded mass of stone in the moonlight. Here, once the intellectual center of the civilized world, bats flew and wild creatures roamed. We talked little, for the moon and the ruins and the shadows were eerie in their beauty.

"It is the night of the *lupi mannari*," Piero murmured.

"It is the night for magic rites and transformations," I whispered in reply, "not into werewolves, but into friends." And I put my arm around him.

Weighted by a sense of the past, we picked our way, alone, through the ruins. At length we came to a semicircular hall with a half dome, decorated with white mosaics which gleamed in the moonlight. Across the façade were four large columns of marble, and in front a silvery pool still fed by running fountains. Along the curved wall were many niches for statues, but one only survived—the weathered and mutilated marble of a nude youth—Antinous, the Greek slave who was the most beloved of Hadrian's many loves. Here we paused, sitting on a massive block of fallen stone, and waited for the day. Now we felt hunger; we opened the baskets my servants had prepared. We ate bread dipped in red wine, and munched on roasted chestnuts. We talked.

After the beginning there had been no formality between us. We talked as though we had known each other from first breath. We talked without reserve or hidden thoughts or insinuations. We talked as though we had been waiting years for this moment, as though we had stored great reservoirs of unsaid things which now came spilling out.

"How did it happen that our eyes met during the coronation?" Piero asked.

"Who can say? Who knows, or can define the curious currents which convey meaning from one person to another without words?" I replied. "But I did not guess you were Pier della Vigna—"

He looked rueful. "I was twice disguised: once as acolyte, once as noble. Borrowed clothes! I am neither priest nor prince—"

"But you yourself, which is enough. Clothes are essentially disguises, not needed by friends. You and I, Piero, in private, must always be naked and equal—the difference between us visible only to angels. . . ."

He smiled, and at last all trace of melancholy uncertainty disappeared from his face. "*Caro Federico!*" he said.

Caro Federico—the tone was unforgettable. This was his salutation to the equality of our friendship; for, outside such intimacy and rapport as we now shared, who would have dared thus to say *dear* Federico . . . ?

In a voice low with the shyness of authorship, he recited for me one of his poems which dealt with the nature of love. He began:

Perocchè Amore non si può vedere
E non si tratta corporalmente,
Quanti ne son di si folle sapere,
Che credono che Amore sia niente . . .

The meaning of the words echoed in my mind: "Since Love cannot be seen, and is unsubstantial—those who are foolishly wise believe that Love is nothing. . . ."

But at the ending, an affirmation: *Amore sia*—"Love is . . . and will always be. . . ."

Love is—indeed no explanation could be found, nor even a definition. For Piero I felt love, and he for me. There was no choice but to accept it as a wondrous thing.

We sat close together, that our bodies might fuse like our minds and emotions. At dawn, the white columns of the ruins changed rapidly from rose to gold. Skylarks soared and sang. The glowing sunlight filled us with the sensuous warmth of true summer, though this was the Summer of San Martino. Rock lizards appeared to bask in the heat. We responded like votaries of the sun god and flung off our clothing. And then . . . friendship was transformed, as the emotion of love and the act of love became one.

Afterward, we bathed in the pool, laughing and splashing like boys. When we were tired, we lay in the sun and slept, primitive and natural as simple shepherds out of the remote and childlike past . . . or perhaps god-men from the dim beginnings of antiquity. The real and the dream were as one, for the reality had been dreamlike, and the dreams were as sweet as the real.

We were awakened to the long shadows of the columns, by the bleat of goats, the clatter of small hoofs across marble, and the high thin notes of a *zefalo*. From out of the underbrush appeared an unkempt, white-bearded old man in rags, mournfully playing the pipe. As he saw us lying together he stopped in his tracks, his shrill melody left unfinished.

"Ai—" he cried, then went on in purest Latin, "you have chosen dangerously, my lords! I know these ruins well, for I commune with the spirit of the Emperor Hadrian. This was the Serapeum, where Hadrian and Antinous made love. O fools—have you learned nothing from that tragedy? You hear not the last gasping breath of the drowning Antinous in the waters of the Nile? Listen—listen: *Can two unequal ever equal be . . .?"* He paused, blew on his pipe again, and began to move away, the black goats bleating and crowding about his heels.

Then suddenly he stopped, turned back to us once more, and pointed his pipe at me. "You, you of the fair hair—" he cried, "you shall die *sub flore*, near an iron door!"

He sucked in air in gasps and tore at his white beard, as though possessed by a demon. Once more he pointed the pipe. "You, you of the dark hair. You shall die—" But the pipe wavered; his words were muffled as he pressed his hands to his face. "Ai, ai—" he shrieked, "my eyes cannot see what yours will not see . . . !"

With a wild cry he crossed himself, turned and ran with his goats into the ruins.

"He is a hermit," I said lightly to Piero. "Like all hermits, the old man is mad—. And who could die in a castle without being near an iron door, or die in Italy without being near flowers? As for seeing one's own death—how unlikely!"

But the terrible tincture of doubt and dread had been injected into our relationship. Piero's face was somber, his eyes shadowed with gloom. An evil omen, to think of death, in the most intense moments of life!

We returned to Rome in oppressive silence. In spite of my skepticism, I too felt disturbed—for who can know the truth of a prophecy until the prophecy is fulfilled?

III

L'AQUILA

I

'Tis true indeed that my beloved Sicily is the "port and navel of all the kingdoms of the world." I have been told by mariners that in faraway China, in the province of Fukien, one Chao Ju Kua has written of us and our volcano. To go beyond China would be to go full circle. If opportunity arises, I would like to outfit an expedition for this purpose. But after my coronation in Rome, I had little time to dream of such exotic exploration: I had my hands full with traitorous barons, truculent clergy, schismatic towns, rebellious Saracens, and an irascible Pope continually urging me to abandon my homeland and sail away to new dangers in the Holy Land—before he himself passed on to Heaven.

So impatient was I to return to the Kingdom of Sicily that I tarried in Rome hardly three days before breaking camp and heading south on the Via Labicana—my ensign now the Imperial Roman Eagle on a golden field: *l'Aquila*. My entourage had shrunk to only a fraction of its precoronation size, as my strategy was not to enter with an army—and most particularly, an army of German knights. I even felt some reluctance at including Hermann von Salza (no doubt Berardo, once again philosophically munching salted watermelon seeds, would have been happy to see him go) but by now he was indispensable. I was eager to get on with the plans I had made—for during the long winter nights in Germany I had given much thought to the problems ahead.

The Pope did not let me escape without extracting one final drop of advantage. I must, he said, issue edicts against heretics paralleling the Church's own strictures against them—the punishment was burning at the stake, or cutting off the tongue. In the Lombard cities heresy was rife, the Pope said, and to go against the Church was also to go against the Empire. The Lombard cities were a sore point with us both, so I acceded. Then, as a final fillip, I proclaimed that I would pay for the restoration of ancient buildings in Rome, if adequate plans were submitted to me. This last, the Pope liked not at all—thinking, no doubt, that I myself intended to occupy some of the buildings so restored. But was it not suitable for a Roman Emperor to restore the architectural glory of Rome . . . ?

My first problem was to extract from the barons the castles which guarded the frontiers of the Realm. I demanded and obtained a cluster of these fortresses without so much as a threat to use force. Already the barons were well aware that I returned to my Kingdom not as a boy but as a seasoned campaigner—a sovereign who had dealt successfully with the difficult German princes, and had humbled that very Otto with whom they treasonably had collaborated. But where was my army to use against them? They were not yet aware—but it was to be assembled from the barons themselves.

When I crossed the slow-flowing Volturno River and entered ancient Capua, the first important town inside the borders of the Realm, I was prepared to lay the foundation of such a State as had not been seen since Roman times—if ever in all the world. I did not wait to reach the capital to begin; at once, in Capua, I made the necessary first moves. I called into conference a group of my ablest Italian advisers, including Berardo as usual, Manfredo Lancia, the Aquino brothers, the jurist Roffredo da Benevento, and—to my special and secret pleasure—his young assistant Pier della Vigna. Some of the older men, and some of the nobles (such as the Aquino brothers) were more than a trifle disconcerted by the presence of Pier della Vigna: the former because of his youth, the latter because of his plebian blood. They said nothing, but they stiffened in his presence.

The basic objective was to develop a plan for reducing to manageable proportions the power of the barons, which had grown inordinately during my absence. I wanted to avoid both the fragmentation I had seen in Germany, and the interminable warfare between towns as in northern Italy. I took an unsympathetic view of the feudal structure; I wanted a strong and efficient central government. But if wishes were horses, beggars would ride. Like the Norman Roger de Hauteville, I needed a horse. This was the problem I put to my advisers. The answers ran about as follows:

Berardo: "I would recall to mind the considerable resources in lands and treasure acquired by the highest prelates of the Church. It may be that a little loss to them would prove a great gain to our noble Lord—for his goal, peace, is surely the most Christian of all worldly goals. So in the end, the Church's bread, cast upon the waters, will return an hundredfold."

Landolfo d'Aquino: "Of what effect are words, without the power of arms to give words substance? Why not consider first a threat of force backed by force?"

Tommaso d'Aquino (the elder): "The might of the state should be based on a body of law, derived from God and collated by man, enforced by dully designated authorities, under the supreme direction of the head of the state. We find now a state reduced to chaos; so let us begin in the beginning, and reëstablish a respect for the processes of law."

Roffredo da Benevento: "The problem now, your Majesty, would seem to be a codification of law, plus the development of means of enforcement. To turn to force without the objective of establishing order maintained by law, is fruitless. The existing laws are a contradictory jumble of nonsense. First we must have clarification, then action."

I: "Messer Piero, you sit in silence. What say you?"

Pier della Vigna: "What has been said thus far is well said and true enough. But it seems, my Lord, that rapid action is needed—else the state expire before it has time to breathe. Why not turn therefore to the statutes enacted by the last legitimate Norman King, Guglielmo the Good, and use them as a point of departure? Under them the income of the clergy can be modified, the military forces of the barons curbed, a respect for law reëstablished, and a new codification begun."

Others: "He speaks well . . . !"

I: "How, then, might the laws of King Guglielmo be reapplied?"

Pier della Vigna: "If it pleases your Majesty, we may cite a few examples. The Church, under the then existing law, might acquire lands for short terms only, thus restricting the acquisition of wealth. No noble might leave his castle with an escort of more than four armed men, without express permission of the King. Through an edict returning to Guglielmo's laws, it could be decreed that no family may now bear arms unless it had done so in Guglielmo's time; that all castles built or seized since

Guglielmo's reign must now be ceded to the Crown; that all rights and privileges obtained since then (many, incidentally, are forged) must be submitted to the Crown for reëxamination; that the children of fief-holders may no longer inherit fiefs without royal consent; and so on. In this manner, my Lord, barons, abbots, and bishops who have enriched themselves illegally or by force during the last thirty years will be returned to their former status—and some, in all likelihood, to poverty. This move will be unexpected. The power of your adversaries will be shaken—while you gain time for fundamental reforms."

I: "Messer Piero, your words are weighted with wisdom. The reaction will be violent, but we will stand on the law. And we will use force if forced. It appears that we have found, for the moment, a way. . . ."

Afterward, privately, Piero came to me and suggested that Count Tommaso d'Aquino be named Chief Justice of the province, and that Landolfo, his brother, be assigned direction of the military forces. At once I recognized the astuteness of Piero's methods, and promised to give serious consideration to his proposals.

I recognized something else: Pier della Vigna had much more to offer than mere facility with his pen. Irrespective of my favor, he was a young man who would go far. And with my favor? What heights might not the two of us together—perfect counterparts of one another—attain?

I issued the edict restoring the laws of Guglielmo the Good. At first the barons and bishops were stunned by this blow; then, very quickly, as anticipated, arms were taken up against me. As always, the wealthy whose possessions are threatened have recourse to force. I prepared to enforce respect for law. These rebels would find my sword and Piero's pen more than a little difficult to blunt.

The first step in my defense was to divide the nobles among themselves. I made concessions to some of the minor nobility, and, as vassals, required them to report with levies of armed men. If they failed to arrive at once, I had them arrested and imprisoned. Most responded with alacrity, and in a short time I had the core of an army. Certain fief-holders, in Norman times, had been required to submit, too, timbers for ships and men as sailors. I reinvigorated these demands so effectively that in less than a year I had two squadrons of galleys at sea—the core of a fleet. A number of merchantmen, anchored in my harbors, I acquired by forced sale—for I had sore need of them.

Then I moved to seize the castles I wanted, or level those I did not. Since I was concerned chiefly with defense, my procedure was simplicity itself. I established castles as fortified strong points, and not as habitations for feudal vassals, their families and dependents. My castles were to be garrisoned in peacetime only by a castellan and a handful of professional soldiers with arms in storage. Men of surrounding villages were to be responsible for each castle's upkeep, and to aid in its defense in case of war. All were subordinate to a department of defense in the capital. The implications were far-reaching.

I now had an opportunity to settle a number of old scores, such as my loathing for that Diepold von Schweinspeunt who had intrigued with both Otto and my Bishop-Chancellor Gualtiero di Palearia. By one of my usual ruses I made Diepold my prisoner, and held him hostage until Diepold's brother disgorged two powerful fortresses. I arranged for Diepold to be received into the Teutonic Knights, and packed him off to the frigid Baltic to Christianize the heathen Prussians.

That sterling character Gualtiero di Palearia himself turned up when I had been hardly a week in Capua. In eight years he had become balder, more unctuous in manner, and fouler in breath. When he was ushered into my presence he had a terrible fright, for apparently he still visualized me as a boy. He must have thought from my face that I was an avenging angel, for he turned white and flung himself to his knees.

"I beseech thy mercy, Lord!" he cried, as if in prayer. "Mercy, mercy . . . !"

"Rise up, honest Bishop-Chancellor," I said. "We hear your supplication, and wonder why mercy is so urgently your need? We have seen already, from the status of our Realm, your unmistakable handiwork—without doubt you have labored long and hard. But why not come to us for praise, and not to plead for mercy . . . ?" I paused a moment, studying the marks of gluttony upon his face, and went on: "Rejoice—we have prepared a reward for you: it is our desire to place in your hands the entire responsibility for recruiting knights for the Pope's Crusade. And it is our intention to report regularly to the Holy Father the measure of your success. . . ."

He actually groaned aloud, and in that moment I came close to sorrow for him—for I am sure he foresaw clearly how I meant eventually to dispose of him.

It also became necessary, unfortunately, to settle scores with some persons I would have preferred to leave untouched. One such was Count Alaman da Costa, that plump, engaging merchant-count whose bawdy tales had seemed inexhaustible on my voyages to Rome and Genova. He had returned to Siracusa, and in the course of time had come to believe that not only the *fondaco* (from Arabic *funouk*) was his, but also the town was his (and Genova's). He was in fact no count at all but a notorious corsair —though he chose to sign himself Count of Siracusa and Officer of the King. By the accidental capture of a Pisan ship laden with arms, he had found the means to attack and subdue the once great Greek city, already sunk to the level of a Pisan pirate nest. This had happened when I was eight years old. I chose now to remind him of my gratitude for all his past favors, how warm I felt toward Genova—but Siracusa was a city of the Realm, and must be wholly subject to my jurisdiction. I was prepared to create him a true count, and assign to him positions of great value. The unhappy man refused. In due course I permitted him to save himself by flight, but I confiscated everything he left behind. How could I allow my personal gratitude to breach the economic foundations of my future state . . . ?

For indeed I aimed at nothing less eventually than the liquidation of the whole feudal system in Sicily. I wanted this land of mine to enjoy, once again, a central government, the prosperity of peaceful trade, the excitement of knowledge, the pleasures of culture. It was to be all or nothing.

And then, at precisely the moment I thought I was fairly launched, the greatest of all my nobles rose the Molise in rebellion against me, and, a sickening disappointment, the Saracens in Sicily fanned smoldering fires of discontent into a flaming war.

I was caught between them, with no alternative but to fight.

2

It was Pier della Vigna who urged me not to be diverted by the rebellion in the mountainous Molise and Abruzzi, but to go straight to the island of Sicily and begin its pacification. In this he was correct, though he had no training in military matters; for the island was so rich and firm a base that I could use it, if need be, to defend myself against half the world. I followed Piero's suggestion, too, that I place the campaign against the Count of Molise in the hands of Landolfo d'Aquino, and name Tommaso d'Aquino, the elder, Chief Justice of the province.

Astute advice, as events proved. Tommaso and his brother were not only completely loyal, but sagacious. In time they drove the Count of Molise from one stronghold to another—though the Count alone could put over fifteen hundred knights and squires into the field. So long had he ruled his lands as a petty king that he could not believe any force might surpass his, or any strategy reduce his castles to rubble. But he reckoned without my men of Aquino and the fury of the lesser nobles who had borne hate so long. Finally his wife opened the gates of the last castle left to him, and cried surrender.

So great were the demands on me, however, that I could not leave Capua until late May, though I had arrived in December. And I was scheduled to sail in August for the Holy Land! I itched to be in movement, like a boy at Mass, and day and night my mind was filled with thoughts of Sicily and of my childhood in Palermo. But despite this urgency, I took time to go with Piero to a village not far away and say good-by to his mother. He had, of course, on our arrival in Capua, rushed to find his mother, and with the change in his own circumstances, had made every effort to effect a change in hers. But she proved uninterested in silks and satins, or new housing, and was merely happy to rejoice in her son's success.

We found her occupying two rooms on the top floor of an old palazzo which was falling into ruin. The stones of the external staircase were green with age; and as we climbed we were regarded with such awe by the host of neighbors who had assembled in the courtyard that hardly one of them drew breath. Even babies and dogs fell silent and the servant girl who opened Monna Maddalena's door almost swooned with fright at seeing a king in the flesh. But Monna Maddalena herself was as calm and dignified as if such visits happened every day. She was sitting by a window which opened on a small loggia, overlooking the tops of acacia trees, the winding Volturno and the rich green fields of the Terra di Lavoro, enjoying the warm spring air. She was a gray-haired woman of about fifty, dressed all in black—in mourning, Piero said, for his invalid sister who had met a bitter death. The resemblance to Piero was striking. Now in her face was the beauty of repose and the satisfaction of not being at odds with life. As we entered, she set down from her lap the white kitten she was stroking, and rose to bow to me.

"Madonna Madre," Piero said, "this is our Lord King Federico. Please kiss his hand in welcome."

"No," I said, "it is better to salute Monna Maddalena for the favor she has done the world in producing such a son—she honors us." And I kissed her hand.

"May the grace of God go with you, my Lord," she said. "I pray daily for your blessing in Heaven, in gratitude for the earthly blessings you have brought my son."

Her voice was sweet and gentle, and for a moment I felt a wispy jealousy of Piero; but how much older my own mother would now be! Piero's mother was just Berardo's age, and that other jealousy tugged once more at my heart.

"The greatest thanks belong to your true friend, the Archbishop Berardo," I said, watching her face closely. "His intercession, more than the stars, fixed our conjunction. . . ."

"Berardo has been very good to us," she said, without the slightest change in face or voice, "we have known him well for many years. He also is included in my prayers. . . ."

I went away—as I will always be—unsatisfied.

On the return to Capua, to restore my spirits, Piero told me that not far distant a Mithrium had been uncovered, complete with altar and frescoes depicting the mysteries of the cult of Mithra. More interesting still was the discovery of a stone madonna of the pre-Roman Samnites, or perhaps the more ancient Oscans, with not one child in arms but a litter of six or seven! I was tempted to remain for further digging, but I contented myself with giving orders to erect the statue of this prolific goddess in the central piazza. Let people ponder the curious ways of virgins . . . !

When once again I set foot on the island of Sicily, I found that before I could deal with my infidel Saracens I had first to deal with my faithful Christians. The "irregularities" (to use the kindest word) of many of Bishop Gualtiero's fellow churchmen were irregular in the extreme—even surpassing my expectations. Individually, I found such flagrant misuse of church funds and personal enrichment that I placed a covey of bishops on trial and demanded of the Pope that he dismiss others outright. (At this time in Sicily there were twenty-one archbishops and one hundred and twenty-four bishops.) I never hesitate to use a surgeon's knife or to cauterize a wound. At Bishop Arduino, of that great Norman Cathedral of Cefalù, I was particularly angry—the record of the trial showed that he would have squandered the cathedral itself if he could. Of the lesser clergy I clapped a considerable portion in jail, and fed them on bread and water for a while to reduce their portly figures.

I found that the Church was gobbling up more than food and gold, for, as in Germany, it hungered after the land as well. I took measures: I reactivated the old Norman law which forbade the acquisition of lands through mortmain, for a time I permitted the purchase of land, provided it was not held more than a year, a month, a week and a day. Finally I prohibited the latter also, and declared publicly that I did so because "the Church before long would have bought up the entire kingdom" with its apparently inexhaustible supply of gold.

The old quarrel over ecclesiastical appointments was resumed, too. In this matter the weak Honorius was quite as obdurate as the strong Innocent, and the quarrel between us became no less acid. I refused flatly to accept certain Papal appointees, on the grounds that I could not tolerate in Sicily "a state within a state." I threatened to close the Realm against all priests appointed from outside Sicily. The Pope, in retaliation, threw open his doors to a multitude of refugees from Sicily—an emigré group which plotted for the overthrow of my regime, while Pope and Curia winked at their activities. However much the world aims of

Holy Roman Empire and Holy Church might coincide, Sicily was itself a nation apart—and I, its Sovereign, was responsible for its national welfare. A radical point of view, no doubt, for a Holy Roman Emperor. But I had found, through practical experience, that the Empire was more concept than reality, and in Sicily I had under my feet the solid substance of the fertile and beautiful earth.

These troubles with the Church were not ameliorated by the approaching deadline for my departure on the Pope's Crusade. It was obvious that to leave Sicily at this moment would only provoke a disaster at home which could not be compensated for by success abroad. I decided, like a peasant, that I had better hoe my own row—but to placate the Pope I provided forty galleys to carry reinforcements to the Christians at Damietta. The knights I placed under the comand of Anslem von Justingen, whom I had created a Marshal as a reward for his services; and the ships I placed under the command of the Admiral Enrico di Malta. But the overall responsibility for decisions and direction I gave to none other than my Bishop-Chancellor Gualtiero di Palearia. To my amusement, he was panic-striken at the honor; but he could not refuse. What would he say to the Pope?

This phase of the Crusade worked itself out with dispatch. The armies at Damietta did not wait for the arrival of my reinforcements, and, commanded by the Papal Legate and King Jean of Jerusalem, attempted to push up the Nile delta to capture Cairo. Their forces were not only insufficient, but they picked the wrong season—for the Nile was coming into flood. The Egyptians opened the dams, and the crusaders found themselves floundering in water and mud. Gualtiero, on my ships' arrival, instead of bargaining for terms, urged defense of Damietta. Another mistake, and Damietta fell into Egyptian hands. The Pope, indeed the whole Church, was stunned by the extent of disaster. Even Sultan al-Kamil's astute restitution of the True Cross failed to soften the blow. Thus ended the Fifth Crusade.

One result of the defeat, however, pleased me greatly: never again did I see the face of good Gualtiero di Palearia! While he was away I publicized a number of his thefts, and he dared not set foot in the Realm again. He fled to Venezia, where he was amply rewarded for his avarice: he died in poverty.

Another result was less pleasing. The failure was laid to me! I had not gone on the Crusade in person. There was nothing for it, the Pope wrote, but for me to go within the following year. . . . But another part of the letter struck a new and ominous note: "We shall spare you no longer if you still neglect your duty; we shall excommunicate you in the face of the Christian world. Take heed, then, like a wise man and a Catholic Prince!"

3

MY LONG-DELAYED and longed-for tour of inspection in Sicily had to be confined to the towns of the coastal areas, for the Saracens had seized almost the whole of the center of the island. Serious trouble with the Muslims actually had begun a few years before my birth. In that chaotic period some rabble-rousing monks had stirred up the Christian populace to a vast letting of Muslim blood. Many Saracens fled to the mountain fastnesses of the interior, nourishing over the years a desire for vengeance with a longing for better land. Eruption of new violence was only a matter of time. To my sorrow this smoldering inheritance was mine.

Indeed, my homecoming to Palermo was spoiled by a simultaneous Saracen raid on Monreale, in the very outskirts of Palermo. While crowds in the streets were cheering the Empress and me, the Bishop of Monreale was prostrated with fear in the cathedral; and I had hardly entered my grandfather Ruggero's suite in the Norman Palace before I was urgently summoned to Monreale's defense. I had no time to indulge in the luxurious memories I had contemplated—visiting again the garden of San Giovanni degli Eremiti and other memorable scenes of my youth. Nor could I introduce Piero to some of the delights of Palermo, as I had described them to him in anticipation. I had hoped too, that I might find in Palermo a tutor like dear Guglielmo for my four-year-old son Enzo; but such a search would require time and patience. Now I had no time and my impatience raged beyond all bounds.

Hardly ten miles from Monreale was the important Saracen fortress of Giato, the lair of the Emir Ibn'Abbad, one of their most important leaders. This Emir I had trusted in the beginning to help me to secure peace without force. He assured me through couriers that he would present my program to the followers of Mohammed, and urge its adoption—for I had a grandiose scheme in my head. In return, I sent valuable gifts as evidence of good faith, for I was most anxious to avoid war. He, like an unclean swine, took my gifts, seized my messengers, tortured and hanged them, then laughed in my face. For his laughter I cared little; but his betrayal I could not abide.

I mobilized all my resources—armament, engines of war, men, supplies of Greek fire (petroleum mixed with sulfur), and a generous number of gallows. I had, before the siege of Giato was ended, ample use for them all. Three months were required—interminable months of heat and frustration. But slowly and surely the defenders were worn down. In a matter of hours the end was in sight.

Then in the night, secretly, the Emir was brought to my tent. He had come to plead for clemency before the surrender. As he entered, he flung himself at my feet.

"From your serene Majesty," he cried, "we crave only our lives. All else we relinquish to your will!"

As I looked at this loathsome creature I could not bring myself to use human speech with him. Like stamping upon vermin, I struck him with my mailed foot and with my spur tore open his side—and had I not controlled my rage I would have trampled him to death on the spot.

"Others shall live, but you shall die, O trusted Emir!" I said, as he was dragged bleeding and gibbering from my presence.

Only the guards and an ashen Piero were witnesses to this scene. Next day the Emir was hanged. And for good measure I hanged with him two Christians: Hugues de Fer, a Marseillais pirate; and my own ex-Admiral Guglielmo Porco, who had turned traitor. (Nor was he the only Christian noble who aided the Muslims because of opposition to my rule.) This fine pair had been running arms from the African coast, and a few years previously had been busily engaged in selling into slavery innocents captured on the Children's Crusade. Such men, I thought, had soiled the earth quite long enough.

With the other thousands of survivors I began at once to put my great plan into effect. It was nothing less than the resettlement of all Muslims, in peace and friendship, in a community all their own. Untouched was their religion, leadership, way of life. They were to leave the barren mountains of Sicily and go to the level plain of Apulia, to become tillers of its rich soil. I chose the town of Lucera, which in Roman times had been a military outpost, as the site. I went so far as to convert the *duomo* into a mosque, and it was not long before the call of the muezzin echoed over the tranquil countryside. With each victory over the Saracens, this was the course I followed. The Pope and the Curia were horrified, and considered this all-Muslim community in a Christian land an affront to all Christendom—a purulent sore, they said.

As for me, I thought it better to have the Saracens as friends than as enemies; nor had I forgotten their worth as fighting men. I planned, after their pacification, when I became sure of their loyalty, to return their arms to them and enlist them in my own forces. I chose the Roman amphitheater as a fitting spot for such a ceremony. I also planned to begin, on a Roman site, a mighty fortress to dominate the coastal plain and the whole region of Monte Gargano. Already another castle was nearby—"Fiorentino" it was called; but I considered it an unimportant, ramshackle affair, of toppling turrets and rusty gateways. One other construction I immediately began in the vicinity: a palace of exquisite design at Foggia—Palermo was entirely too far from Rome, yet I could not live without the beauty and luxury of my Greco-Roman-Arabo-Norman paradise.

Querulous letter upon querulous letter assaulted me from the ninety-six-year-old Pope, who pursued the single idea of the Crusade with the singular enthusiasm of senility. A meeting with Honorius was fixed for the end of April, at Veroli. I decided, with the activities at Lucera in mind, to return to the mainland; the whole court, including the Empress, who wished to rest for a while in Catania, traveled with me.

For once a meeting with the Holy Father posed little difficulty. I had only to point out that I was killing more infidels at home than the crusaders were in the Holy Land; and that I could not rest so long as the Saracen rebellion was a threat. Did His Holiness wish to have repeated the Saracen sacking of the Basilica of San Pietro itself, as had occurred in the middle of the ninth century? My departure on Crusade was again postponed.

When I had taken the Cross the Empress had been wildly enthusiastic, even expressing the desire to go crusading herself; but with the approach of each deadline her enthusiasm had cooled. She had no relish for my long journeys into unknown lands. And just now she was continually distraught by another cause: the fixed idea that her son Enrico was lost to her. On several occasions I had found her in her private chapel, praying for his soul as if he were already dead. In Rome she had whispered that she wished to bear me another heir; but subsequently she had failed to conceive. Her ambition in this matter had no doubt been stimulated by the children I sired by other women: after Enzo had come another boy, whom I called Riccardo di Theate, and three girls—Violante, Margherita and Selvaggia. (For all I had decreed a royal education; and for the boys, eventually a position at court.) Perhaps Costanza was saddened by her own failure, for she seemed to find no happiness other than religion.

When we parted, I was disturbed by her appearance—she looked distinctly ill. Greenish circles ringed her eyes and her face was drawn. Indeed, I felt astonishment at how markedly she had aged—she seemed older than Piero's mother, though she was in fact certainly ten years younger. Nevertheless I was hardly prepared for the news of her death. I registered first shock, then the curious sense of once more being free.

I ordered the body brought to Palermo, and myself took ship to the capital. I selected a Roman marble sarcophagus for Costanza's remains. On it was carved a hunting scene, horsemen and dogs against lions; it was not of the best workmanship, but the best I could find at the time. With her body, wrapped in a veil woven of silver thread, I enclosed her crown, my gift of eagles with wings of lapis lazuli, and a sword of mine. She was placed in the royal crypt of the cathedral, beside my father and my mother and the red porphyry sarcophagus reserved for me. For her I felt one overriding sorrow: I had never loved her.

But on these emotions I had little time to brood. At the Requiem Mass news was brought me that once more the fortress of Giato was in Saracen hands, and Palermo itself was in danger.

4

MY LIFE, for the next several years, was wholly dominated by infidels—infidels at home, infidels abroad. For hardly a moment of any day did we discuss any other subject; and at night I shared my bed with them both literally and figuratively in troubled sleep. Little leisure was to be found for philosophy, art, experiment or even hawking. Nor was there a focal point for the court; I was always traveling—even love had to be taken in camp or on the run. I resolved to devote all my resources to the resolution of the infidel wars; my work for the future required peace.

Though I strengthened the defenses of Palermo, I did not begin my domestic campaign with the reinvestment of Giato—as was expected by my enemies. On the contrary, I ordered attacks at other points all round the island, and only when the Saracens were fully occupied did I attack once more their strongest fortress. My strategy was one of severance of parts from the whole. I wished to chop the Muslims into smaller and smaller units of defense, picking them off piecemeal; and, as each group surrendered, shipping them off, not to prisons, but to Lucera, complete with families, cattle, carts, and asses. All Muslims, of course, are anxious to go to Paradise; but I thought the prospect of good land and good women tilled in peace might be almost equally intriguing. And so it proved: but how stubborn my Saracens! How much blood had to be spilled, how much valuable time lost, before I could get into their thick skulls a recognition of the advantages of the new way of life which lay before them! How hard it is to compete with Paradise!

The struggle, therefore, turned into a war of attrition; and my *pazienza*, in spite of my impatience, was unlimited. Simultaneously I began to prepare with serious intent for that other

Muslim conflict I knew must come. I planned a fleet of a hundred galleys equipped for war and half as many transports—with a total capacity of ten thousand men-at-arms and two thousand knights with squires and three horses each. I myself so designed the transports that each had a ramp which opened from the ship, permitting knights and horses to disembark fully armed and in battle array. I planned something else, which I kept secret: a special corps of Saracen warriors. From each batch of captives I selected those most outstanding—and for them I provided special training. In course of time these men came to consider me their sultan.

But—I needed time. Always I had to placate the Pope. I went to San Germano to meet Honorius and ask for two more years postponement. I could not fight the Muslims on two fronts, I must finish one war before beginning the other. And the Pope agreed—but, as always, at a price. The price he set was another wedding.

The suggested bride was Yolanda, the twelve-year-old heiress to the crown of Jerusalem. Yolanda's father, Jean de Brienne, a thin, red-headed man with pointed beard, fishy eyes, and a nervous twitch, eagerly made the proposal. He had been a commander of the ill-fated expedition up the Nile, simply because he was nominal King of Jerusalem. He had acquired the title as King-Consort to Yolanda's mother. On her death, the title of Queen had passed to the child Yolanda. By marriage to Yolanda, I could become King of Jerusalem. In this, both Pope and von Salza saw an incentive to rekindle my lagging enthusiasm for the Crusade, pointing out how glorious it would be to liberate my newly acquired kingdom from the infidel. At the prospect of such glory I sighed: liberating the old kingdom was enough of a chore.

"Dowry—" I said. "How much gold, how much silver, how many knights, will the bride bring to the campaign?"

She was, of course, impoverished. Her only asset was her title—and, von Salza added, her Syrian beauty (she lived not in Jerusalem but in Antioch). I should be an Emperor whose domains stretched from the North and Baltic Seas to the Dead Sea itself—with a fresh young virgin in my bed. When I sailed to the Holy Land, I should only be reclaiming my own—for my own.

In the end, I agreed. It was a relatively cheap price to pay for my two years' delay, though the bait was hardly worth the taking. I was betrothed. But I too had a price: I insisted that the Pope send von Salza as ambassador to recruit aid from all the other princes of Europe. I wanted the balance sheet to be open to all, with my own investment clearly revealed in the ledger.

All wars are costly affairs—even holy ones. With reluctance I increased taxes, not exempting the clergy; and, to avoid additional increases, developed other ways of raising money. I forbade all export of foodstuffs from Sicily, and prices dropped to rock bottom. Thereupon I bought up massive supplies in the name of the Crown, which in due course I sold to foreign traders at a handsome profit. In so far as possible I also monopolized the shipping of wheat, forbidding its passage in bottoms other than those belonging to the State; thus I was able to take advantage of the high prices offered for grain in deficit areas, again making a handsome profit. The proceeds of these operations all went into the coffers of the State; but I wondered a bit what might happen if some very wealthy individual attempted similar control of the market—what sort of crisis might ensue? To stabilize the currency I issued a new silver coin, the "imperial," and guaranteed its value. I embargoed all export of precious metals. I wanted no monetary panic to complicate further my already complicated problems.

Then, in the midst of war and preparations for war, I paused to establish a university—the University of Napoli, in the year 1224. It was clear that, for the State I was building, a new type of administrator was needed, and education was of primary importance. If I wished to revive the judicial and trading systems, maintain a national defense system including a fleet, improve medicine, and finally to reform clerical abuses, I needed men of intelligence and learning. Since they could not be created from clay, they had to be trained from the raw material available. I proposed to begin at once.

My university was to have schools of law, philosophy, mathematics, medicine, languages, and special studies of antiquity. Theology was to be left to the theologians. I sought all over Europe for the most outstanding scholars to fill the professorial chairs. I offered special attractions to students: lodgings at fixed rates; loans to students in need; State posts for the most promising students. And finally, I forbade study abroad until a student of the Realm had first completed his course at Napoli. I myself dictated a statement concerning the advantage of the new university, and I thought to add certain points which would appeal to fathers and mothers: "We keep the students within view of their parents; we save them many toils and long foreign journeys; we protect them from robbers; they may now study with small cost and short wayfaring." Because Pier della Vigna knew far better than I the ways of university life (I, who had had only the streets and a handful of tutors), I deputized him to keep an eye on developments. Then how enthusiastically I waited for the first harvest from my new crop . . . !

By a curious anomaly, my university was to produce a famous churchman, Tommaso (the younger) d'Aquino, son of Count Landolfo, at Napoli. He learned much of that very Aristotle whose books had been banned by Innocent III and whose philosophy Tommaso now attempted to integrate with Church doctrine. He was a clever boy, and I joined his family in urging him not to enter the Church but to come to Court. He might have gone far—but his abstract turn of mind seemed wholly lacking in reality.

But could I have imagined that despite the ecclesiastical labors of Tommaso d'Aquino my university—my "fountain of science" —would be considered a veritable instrument of the Devil?

5

I SHOULD have taken warning because I myself came under fire from the Cardinal Ugolino of Ostia (from whom I had received the Cross at my coronation in Rome). He had become the Pope's closest adviser, and, oddly, also a friend and confidant to Francesco d'Assisi. It was the Cardinal who had been named by Francesco as protector of his Order, the Cardinal who helped to organize the brotherhood in the towns, the Cardinal who played a significant role in making palatable to the Church Francesco's potential heresies. And when I met and talked with Francesco, I was sure that Cardinal Ugolino would hear about it, and that I myself would be labeled (as I was) an instrument of the Devil.

It was curious, devil though I was, that Francesco and I should agree at so many points on the need for reform of the Church. He, however, as a mystic, was willing to submerge himself in the universal hierarchy, trusting that in time the goodness of God would bring repentance, poverty, and a return of the early Christian spirit to that vast organization which now dominated all Europe. I, who talked not with birds, but studied their habits, was more skeptical.

My skepticism, in fact, extended to Francesco himself—for many times had I listened to friars who preached one thing and did another. This Francesco, who had become so famous for his preaching to the poor and ignorant, I resolved to test—and to observe with my own eyes the result of the test. I was then holding court in Bari, in the castle on the harbor, and Francesco came to preach beneath the walls. Berardo was greatly disturbed, and would have reasoned with him; but I said to let him alone. Not long since he had returned from the Pope's fiasco in Egypt, and was himself both hurt and humiliated at his failure to convert the Sultan al-Kamil. Perhaps he thought to try his powers (he was renowned as a worker of miracles) on me—if, according to his own account, he had managed to convert the largest, most terrible and ferocious wolf of Agobio, why not me? He began to cry out in a loud voice against the licentiousness of the court and the sins of the flesh. Thus he gathered a sizable throng, who beat their chests and also cried out against sin, while savoring to the full the details the good monk had just been describing. It was indeed a delicious sense of shock they felt, and no doubt their hearts beat fast with vicarious excitement. But in the voice of Francesco was only pain and sorrow.

At dusk, when he had finished, I sent a messenger to say that the Emperor would speak with him, and he accepted at once. My "conversion" would have been a feather in his cap second only to the infidel Sultan of Egypt.

I had him escorted to a pleasant chamber in the castle, a room with a great bed and many cushions covered in gold satin. In it, also, were some of the antique sculptures I had collected —bronzes and marbles of nude youths and girls, fauns and satyrs, dancers and bacchantes. It was a little hideaway of my own, where I could go in private with some new favorite and spend an hour or two in precious escape. It was a room with the odor not of incense but of flowers, perfume and human love. Indeed when Francesco entered, he sniffed suspiciously; for I was watching through a slit in the wall (a slit I used when I wished to observe my favorites all unobserved—so I have seen some very surprising things). He gathered his ash-gray robe about him as though he would not have it contaminated by the articles in the room, and lowered his eyes when he saw the statues unashamedly nude (as God had once made man). He dropped the cowl from his tonsured head, and turned toward the slit; I saw ascetic, gentle eyes which seemed not quite in focus and thus glazed with a hazy, dreamy film. His face was haloed by a soft, thin beard. He dropped to his knees, clasped hands, and prayed. Then with alacrity he rose and in evident gratitude warmed his hands over the charcoal brazier—for the night was a little chill and I wanted warmth in the room. After his hands, he took off his sandals and warmed his feet, and, like a physician, I wondered about his circulation.

Servants arrived with portions of the supper prepared for my own table—a simple meal of *pasta* with clam sauce, *gam-*

beroni, scapece (my favorite dish: made with fish fried in olive oil, marinated in a sauce of white wine and saffron), green salad, fresh fruit, and wine of Gallipoli. He ate and drank as though he hardly knew what food he took or what liquid passed his mouth, for his mind was on other things. I think he was not aware when the meal was finished and the servant took away the dishes. But abruptly he came to sharp perception when the sweets arrived, for the plate was brought by one of the loveliest of my dancing girls. She was dressed only in golden sandals and a transparent veil; her nails were painted scarlet, her eyes shadowed blue-black, and her lips and breasts were tinted to a rosy glow. Francesco sprang like a boy to his feet, but held out his hands in defense before him.

"Away, woman, away!" he cried. "Cover your nakedness and pray for forgiveness—repent, repent—God will forgive you!"

"For what, holy monk?" the girl said. "Before Allah I have committed no sin, for I have not gone unveiled on the streets. And is not woman made for man—"

Francesco moaned, almost weeping, "Out of my sight naked woman, else I sear your sins with these coals of fire!" He took up the brazier and flung the red-hot charcoal between them as a barrier to her passage.

She screamed, dropped the sweets, and ran. Thus arose the legend that I had assaulted Francesco with a temptress, and an angel had come to his defense with a flaming sword.

But I was content.

When I opened the door to the room, Francesco looked up with dilated eyes, as if afraid of seeing another woman. Had I been so fearsome as a demon, I think he would have greeted me with relief. I had tested him, and he had survived the test: now we could talk to one another without harangue.

"Congratulations, Fra Francesco," I said. "You are a man after our own heart, because you act upon your beliefs. Would that all clergy were like you!"

He rose and bowed. "Would that your Highness also approved of the rejection of your own temptations," he said politely. "Then I could pray that the blessing of God be showered upon you—"

"We believe in the power of God in man," I said, "while you believe in the power of God in the Church."

He frowned. "In the grace of God as mediated through the

Church. It is written: 'Man must love God and keep His commandments.' "

"Does this mean we must also love the Pope?" I asked.

"Man must love the word of God when spoken by the Pope, or by God Himself," he answered eliptically. "Man must know God—but Holy Church shows him the way to God. Thus man must love, honor, and venerate the Church and its Pontiff . . ."

In this manner began a conversation which lasted four hours and ranged over the face of the earth. We discussed the Bible, Sultan al-Kamil, corruption, French literature. Francesco burst into French songs, and finally recited for me one of his poems —the ecstatic *cantica* on Divine Love, in which he has our Lord Christ speak, beginning:

"Set Love in order, thou that Lovest Me.
Never was virtue out of order found;
And though I fill thy heart desirously,
By thine own virtue I must keep my ground. . . ."

Such was Francesco d'Assisi—a man of utmost simplicity, sincerity, honesty, and filled with the love of all living things. He had submerged himself in God, and considered himself at one with God. He had preached to the multitudes about the nearness of God, and had moved them greatly. The reaction of Pope Innocent III had been to increase the significance of the priest as intermediary between God and man; but this was no answer to the need for reformation of the abuses of a Church directed by worldly men. It was easy to see why the Church had been forced to come to terms with the saintly Francesco and take him into its own fold.

Francesco d'Assisi—a moving spirit of his age. So soon to die; so soon to be canonized.

Alleluia, alleluia—Franciscus pauper
et humilis, caelum dives ingreditur,
hymnis caelestibus honoratur. Alleluia.

His danger to the Church passed away with his life. His danger to me began with his death.

6

THE YEARS of postponement of the new Crusade stretched out from two to four—though this time, however welcome the delay, I was not primarily responsible. During the interlude, in Sicily the Saracen war was successfully concluded; in Lombardia, incipient revolts of the towns were an ominous foreshadowing of the future. As for my "private" life, I learned to play a new and fantastically complicated mathematical game; I took a child-wife, and I fell completely and genuinely "in love."

Pope Honorius himself made it known that he would be willing to accept another extension of embarkation time for the Holy Land, but he wanted stiff penalties to guarantee that my embarkation would actually occur. Though he was ninety-nine, his faith was such that he felt sure that he would live to see the great day of liberation of the Sacred Places. He was, however, himself in grave trouble with the people of Rome—and the city was in a stage of semirevolt. For his own safety he felt it necessary to flee, while he called on me to use my prestige and authority to placate the nobles and calm the masses. So, actually, we had something to exchange when once again we met in the lofty monastery at San Germano.

He had been deeply disturbed, too, by the reports brought from the rest of Europe by Hermann von Salza. Nowhere—Germany, France, England, Spain—was any true enthusiasm for the Crusade to be found. Most of the princes in these lands were too preoccupied with their own problems, too conscious of the cost, too fearful of another failure. From the Near East, Jean de Brienne, still jauntily wearing the crown of Jerusalem, reported dissension in the ranks of the Christians and a serious decline in crusading zeal. It was evident that both the leadership and the financing of the expedition had fallen upon my less than willing shoulders. But this responsibility also opened a magnificent opportunity: to become the leader of all Christendom.

The Pope was astonished at the lightness with which I agreed to his onerous conditions—that I transport and maintain one thousand fully equipped knights in the Holy Land for two years; that I prepare an additional two thousand; that I maintain a fleet to protect communications; that I pay one hundred thousand ounces of gold into a Crusade fund (to be forfeit if I failed to go); that I should fall under the Papal ban if I failed to honor the promised date. The Pope meant to have a Crusade—but so did I.

I began to consolidate as rapidly as possible all my affairs.

With the end of the Saracen war in Sicily (I had resettled almost twenty thousand Muslims), had come incipient conflict in Lombardia. There the situation was extremely complex. Both guildsmen and the growing class of banker-merchants found themselves united against the old nobility. The nobility by vow and fief were sworn to support the Empire, but in fact preferred to rule their lands without a central power. The aristocratic Church—its ecclesiastical princes—looked with loathing upon the merchant class and common people. With the feuding of Guelf and Ghilbelline, the confusion grew. Nowhere were lines clear-cut. When Emperor and Church were at odds, the nobility found themselves divided between temporal and spiritual authority; the merchants found themselves backing the Church; and the common people found themselves in the camp of the Emperor. As the power of the nobility waned and the power of the merchants waxed, the towns tended to assume a new autonomy, breeding both heretics and rebels, and attempting to escape alike from rule of Church and Empire. And, in the interludes when the towns found "freedom," they fell immediately to fighting in the most savage type of internecine warfare. This fragmentation I wished to avoid. I wanted unity, trade, culture, peace.

The Lombard towns had heard of the army I was collecting, and jumped to the conclusion that it was to be used not for a crusade but against them. Promptly they formed a league, though they were sharply divided among themselves for and against me. Under the leadership of Milano, they renewed the Lombard Confederation, and extended its term of membership for twenty-five years. I saw it as a rebel state within a state; but the Church secretly aided its organization, in spite of the fact that, in the Pope's own words, Milano was "saturated with the poison of heresy." The Church wanted in northern Italy no state comparable to the Sicilian state—for already my reforms were becoming anathema to the Curia. And, for the Church, a united Italy was to be avoided at all costs: the only united Italy acceptable to the Church was an Italy entirely under the domination of the Pope. Already the Curia was in deadly fear of temporal union.

I called a Diet of Empire representatives to meet in Cremona. I marched north without the Pope's permission to cross the lands of the Church which sliced Italy in half. The Pope trembled at this effrontery, the Curia raged. Acid letters (mine penned by Pier della Vigna) passed between us. Actually, these lands had been an Imperial concession, which the Emperor at any moment had the power to revoke. Just now I wished to demonstrate to north and south the need for unity. And, to stress my peaceful intent, I marched without an army.

The Lombard towns mistook this gesture for weakness, and rebuffed me with unprecedented insolence. They closed the Brenner Pass at Trento so that my son King Heinrich could not enter Italy. I was particularly anxious to see him because his guardian, the Archbishop Engelbert of Köln, recently had been murdered, and I liked not at all some of the things I was hearing about Heinrich's behavior. In Faenza a knight was stabbed to death in the mistaken belief that he was the Emperor. My meeting was an utter failure, and I was reduced to verbal imprecations. I revoked all Imperial privileges and threatened the ban of Empire. As a crusader whose overtures for the Crusade had been rejected, I sent von Salza to the Pope to demand an interdict on the Lombard League, and then (like pinning him with an arrow) called His Holiness to arbitrate our differences. How could he do otherwise than defend the rights of his chief crusader? Nevertheless, all my acts were a series of mistakes. (At that moment, perhaps, I should have allied myself openly with all anti-Papal forces?) I controlled my wrath and bided my time.

I took warning from the attempt on my life, and called on the loyal Pisans to send me a sizable armed escort. They did so, and took me directly to their city. This, as things turned out, was the only fortuitous event of my entire journey, for I met the famed mathematician Leonardo Fibonacci. He had studied in Syria, Egypt, Greece and Spain, and his name was well known to me. He was a small man with a bald head, very reserved and precise in manner, and a great lover of music played on the flute. He could use an abacus with the skill of any counting clerk. He was then working on his treatise on squared numbers, the *Liber Quadratum,* which he chose to dedicate to me because "it pleases you from time to time to hear subtle reasoning in geometry and arithmetic." I put to him a number of problems which I thought difficult, and which, to my delight, he solved with ease. They related mainly to the asymptote, the straight line always approaching nearer but never meeting a curve: I was concerned with its aspects in infinity. Neither he nor I could resolve the Delian Problem of the duplication of the cube, nor square the circle.

But far more important was Messer Leonardo's advocacy of the use of the Arabic numerals and the zero, reckoning, as he said, "after the manner of the Indiani"- for they were Hindu in origin. The old Roman numerals were entirely too cumbersome, and the Greeks had to memorize twenty-seven different symbols just for the numbers 1 to 999. Both Leonardo and I had read al-Khowarizmi's book, written in the ninth century, on the virtues of the "Indian" numerals. I agreed to help him promote use of the place system, though it had been denounced as pagan. It does take a while for these new ideas to get around! Finally, Leonardo taught me a number game called "*rithmomachy*"—played on a double chessboard with eight cells on one side and sixteen cells on the other, with pieces in the shape of triangles, squares and circles. Though it was extremely complicated, I must say that I enjoyed it, and felt relaxed and refreshed when we had finished. We played three times, and he won two of the three encounters—which he politely ascribed to the fact that I was new at the game.

I laughed and said that the game for me was a *pons asinorum*—which is the fifth proposition of the First Book of Euclid (the base angles of an isosceles triangle are equal), and has come to mean any problem difficult for beginners.

But playing mathematical games was not my only means of refreshment in those days. I also knew the *divertimento* of love.

7

I WAS six weeks short of my thirty-first birthday, and the bride was just fourteen, when the wedding took place. In August I had sent a fleet of galleys to Acre to pick up Yolanda, and we were pledged at once by proxy. Since Yolanda was not yet of age, it was necessary that she be crowned Queen of Jerusalem. The ceremony took place at Tyre, and all the crusader-barons of the Holy Land, and the Church's Military Orders, paid her homage. She was accompanied by her brother Count Walter, who had not long since married a cousin named Balian. The necessary preludes completed, the whole party embarked aboard my ships, and sailed for Italy.

At about the same time, my son Heinrich, now fifteen and a strapping fellow (so his guardian had reported) was married to Margarete, daughter of the Duke of Austria. I sent rich presents, and regrets that I could not attend the ceremony. The consolidation of the Empire seemed well in hand. In my mind's eye I liked to follow a flight of the Imperial Eagle: from the mists of the northern seas up the Rhine, eastward along the soft green hills of the Danube, south through the boot of Italy, and now—by the simple exchange of rings—across the Mediterranean into the Holy Land. What matter if the bride came impoverished? The Pope was the Pontiff of the Holy Apostolic See—but I was to become King of Jerusalem. To the Catholic Christian mind, this was a fact, I thought, of supreme importance if Jerusalem once more passed into Christian hands. And I recalled the prophecy that "he who rides into Jerusalem as King will bring the long-awaited Reign of Peace before the Antichrist shall come."

With Yolanda's father, Jean de Brienne, I traveled from Foggia early in November to meet my galleys in Brindisi harbor. I did him the courtesy of calling him King Jean—and he basked in the title as I basked in the strong autumn sun. I was in a good mood because I liked particularly the landscape we passed through —the country of the *trulli,* those round beehive houses of white stone and conical roofs of gray slate. (Once I had asked a peasant why the houses were built that way, and he answered, "Is there any other way?") I was happy to honor my betrothed's arrival not only with much pomp, but also in person—unlike that stiff-necked fourteen-year-old king in Palermo who had forced his older bride-to-be to come to him. As an Emperor I had learned *noblesse oblige.*

Indeed I had need of graciousness when Yolanda's party left the galley, and, to the sound of trumpets, entered the Imperial pavilion to greet me. I should never have guessed that she was the Queen of Jerusalem had not her father stepped forward to perform the introduction. I came near staring in astonishment at this bony little squab which had been foisted upon me; and as she dropped her veil I saw a beaklike face and dilated, bewildered, childish eyes very near to brimming with tears. I was sorry for her, but I could not smother a sense of indignation—for, dowerless, at least she should have been beautiful. I turned and glanced at Piero, and he read my thoughts at once, shaking his head with compassion for my plight. Then to Berardo, who was to perform the ceremony, a plea for help. Then at Hermann von Salza, who was beaming with satisfaction, I simply glared.

Yet compensation was imminent: Count Walter de Brienne and his young cousin-wife were presented to me next. He was a small man with a scanty red beard not unlike his father's, but he lacked the fishy eye. His age was about the same as mine, though already he was balding. As his wife kissed my hand it was a sensuous velvet touch. Her great dark ancient Syrian eyes hinted a smile. It was like a caress of eyelashes. I wondered about the lips hidden behind the veil. I was suddenly aware of her perfume, suddenly conscious of crimson-lacquered toenails in golden sandals. The perfume was a scent I had never smelled before; the small delicate feet were the most perfect I had ever seen. I repaid her smile with a fleeting quizzical look. Instantly we were at one. Or, as it is said, "in love."

How did it happen? Who can explain? Had I not been the Emperor, surely I would have murdered her husband, so filled was I with desire. As it was, very shortly I had him detained in a tower —while she and I disappeared.

I could not, of course, escape the marriage, and I became most impatient for the completion of the rite. I wished to assume at once the title "King of Jerusalem," which I did—to the disgruntlement of Jean de Brienne. Apparently he had cherished the notion that the title was his until Yolanda should come of age. He was not satisfied as father-in-law to the Emperor. We quarreled and I dismissed him curtly from my presence.

"Has my Lord the Emperor and King of Jerusalem considered the consequences of his brusque actions?" he asked harshly as he bowed himself out.

As for Yolanda, I curbed my eagerness to be elsewhere, and visited her chambers. I was courteous and gentle with her, but she was so frightened she could hardly speak. She was dressed in an elegant nightgown embroidered with scenes from the tale of the tragic lovers Tristan and Isolde. Nothing, to my mind, could have been more inappropriate for this breastless girl.

"*Madonna mia*," I said, "dismiss the ladies-in-waiting. Let us talk alone."

She did so with a gesture, then bowed awkwardly to me. "My Lord," she gasped, "I await your pleasure."

Luckily she did not know the ironic sound of her words in my ears. "Yolanda, *cara*," I said, as to a tiny child, "now you are indeed the Empress, and this is our wedding night. But as your husband is not feeling well, we will postpone the consummation to another time. You understand . . . ?"

"But—but my Lord," she cried in obvious disappointment, "the nuptial bed is all prepared!"

It was an affront, but I could not bed with her. My fish wanted to swim in another pond. I kissed her on the forehead, and said good night. Behind me, she stood forlornly at the half-open door, with flickering candle, clearly on the verge of tears.

I had done no more than send word to Balian that the Emperor desired her presence, and she came willingly. Horses were saddled and all was in readiness for flight by the time she reached my apartment. I took both her hands and kissed one and then the other.

"No doubt the stars have arranged our introduction, Contessa," I said in Arabic, "but the Emperor himself has arranged a rendezvous. Since we may not deny the wishes of either, shall we make all haste toward their fulfillment . . . ?"

She smiled—a slow, sensuous, devastating smile, and replied in Arabic: "Indeed, my Lord, the utmost haste toward the utmost fulfillment!"

We left the castle secretly by a small door, extinguishing the torches before we stepped outside the walls. The town was sleeping; only here and there a barking dog disturbed the peace. With but a handful of Saracen guards, my two favorite body servants, and Balian heavily veiled, we made our way toward the countryside.

I had told no one of our going save Berardo. As for Piero, he was not informed because I was sure that, in spite of himself, he would be jealous—he knew as well as I that this affair was not the ordinary.

We paused to water our horses at the oriental fountain built by Tancred for crusaders a few years before my birth—Tancred, that unfortunate illegitimate Norman King whose corpse had been dealt with so gruesomely by my father. By a quirk of fate, Balian was one of Tancred's descendants, and therefore not only my new wife's cousin but remotely my own.

After remarking on this coincidence we took the ancient Via Appia in the direction of Taranto. The long, straight, powdery white road was lighted by thc sliver of a moon; and to the vineyards still clung the sweet, ripe odor of the grape harvest. We talked little, but rode hard, kicking up small clouds of billowing dust. We had, actually, not far to go: only to Oria, where I was building a castle, and where, with a wave of my hand, I could command privacy. Hidden there, we would be safe from the intrusive world.

At length the white houses of the town loomed ahead on a hillock, and the tall round towers of the castle cast long dark shadows in the moonlight. We entered not through the town, but through a secret passage which opened into a vineyard (I had never forgotten our blocked escape when Markward's soldiers pressed into the Castello di Maredolce). The passage led into the castle courtyard, into a subterranean room lined with broken columns. Here I sent the guard ahead, and paused with Balian.

I took her into my arms. "*Carissima*," I said softly, not to disturb the past, "this was the temple of Venus: I shall dedicate it anew to Balian . . ." Then I whispered a few lines I had composed on the road:

> *"Poi che ti piace, Amore,*
> *che io deggia trovare,*
> *faronne mia possanza. . . ."*

I kissed her, and, like a boy, I felt the full first excitement of love.

Never have I known such a woman. She was the fullest expression of sexuality—surely Venus herself. She had none of the guilt-modesty of Western Christian women, but matched me act for act and in total passion. As I kissed and bit her naked body, likewise she kissed and bit mine. As I gave extraordinary form or shape or motion to our contact, likewise she gave extraordinary form or shape or motion to the act of love. And her beauty was unsurpassed. Never have I seen such a body—surely Venus herself. The great, dark, love-taunting Syrian eyes; the whimsical, sensuous mouth; the graceful arms and legs; the sculptured feet; the tickling fingers; the luscious breasts; the soft buttocks; the tawny flesh; the hot thighs. Now indeed I knew why the Arab poets sang of love exotic. And I recalled the words of the ancient pagan hymn: "*O admirabile Veneris idolum!*"

All this, I thought, is a dream: she is too perfect. Time alone would reveal that her only imperfection was within.

For a week we made love thus, at whatever hour desire struck us. Once at sunset we walked on the battlements to a watch tower, where I showed her the marble map I had devised to aid the lookout. All about was an endless plain without distinctive feature. Two turns around the tower, and it was hard to know in which direction lay Taranto and in which lay Brindisi. My map located towns and streams and roads at a glance, so that a sentry spying advancing horsemen could make no error.

Balian admired the map, as she continually admired me, and then fell silent. The sun dipped down into the red-purple haze across the dusty plain, and the cool, fresh breeze of night sprang up. The evening stars were the jewels of the southern sky.

Balian sighed. "Look, my Lord, at Venus. When I have left your arms, and am far away, you will remember when you see that star that I, like Venus, am very lonely. . . ."

"Not now," I said, "not now!" And there, on my cloak, on the marble map, once more we made love.

All too quickly this idyl of ours came to an end. I could not, like a monk or a hermit, forever hide myself from the pressing world. Neither Balian nor I concealed our sadness as we rode back along the straight white road to Brindisi. Would we ever again know such joy? How strange that ephemeral happiness brings lasting sadness. . . .

We arrived late at night, disguised, as I preferred not to be seen or recognized. The fanciful story of this *amore* I would leave to legend; but the facts would be known only to Balian and me . . . and the man I had usurped.

"Tell your husband that if he harms you, he will be killed." These were my parting words to Balian.

I felt, in fact, but little concern—for the rights of the Emperor were all-inclusive. I thought that Count Walter would acquiesce graciously to my relationship with his wife, and profit from it, as most men would. But not he. I had some unpleasant surprises awaiting.

I found that his father, Jean de Brienne, in disgust at the loss of his crown, had fled to Rome—there to join the Sicilian refugees and other malcontents who wept on the Pope's shoulder and plotted my overthrow. With a certain regret I ordered Count Walter's release, but I felt I could not do otherwise—he was, after all, my brother-in-law. (And I recalled that the onerous duty of consummation yet hung over me.) On the following day, both Count Walter and Balian disappeared, leaving not a trace. They were spirited away in disguise, I discovered later, by one of the mendicant orders—so the long arm of the Church was involved.

For some weeks I waited anxiously for news of them, and at last one of my agents in Rome reported that Count Walter had joined his father at the Papal court. But of Balian, nothing. I grieved, and swore vengeance if I learned of injury to her.

I was on the verge of action when a letter came to me from Syria. It was from Balian, written in Arabic. She had been returned under guard, and was now shut away from the world in Antioch. The letter continued: "Take warning. Beware of my husband. He hates you. He has called down a malediction upon you! But above all rescue me—I am with your child . . . !"

I replied at once by a special messenger on a fast ship. The letter was addressed to the Flower of Syria, and I enclosed a poem which had this final stanza, for indeed my heart was in her prison:

Canzonetta gioiosa,
va a la fior di Soria,
a quella c'a in pregione lo mio core . . .

Of course I would rescue her. I had but to leave on the Crusade to rescue Jerusalem. . . .

8

Honorius did indeed reach the age of one-hundred-and-one; but a scant few months before the Crusade was to begin, he died. In an astonishingly short meeting, the cardinals chose one of their number, Ugolino of Ostia, as successor to the Apostolic Throne. He chose the name Gregory IX—a name not without significance, for the predecessor Gregory had brought an Emperor to his knees in the snow.

This new Gregory was a nephew of Innocent III; as Cardinal, the protector of Francesco d'Assisi; and the grim-faced man from whom I had received the Cross in Rome. Now he was a vigorous eighty, of dignified mien and majestic presence; but ambitious, violent, unscrupulous, and ferociously intolerant. Of him I said publicly, "He is a man of spotless reputation, renowned for piety, erudition and eloquence. He shines among the rest like a brilliant star."

I completely underestimated his hostility toward me, though I should have guessed from one of his first letters, focusing on my private life. He wrote (perhaps alluding to my affair with Balian), "God has bestowed upon you the gift of knowledge and of perfect imagination, and all Christendom follows you. Take heed that you do not place your intellect, which you have in common with the angels, below your senses, which you have in common with beasts and plants. Your intellect is weakened if you are the slave of your senses. . . ." To this rebuke I made no answer.

I was intensely busy with preparations for the Crusade. Brindisi hummed and palpitated with activity, as so often with the Crusades of the past. Not for nothing had the Romans erected two columns of gray marble to mark the end of the Via Appia at that port. Here was the jumping-off point for the East. Now my galleys rode at anchor where Caesar had blockaded Pompey's fleet; and where, long before, Greek galleys anchored, bringing Hellenic culture to the Messapians and the Palasgians who lived along the Adriatic coast. But, as always, for much musing I had no time. I did not even pause to celebrate the birth of a son to my son Heinrich—at the age of thirty-one I became a grandfather. The grandchild was named Friedrich, in my honor. I was occupied, not with lullabies and cradles, but with such problems as stable space for horses and storage of armor aboard ship.

No, not wholly. The Sultan of Egypt, al-Kamil, had sent to my court an Ambassador, the Emir Fakhr ad-Din. He was bland, plump, Arab in appearance only because of his beard, and learned in philosophy, poetry, arms, horseflesh, and falconry. He was, in fact, a fair representative of his master, and we took to one another at once. Al-Kamil had troubles at home, and now I was about to launch a Crusade bringing more. Let us talk, let us negotiate, said al-Kamil through his Ambassador. Let us explore each other's minds, evaluate each other's positions, and perhaps we can reach an agreement. I was noncommittal, but I sent Berardo to Egypt to talk to the Sultan. One point was already clear to us both: each of us preferred not to fight, and valued peace. But in my camp were Christians who believed that only the sword was an answer; and in his camp Muslims who believed that only the sword was an answer. Our mutual problem was: how could peace prevail . . . ?

In midsummer, pilgrims and knights began flocking into Brindisi, for the scheduled sailing time was near at hand. Hermann von Salza, by the liberal use of my gold, and Pope Honorius, by the liberal use of indulgences, had been far more successful in enticing crusaders than anyone expected. The tent encampment outside Brindisi grew daily, hourly—swarming with knights, squires, servants, holy men, pilgrims, monks, horses, dogs, and prostitutes. With such a multitude came confusion. Von Salza began to worry as to whether we had galleys enough to transport men and cargo; I began to worry as to whether men and cargo would ever be embarked. Food grew short. The August sun beat down, baking, broiling, burning. The men from beyond the Alps knew nothing of this climate, nothing of sanitation. The camps began to stink with offal. Flies and rats were everywhere. I recalled with apprehension the fearful demise of Costanza's Aragon knights in Sicily.

My fears were all too justified. The pest appeared in camp, and men began to die in tens and hundreds. Some fled in panic; others patiently waited for the will of God. I did not wait, but removed Yolanda—who was pregnant at last (and almost pretty)—and as much of the court as possible to Otranto. There, on the tip of the heel of Italy, the air was cooler and the sea fresher. Piero refused to stay, but returned with me to Brindisi. In the hope of safety, we moved from the castle to the Island of Sant' Andrea in the harbor—but the hope was in vain. One morning I awoke with a light fever, nausea, and a feeling of deep malaise. Yet, unlike others who took the sickness, I seemed to get no worse. Days dragged on. I did not die, but I got no better. I fretted. A large detachment of my forces had sailed in the middle of August; I could wait no longer. I decided to fulfill my vow.

On the morning of September 9, my stomach rolling and heaving like the ship, I managed to walk aboard the Imperial flagship. Church bells clanged and pilgrims cheered; in my sensitive ears they were but a raucous noise. I gave the order to cast off the hawsers; I was, I announced to the crew, a little seasick, though the voyage had just begun. But the truth would not down. The Landgrave of Thuringia, whom I had named Commander-in-Chief, suddenly took to his bunk. In delirium he cried out that his cabin was full of white doves heaven-sent. Von Salza gravely reported that they had come to bear souls home to God. Not mine, not yet, I thought; and gave orders to put in to Otranto. There, after receiving the last Sacrament, the Landgrave died, and the doves winged away. Of my fifty galleys, I sent twenty on—under the command of Hermann von Salza. This blessed man left, complaining not about this new burden, but that he was never able to adapt "sea feet."

Great was my rage and disgust at the situation. I was miserably ill. Not the least of my frustrations was the delay in seeing Balian. I permitted only Piero to be with me constantly, and he acted, in effect, as the Emperor. Even through the film on my eyes I could see him gain a new dimension. I improved a little, and sent a mission to the Pope to explain. Then I myself set off to the volcanic baths of Pozzuoli, near Napoli, to convalesce.

There, floating in a marble basin of hot sulphur waters, I received the ambassadors I had sent to the Pope. I was so unprepared for the news they brought that I came close to foundering on the spot. Gregory had refused to see or speak with my representatives. Further, he had called a secret consistory and declared me an excommunicate. For reasons which seemed obscure but speedily clarified, he postponed public announcement of the ban for about six weeks—though he knew, of course, I would be informed through private channels.

He used the intervening period for a series of attacks on my character. He blamed me for everything: for first taking the Cross without permission of the Apostolic See; for continued delays in the Crusade; for the earlier disaster at Damietta; for detaining the pilgrims in the summer heat; for not providing sufficient ships; for exposing the army to the pest and thus taking their lives; for turning back when once I had embarked. He did not believe for a moment that I was truly sick: I had feigned illness to avoid going on the Crusade. Then, to cap all, from Rome came rumors that I myself had poisoned the Landgrave of Thuringia aboard my galley.

Once more I offered proof of my malady. The Pope was not interested in proof. In an address to a great assembly of the clergy he bewailed my treachery and pronounced the interdict itself:

> The Church of Christ, while she thinks she is nursing her children, is fostering in her bosom serpents and basilisks, which would destroy everything by their fire, their breath and their burning. To combat these monsters, to triumph over hostile armies, to appease these restless tempests, the Holy Apostolic See reckoned on a nursling whom she brought up with tenderest care; the Church took the Imperator Fridericus from his mother's womb, so to speak, fed him at her breast, bore him on her shoulders. Often Holy Church rescued him from those who sought his life; then instructed him, educated him with care and pain to manhood; invested him with the royal dignity; and to all these blessings bestowed upon him the title of Imperator hoping to find in him a protecting support, a staff for her old age . . .
>
> How has he fulfilled his covenant . . . ?
>
> He, breaking all promises, bursting every bond, trampling underfoot the fear of God, despising all reverence for Christ Jesus, scorning the censures of the Church, deserting the Christian army, abandoning the Holy Land to the Unbelievers—to his own disgrace and that of all Christendom, withdrew to the luxuries and habitual delights of his king-

> dom, seeking to palliate his offense by frivolous excuses of bodily sickness. . . .
>
> That we may not be esteemed as dumb dogs, who dare not bark, or fear to take vengeance upon him, the Imperator Fridericus Secundus, who has caused such ruin to the people of God, WE PROCLAIM THE SAID IMPERATOR EXCOMMUNICATE . . . !

I received the sentence with such calm that all men were amazed. I did not contest the Pope's right to excommunicate me, for in fact I had not gone on the Crusade. I paid in forfeit the one hundred thousand ounces of gold. To lift the ban I offered to do penance, and promised to sail to the Holy Land within the coming year.

The Pope's response was: NO! No penance was acceptable—no hair shirt, no fasting on bread and water, no pilgrimage barefoot or on all fours to any shrine. Nothing was acceptable save my relinquishing the Kingdom of Sicily to the rule of the Pope.

Now I clearly understood what had hitherto been obscure, for Pope Gregory had brought into the open the latent conflict. He was a man of great foresight, and these were his fears: the growth of the lay state, and reformation of the Church. I was a double heretic, for I held both objectives. He had controlled the revolutionary preaching of Francesco d'Assisi and channeled its course; now he would control me and determine my course. He declared war on my person—war without quarter—unless, of course, he saw the prospect of defeat.

I struck back. I ordered all Sicilian clergy to perform religious rites as usual. Then with Berardo and Piero I held fevered consultations. We prepared draft after draft of letters to be issued to all the princes of Europe, to be read in every market place of the Empire. At length we arrived at a final draft, which Piero wrote with the words taken from my mouth. I resolved to be calm and reasonable at all costs—regardless of the Pope's invective:

> WE grieve to say that our hopes have been deceived; the end of all things is at hand, for love is waxing cold not only in its branches but in its roots.
>
> The Roman Empire, the bulwark of the Faith, is being assailed by its own fathers. If an enemy were to attack us, we would grasp the sword; but when the Vicar of Christ

arises against us, our reverence for the blessed San Pietro causes us to pause in amazement. Let all men hear the provocations we have received!

Our Apostolic Lord did not deal fairly with the ambassadors we sent him. They were ready to explain all, but he would not listen to them. It is said that, before the defense made by our envoys to the Curia, the Pope had already consulted with each Prelate secretly, warning each not to depart from the sentence already arranged. Thus the council arrived at a conclusion before hearing the defense.

All this we desire to make known to the whole world, for in spite of injustice we shall not desist from the service of Christ.

In Rome, I arranged through certain of my friends, chiefly the Frangipani family, that the letter be read aloud on the Campidoglio to as large a crowd as could be mustered. And as it was read, mutterings and restiveness arose among the people. In the Basilica of San Pietro, soon after, mutterings arose while the Pope was saying Mass. When he elevated the Host, the people ceased to be dumb dogs, and began to bark. As the Pope fled to the Laterano, he was mobbed in the streets. Then, in fear, he fled from Rome.

But Gregory needed more than a bark. He needed a bite. And bite I could and would. Was it possible for an excommunicant, unabsolved, to lead a Crusade?

Let Gregory wait and see . . . !

9

I SAILED without fanfare for the Holy Land on the twenty-eighth day of June of the year 1228, according to the Christian calendar, or 606 according to the calendar of Islam. Gregory hurled a parting shaft. I sailed, he said, "more as a pirate than as an Emperor!"

Once before I had gambled for the highest stakes, when as a boy king I had set out for Germany to become a Roman Emperor; but that gamble was as nothing compared to the chance I was now about to take. I had no alternative to victory. Nor did anyone except me—not even Piero—believe I would dare to do this thing. As the news spread, all Christendom was horrified and thrilled. I had acted, said Gregory, "with devilish cunning." He had been convinced that he had finished me.

My position had been made the more difficult by one unexpected setback shortly before I sailed—Yolanda's death in childbirth. She was sixteen. She, poor thing, struggled agonizingly for hours before delivery of a boy—a new heir whom I named Corrado. She was so greatly weakened that, when the fever struck her, she did not survive for long. I myself crossed her bony bird hands across breasts at last enlarged by milk, then kissed sorrowfully the pallid forehead. In her had been no malice, and even the dual hatred of her father and brother toward me had not served to engender hatred. Toward her I had behaved as kindly as I could—once the madness for Balian had passed. But this ill-fated child and I lived in different worlds; she could not enter mine, nor I, hers. I buried her hastily in the Cathedral of San Riccardo, in the town of Andria, under a flat stone slab, in the floor of a ninth-century crypt. I had no time for long journeys to and from Palermo, or elaborate ceremonies consuming many days. Thus, technically, I ceased to be the King of Jerusalem, becoming only

Regent for my newborn son. This change endangered the loyalty of the barons in the Holy Land and created advantages for the divisive activities of Jean de Brienne and his son Count Walter, my increasingly bitter enemies.

My flag was not the Cross, which Gregory had withdrawn, but the Imperial Eagle. And I myself was known as *l'Aquila*. The name of my ship was *l'Aquila*. And once more I was called *al-Tair*, for the Sultan al-Kamil had said that the Emperor of the Franks (the Muslims called all crusaders "Franks") was an eagle among men. Thus I was known to the Saracen detachment I brought with me aboard ship; and the name spread among their brothers. So by both Muslim and Christian I was called "The Eagle."

As we sailed eastward I mused on the fantastic pageant of the Crusades, as I read their history in both Christian and Muslim accounts. Activated in the beginning by religious zeal, every Crusade had been corroded by plunder. Great were the names of the leaders, slim the achievements. Godfrey de Bouillon, Konrad III, Louis VII, Philip Augustus, Richard Coeur de Lion, my grandfather Barbarossa—the Christians. And, for the Muslims, the towering figure of Saladin. In 1099 the First Crusade had captured Jerusalem; the Second had attempted to defend it; the Third, in which my grandfather lost his life, tried to recapture it; the Fourth never reached Palestine, but dissipated its force attacking Christian cities and sacking Constantinople; and the Fifth had ended with ignominious defeat on the banks of the Nile. Was my Crusade the Sixth Crusade?—or would it be known to history as the Crusade of the Excommunicated? How could it—in the face of so many failures—succeed? Indeed, the world was soon to be treated to the sight of an amazing and bewildering paradox: the Vicar of Christ doing all in his power to defeat the crusading forces of Christ. Who, then, men said, served God and who served the Devil?

My grandfather Barbarossa, in spite of his quarrels with the Papacy, had labored under no such disadvantage in this effort to retake Jerusalem. Reading, in Arabic, the account of my grandfather's drowning, I thought of his death for the first time impersonally and from the Muslim point of view.

Said the writer, Ibn al-Athir: "Thus Allah freed us from the evil of Barbarossa." Again, an old-new conflict of god against god, aided and abetted by man against man. Thus wrote a Christian about the fall of Jerusalem in 1099:

> HAVING overcome the pagans, our knights seized a great number of men and women, and they killed whom they wished and whom they wished they let live. . . . Soon the crusaders ran through the city, seizing gold, silver, horses, mules, and houses full of all kinds of goods. . . .

I paused in melancholy, and was not cheered even by the long satirical poem Piero was writing in Latin about the greed of monks and prelates. But my spirits lightened a little when I chanced across the description, by Imàd ad-Din, of a shipload of "three hundred beautiful young women of the Franks," which arrived in the Holy Land during the Third Crusade.

> THEY had gathered together from over the seas and volunteered to commit sin. They wished to make the unfortunate crusaders happy, and they eagerly awaited the opportunity for carnal union. They were all frantic *fornicatrici*, superb and tantalizing, firm of flesh and seductive. Each one marched proudly, with a cross on her breast. They had dedicated their bodies to a pious ideal, even offering to prostitution the best and most chaste among them. They said that when they began this voyage, they had promised to consecrate their charms, and never refuse them, to the unmarried crusaders; and they deeply believed that no sacrifice would be more acceptable to God than this.
>
> They settled down in tents and pavilions and opened the doors to lust, consecrating in a pious offering what they had between their thighs. They were ready for any pleasure or any vice, manifesting every license. They lay on the carpets to make love, their anklets near their earrings; they offered their bodies to the blows of staves; they made themselves targets for arrows; they invited the swords to enter their vaginas; they smoothed their earth for the planting; they excited the plows to plow; they allowed the beaks to look inside; they cavorted with those who rode them using spurs; they caught in their nets the horns of rutting rams; they gathered birds into the nests of their thighs; they entwined leg with leg and satisfied their lovers' thirst.
>
> They maintained theirs was a pious work no less than any other. When they had finished, they poured wine and demanded their price. . . .

The weather held fair with a fresh breeze, so that our oarsmen were needed hardly at all, and we made exceptional speed. Another factor in our progress was kept secret from all except Piero and the captain of my flagship. We used for our guidance the compass—a magnetic needle so balanced on a pivot that it swings always to point north. The invention is considered black magic. Our sailors would not have sailed if they had learned of its use, and we might even have been faced with a mutiny. Hence the Captain insisted I keep the compass in a box in my cabin; each time he consulted it he eyed it most warily. But I told him to be of good cheer, as his voyage might set a record.

In three weeks and two days we sighted the Island of Cyprus, where Venus had been born from the sea foam. We put in for more than a month while I untangled some of the affairs of the barons. Cyprus was a part of the Empire, but its connections were entirely too tenuous for my liking. It is a chronic disease of the barons that each one wants to be a king. But in Cyprus, in the nights, I had thoughts other than how to control the barons—for I dreamed again and again of Balian. The closer I drew to the Levante the more fevered became my eagerness to see her once more. Accordingly, I dispatched secret envoys to Antioch, with instructions to bring her to me in Palestine at the earliest possible moment, at whatever cost in gold or lives. I had waited long enough.

I think I half expected to see her among the throng which greeted me at Acre, when at last, early in September, I set foot upon the Holy Land—but of course she was not there. I was welcomed by cries of "Saviour of Israel" and wild shouts of joy, for my coming was seen as a deliverance. For the moment, my excommunication seemed to have made little impression. The Templars, the Hospitalers, the Knights of San Giovanni, and of course the Teutonic Knights—all in armor—bent the knee in submission; also the barons of Outremer; even the clergy was present, led by the Pope's own Legate, Gerold, the stiff-necked Patriarch of Jerusalem—but the clergy refused the kiss of homage.

Behind the Christians, crowding the *molo* in curiosity and perhaps fear, were hundreds of Muslims, some wearing the white headdresses called *araghia*, others the brown woolen robes called *taghis*, and still others the *kaftan*, a footlength robe tied with a girdle. It was a polyglot scene. Peddlers sold sweetmeats, nuts, beads, religious trinkets, and (to Christians) wine, while brown-faced Arab boys vended fresh water from sweating goatskins slung across their shoulders. A haze, a film of dust lay over all. The earth was baked brown from the autumn sun; the sky was a brilliant aquamarine blue with wispy clouds presaging a change of weather. Glancing upward, I saw two vultures—the great black and white bird named *Neophron*—hovering on outspread wings. They were not, I thought, a happy omen.

And indeed, hardly had I landed before two cowled messengers,—members of the Francescan Order—arrived direct from the Pope. No one, the Holy Father warned, knight or cleric, was to render obeisance or assistance to the excommunicated crusader—on pain of likewise suffering immediate ban. In the old folk-saying, I had *un pugno di mosche*—"a fistfull of flies."

Was I to be forced to rely solely on my own Saracen warriors to conquer Jerusalem for Christendom?

10

DESPITE the fact that I came to Palestine with an army, I had not planned to make war. I hoped and believed that certain areas of agreement could be found between Christian and Muslim—and that agreement would be more productive to both than a long-drawn-out and costly war. Futhermore my forces—even had they been united—would have been inadequate for a truly successful campaign in this foreign land. And lastly, the leadership of the forces opposing us was of the very highest caliber—al Kamil was a worthy nephew of the great Saladin. True, my knowledge of Arabic and my experience with Saracen warfare made me no mean opponent of al-Kamil. Our tastes were very similar, and from the first moment of contact between us, we had the greatest respect for one another.

I took up headquarters in a castle not far from Acre (and not far from Nazareth, either), and immediately launched my first mission to al-Kamil. As if he wished to expedite exchanges between us, he had set up court at Nablus—equally close to Nazareth—and for months the roads were dusty with our messengers traveling back and forth. As my chief Ambassador I sent my trusted Count Tommaso d'Aquino, with jewels, vessels of gold and silver, a superb charger with a saddle of gold, and a beautifully illuminated edition of Aristotle's *Nicomachean Ethics* as gifts. Count Tommaso was instructed to say that I had no interest in a war of conquest, that I did not want lands which did not belong to me. But, as the Sultan knew well, the city of Jerusalem contained not only Holy Places sacred to Mohammed, but also Holy Places sacred to Christ—and I wished for Christians the same access to Jerusalem enjoyed by Mohammedans. (This idea was not dissimilar to a plan once tantatively explored by Richard Coeur de Lion and Saladin.)

Back came an embassy from al-Kamil, led by my good friend Fakhr ad-Din, bringing jewels more magnificent than the ones I had sent, Arab mares perfect in every point, ten of the famed mehari camels, bears, monkeys, an elephant—and a polite refusal to relinquish Jerusalem, on the grounds that all Muslims would be incensed at its loss to Islam. I had expected some such reply as this in the beginning, and thus far I was not perturbed.

I was well informed as to al-Kamil's actual situation, which recently had developed in a way by no means favorable to me. Malik al-Kamil was one of the three Ayyubit brothers who had divided the empire of Saladin, and amongst whom had existed the most uneasy of truces. Malik al-Kamil, before I sailed, had sought my aid against his brother al-Mu'azzam, the Sultan of Damascus who had controlled Jerusalem and who died leaving as heir the young boy an-Nasir Dawid. Al-Kamil had swooped, conquering Jerusalem, and then united with his remaining brother against their nephew; together they laid siege to Damascus. So the disgruntling question arose: why should al-Kamil relinquish the Jerusalem so recently won?

I was sure that al-Kamil was as well informed about my situation as I of his—and my heart sank at its contemplation. The rivalries between the barons of Outremer were intense, and the Military Orders were jealous of one another to the point of hatred. Only on the Teutonic Knights, under their Grand Master Hermann von Salza, could I depend. Added to these difficulties was the interdict, with the Patriarch of Jerusalem already doing all in his power to obstruct my every move. After the arrival of the Pope's messengers, the French and English crusaders openly refused to obey my orders. Only von Salza's wise and politic suggestion that all orders be issued in the name of Jesus Christ saved the day. I agreed at once. Then, to my disgust, intercepted letters proved that Pope Gregory had communicated directly with the Sultan al-Kamil, urging him under no circumstances to permit Jerusalem to fall into my hands. The reason of course was clear: my success in the Crusade, as an excommunicant, would mean that the judgment of God was against Gregory. But, as yet, such success was far afield.

I decided not only to continue negotiations, but also to make a show of force. Accordingly, I marched the crusading army of eleven thousand (including even the reluctant Templars) toward Jaffa, and began construction of new fortifications. The results of both moves were negative: al-Kamil, who had a great army of his own, remained singularly unimpressed. He canceled negotiations altogether.

Then nature combined with the Pope against me. A storm at sea, one of those sudden, violent aberrations of the Mediterranean, sank a number of badly needed supply ships, and food began to run short. Even an army dedicated to a Holy Cause does not function without the mess pot and the payroll, and I began to wonder if I ought to turn back before my army disintegrated before my eyes. But this act of nature was as nothing compared to the next foul blow against me: a Papal army, under the command of Jean and Walter de Brienne, invaded the Kingdom of Sicily. And Papal agents, Francescan monks, went up and down the Realm telling my people that I was dead.

I wept with rage and fury. I paced the floor during sleepless nights. Nevertheless, as I scribbled in a note to Piero (then at Acre): "I talk of agreements and of peace, while hastening preparations for my return. I conceal my consuming pain behind a cheerful countenance, so that the enemy may not triumph and rejoice. . . ."

At the darkest hour of one such haggard night, a woman was brought to me. I saw her veiled and in torchlight, but I sensed at once that she was Balian. The child, however, I noticed only on a second glance.

I held the boy up to the torchlight. He had an enchanting face—the face of Balian. I kissed him with delight. He smiled contentedly in my arms, and had no fear of me. "*Bel fanciullo!*" I exclaimed.

"I have named him *Federico*," Balian said timidly.

"Bravo!" I said. "We will call him Federico of Antioch. . . ." I put him down, but he clung to my hand.

"He is almost two, but small for his age," his mother said. An apology, a defensive note crept into her murmurous voice.

Then I noticed. He was lame in one leg.

My heart cringed. From Balian's perfect body, from our perfect union, had sprung a cripple. Of all my children (eventually at least fifteen), he was the only one born with a blemish. Had I thought like other men, I would have said this was a judgment of God against us; but I had observed too closely the lives of animals, and I knew that variants appeared among the most perfect strains. Somewhere, somewhere in the past, was a reason—but a reason I would never know.

Balian was waiting. From me she wanted consolation. "My love for the boy," I said, without direct allusion to hurt him, "is not the less but the more. He will compensate with his mind what his body lacks. And one day he will become equal to a king."

She was comforted, and flung herself into my arms.

Exhausted I was; nevertheless I was astonished at the vigor of my response. I was alive, virile, full of power. How could a man of such vitality even consider the word "defeat"?

II

It is commonly said among Christians that the Lord God moves in mysterious ways His wonders to perform. Indeed He does. Through the roly-poly Muslim body of my suave friend and al-Kamil's ambassador, Fakhr ad-Din, was one wonder performed; and through the lanky Frankish body of a Christian turned Muslim, was another.

One day when I was busily concealing the depths of my despair, Fakhr ad-Din came to me and suggested that the time might be ripe to send another embassy to his master the Sultan. This was, he said, purely a personal suggestion on his part. He knew what I did not: that a Hospitaler, convert to Mohammed, had married the boy an-Nasir's mother, and had taken up the defense of Damascus by an effective attack on al-Kamil's line of supply. The siege promised to drag on endlessly, with al-Kamil far from sure of success. The removal of the Christian crusaders from the Holy Land—by a negotiated peace—would free all his forces to deal with Damascus. This was a valid argument he could use with his compatriots who believed that only the sword could dislodge my army. I took ad-Din's hint, and dispatched envoys at once. Since new and impressive presents could not be obtained on the spur of the moment, I sent to al-Kamil a set of geometrical problems which I thought would tickle his intellect and delight his fancy. One, for example, was to construct a quadrilateral of the same superficial area as a segment of a given circle.

The Sultan was delighted. He sent back answers to a number of my problems at once, together with proposals for a ten-year truce between Christians and Muslims. The Christians were to receive Jerusalem, though it was not to be fortified. The Mosque of Omar, once the Temple of Solomon, was to remain in Muslim hands, but Christians were to be admitted to worship. The Christians were to receive Nazareth, but Muslims were to be admitted to Bethlehem, also a Mohammedan Holy Place. In addition, the Christians were to receive Sidon, Jaffa, Caesarea and Acre. Antioch, Tripoli, and some other towns were to be retained, but without military reinforcement. And finally, I must agree not to aid any Christians who might attack al-Kamil during the term of the truce.

All these were essentially the same points I had made in the beginning of the negotiations; and, as I told Fakhr ad-Din, I would never have demanded so much of al-Kamil had not my whole prestige in Christendom hung in the balance. Hermann von Salza was ecstatic, for the great aim of his life had been achieved, and Jerusalem was at last again in Christian hands. He skipped around my tent, forgetting his tired feet. He foresaw criticism, however, and wrote to the cardinals a letter of explanation, gently taking the Pope to task while pointing out that in Muslim lands Christians were generally free to practice their religion. But alas, my honest von Salza, of all the crusaders, was the only one to express approval.

All of the Pope's adherents were furious, and the Patriarch Gerold promptly reaffirmed the interdict against me, placing Jerusalem and even the burial place of Christ Himself—the Church of the Holy Sepulcher—under the ban. He sent a long document of half-truths to the Pope; and the Pope, adding his own touches, issued the letter in an effort to denigrate my achievement. It was evident, too, he said, that the Emperor "preferred Mohammed to Christ." Among the crusaders, the Templars were particularly angry that the Temple of Solomon remained in Muslim hands, and began a campaign of revilement while they plotted my life.

The Muslims were as angry at the Sultan al-Kamil as the Christians at me. Al-Kamil was attacked from all sides by the orthodox as having betrayed Mohammed, as having desecrated the Holy places of Islam by permitting the entrance of Christians (swine), as having formed a friendship with one of the "unclean" (me), and as preferring Christ to Mohammed. When a service of protest was held in the great mosque, he retaliated simply by confiscating its treasure (and the uproar abruptly died down —such was the Will of Allah). I sent my profound thanks to al-Kamil, and our friendship truly began. Without any objection from the Sultan, I made Fakhr ad-Din a knight, and vested in him the privilege of wearing the Imperial Eagle on his arms.

As for the general Muslim attitude toward me, this was quite another matter. They seemed torn between scorn and admiration—scorn because my physical appearance was so utterly different from their own, and admiration because I was the ruler of so great a domain with so many titles. Usually the Semitic face was swarthy, black-bearded, sharp-eyed and peaked with an aquiline nose. But, wrote an Arab chronicler, "The Emperor of the Franks, who comes from the Long Land, near Spain, is blond, beardless, short, myopic: were he a slave, he would not be worth two hundred dirham." In a state of profound religious shock, this highly orthodox writer continued: "It is evident from his discourses that the Emperor is a materialist who makes of Christianity simply a game." And another Muslim wrote: "Among the Christians, the King Emperor is a man of great power because he dares to challenge their Caliph, the Pope. No one in Europe has equaled him from the time of Alexander the Great until today."

Such is the mirror when one views oneself in foreign eyes.

Though the Pope's soldiers were pressing against my Realm, and I was most anxious to sail for Italy, that "Long Land," I decided to hold a coronation ceremony in the Church of the Holy Sepulcher—ignoring the interdict on Jerusalem. Since a coronation without a religious service was unthinkable, some of my hotheads (including Piero) advised a Holy Mass despite the ban. But both von Salza and Berardo united in urging otherwise, and declared for a ceremony without any religious note whatever. To my mind, one was hardly less provocative than the other; yet I had no wish deliberately to disturb pious souls who were more concerned with the spiritual than the political aspects of religion. So I thought of a way out.

The truce had been signed in mid-February, and a month later, at night, I was able to enter Jerusalem. Thanks to the efforts of von Salza and his German followers, the town was everywhere illuminated with oil lamps—and I recalled my triumphant progress down the Rhine when first I came to Germany. Now hosannas were sung and palm fronds waved, and some among my followers recalled another entry into Jerusalem by a Prince of Peace. The pilgrims who greeted me were truly filled with joy, for their cherished wish to worship at Christ's tomb was at last fulfilled. But the Muslims wailed and beat themselves in lamentation.

I entered the Church of the Holy Sepulcher dressed in majestic robes and followed in solemn procession by my adherents, all bearing tapers. Among them, only Berardo wore the miter of an Archbishop. Without blessing, without absolution, without Communion, without Holy Mass, I approached the high altar and took from it the crown of the Kingdom of Jerusalem. In a sepulchral silence, with my own hands I placed the crown upon my head. Then I turned to the assembly and addressed them in Latin; and Herman von Salza, in white surcoat marked with a black cross, translated each sentence into German and into French. Thus I began, listening to the solemn echo of my own words in three languages among the vaults:

> "LET all who are pure in heart rejoice and give thanks unto the Lord, who hath taken pleasure in His people as they praised the Emperor of Peace. Let us praise Him whom the angels praise. . . .
>
> "God, He is the Lord, and it is He alone who worketh great wonders. It is He who, mindful of His own mercy, renews in our day the marvels that He wrought of old. It is written that God, when He would make known His might, hath need neither of chariots nor of horses. . . . For in these last few days—more by the power of His wonders than by men's courage—He hath happily caused that work to be accomplished which, for long times past, many mighty princes with the multitudes of their peoples, have all essayed in vain. . . ."

So not from the Church, not from the Pope, but from God alone was derived the power to liberate Jerusalem—God, using His instrument, an Emperor of Peace. From God alone was derived the power of the Emperor, who ascribed to the glory of God the very works he himself had accomplished.

For those who had ears to hear, the implications were plain—and frightening. The very foundations of the temporal structure of the Roman Church were being demolished. Mine was a dangerous doctrine—dangerous in the extreme. Some called it heresy. . . .

But from heresy my thoughts turned to Balian, and I hastened from the church to be with her. I was staying in the house of the Qadi Shams ad-Din, a house not small, but in no sense a palace. I had brought Balian there secretly as part of my retinue, for I deplored every hour spent apart from her. When I returned from the high excitement of self-coronation, I went at once to Balian's chamber; this was to be another night of nights.

I found her sprawled on bloody cushions with a knife in her back, and the child Federico sobbing in the arms of his nurse.

Over the body I stood for a long time in a kind of paralysis, while gradually the shock receded and the ache seeped through to my numbed heart. The treasure I had stolen had been retrieved, and now to me was forever lost. My throat, like my eyes, was desert dry; I could neither sob nor talk nor hear. But at length, from the lisping child and the incoherent babbling of the nurse, I understood and pieced together the story.

Balian had been playing with Federico on the dais, her back to the open window. Out of the night, reflecting light from the hanging lamps, had come the flash of a dagger hurled through the air. Balian had screamed and crumpled; at the scream, the nurse had entered the room and run to the boy. That was the tale.

Count Walter de Brienne had been avenged.

Secretly Balian had come to me; secretly she must go. Without absolution, without Christian burial; but Berardo would pray for forgiveness of her sins. I myself withdrew the dagger, and called the Qadi.

"This slave, who attended me, has killed herself in an insane fit," I said, controlling the pain in my voice. "Bury her quickly, as you bury slaves."

The Qadi was most upset. "I am deeply grieved," he said, smoothing his hands on his *kaftan,* then clasping them again and again as if in prayer, "deeply distressed that your Serene Majesty should suffer such an inconvenience in my house. The matter will be attended to at once. Shall the slave's child be disposed of as well?"

"Leave the child with us," I said. "He is a sad little thing, a cripple; but we have affection for children, and will find him a home. . . ."

The dagger I kept; I have it to this day.

I gave instructions to my Saracens to guard Federico as they guarded me, on pain of their lives. I held him in my arms, soothing him, until he dropped exhausted into sleep. And at last, in repose on my own cushions, I controlled myself no longer, and wept as a child might weep. Yet more was signified by my tears: I was full to the teeth of this charade, this mummery, this jousting by unwashed priests and imams for a pile of old ruins and fantastic legends. Mohammed's flight from the Rock into Heaven . . . Christ risen from the dead . . . could such things be . . . ?

Bitterness overflowed within me: it was not the legends, but the perverters of the legends, who drove men to stupidity upon stupidity, madness, and death.

Would never be seen an end . . . ?

12

THAT NIGHT, as I lay awake and suffering, I heard no calls from the muezzin atop the minaret. With the morning light I summoned my host. "O Qadi," I said, "why have the muezzin not made the call to prayer according to their usual custom?"

He bowed repeatedly to the ground. "This humble slave," he replied, "has stopped them, out of regard and respect for your Majesty."

"You have made a mistake in acting thus," I said as gravely as if I had never heard the cry of a muezzin in my life. "Our major purpose in remaining in Jerusalem was to hear, during the night, the call to prayer of the muezzin and their praise of God. Would you alter your rites and your law and your faith merely to please me? When you come to my country, do you think I would silence the church bells to please you? By God—no!" Then I gave him a sum of money to send to the muezzin.

So overcome with self-blame and apology was the Qadi that I submitted patiently to the schedule he had arranged for me. It was better so, for I wanted no wondering talk about a too abrupt departure from Jerusalem, or conjecture on the hurried burial of a female slave.

It was a dreamlike tour of Muslim and Christian Holy Places—the holy causes of a holy war which already had lasted more than one hundred and thirty years. And now my truce, I thought, was but a puny interlude. . . . With Piero as my companion, I examined the Mosque of al-Aqsa. I admired the beauty of the prayer niche and the detail of the pulpit, which I ascended. I was impressed with the magnificence of the Sanctuary of the Sacred Rock, built on the site of the Temple of Solomon. It was an octagonal structure, with a lofty cupola of green and gold. Within were hundreds of hanging lamps on golden chains, lush carpets, brilliant mosaics. As we entered, like any Muslim worshiper I removed my shoes, and Piero followed my example. The Qadi glanced at me in astonishment, for he had not expected this of a Christian Emperor.

In the Sanctuary I noted an inscription which read: "Saladin cleansed Jerusalem of the Polytheists."

Said I, innocently, to the Qadi, "Who are these Polytheists?"

Once again he became flustered, and twitched from embarrassment. "I offer a thousand pardons to your Majesty," he cried, "but by *Polytheists* is meant the Christians, who worship, as you so well know, the Father, Son and Holy Ghost *and* a woman as well—Mary the mother of Jesus."

This last seemed to him incomprehensible, and he muttered something in an Arab dialect I did not understand.

The Sacred Rock itself was the slab of stone from which Mohammed was said to have taken flight into heaven. Aside from the imprint of the sacred feet, to my eyes it seemed a very ordinary rock. I was careful to maintain a solemn face, and my Muslim host seemed not dissatisfied that he had obeyed the Sultan and brought me here—an act without precedent and certain to be furiously condemned by the orthodox.

As we turned to leave, we were surprised by a priest clutching a scroll of the Gospels. Still shod in dusty sandals, he had forced his way into the very heart of the Sanctuary. Certain hours had been proclaimed when Christians might enter and pray, but not, of course upon the Sacred Rock. At the sight of the priest I lost control of myself and with a blow of my fist smashed him down.

"Pig!" I shouted. "Why are you here at this hour? The Sultan Malik al-Kamil has graciously given us permission to use these structures, but it is not a right to be abused. If one of you enters the Holy Place improperly, I will snatch out his eyes and flay him alive!"

Piero's face went white; he could not bear such scenes of violence. The priest, trembling with fear, picked himself up and fled. I stalked from the Sanctuary, still in a fury, while behind me followed the Qadi in respectful silence. By nightfall all Jerusalem would hear of the incident . . . but I did not care.

"Imperatore—perhaps the priest made an honest mistake?" Piero murmured in reproof. "It's always possible. . . ."

"Possible, but not probable," I snapped. "More likely the gesture was a considered provocation."

In a matter of hours I was to learn more of Christian intransigence. I had planned in advance to leave Jerusalem to bathe in the waters of the river Jordan, near the spot where Christ was said to have been baptized. At dawn, with deep breaths of relief, I left both the house of the Qadi and Jerusalem. O Jerusalem, of bitter memories, I thought; I would cleanse you, if I could, of both polytheists and monotheists, and leave you in peace. And somewhere in Jerusalem was another, a new, sepulcher—the unmarked grave of Balian. . . .

I pushed the horses to their utmost, for I sought release and forgetfulness in physical violence. It was easy to make speed, for I had with me only a handful of guards (we were in territory under Christian control)—all the rest of my company I had sent on to Acre, not wishing to talk with anyone, even Piero. Later I would recount these events, but just then I was unprepared for both the sympathy and the reproach I would see in his eyes—so sensitively was he attuned that, from Balian's absence and the child's presence, he guessed her dead. I was oppressed, too, by the barrenness of the countryside, and recalled how the Romans had made it bloom.

When at last, under a blue and cloudless sky, the ribbon of the Jordan came into view, winding along an escarpment toward the salt-laden waters of the Dead Sea, I shouted aloud. Within the hour, I had taken my ceremonial bath, attended only by Saracens, and gratefully relaxed a little in the rays of the hot spring sun. I dallied, remembering the swims of my boyhood with Muslims, naked all of us, and indistinguishable one from the other as children of God. Perhaps the basic error of all time was the moment man put on clothes . . . ?

Almost at the instant of that thought, my sense of majesty was put to its severest test. A band of Arab warriors appeared suddenly over an embankment, waving lances and spurring their horses so that their *kaffiyeh* flared out in the wind. We were outnumbered twenty to one; and I was—naked. I made no effort to be clothed in embarrassed haste, but unsheathed my sword and with my shield leaped upon a massive boulder which increased my height and served as a kind of throne. Half my guard, the archers, grouped around my feet, while the lancers vaulted into their saddles. What a sight I must have made—standing at bay on the rock, nude, bearing only shield and sword, the sunlight playing on my wind-blown long blond curls!

With a crested helmet, I might have been an ancient Greek, for in remote antiquity all Greek warriors fought nude—and why not I?

We were completely trapped. My heart pounded in anticipation of a violent end, but the Arabs stopped at a distance, and their leader called my name. It echoed curiously in the Jordan hills.

I raised my sword like a cross, and replied with a cadenced shout: "We are the Christian Emperor you seek! Approach in peace!"

They dismounted, dropped their lances, bowed, and advanced on foot. As their leader approached, he stared at me in amazement; but he was much too polite to comment (perhaps it was the custom of Christian Kings to go naked in the desert—how could he know?). They were, I think, far more impressed by my dignity in the nude than by any splendid robes I might have worn.

The leader made a deep obesiance. "We bring a letter from the mighty Sultan Malik al-Kamil."

From a pouch of camel-skin, inlaid with semiprecious stone, he produced a parchment case sealed with wax and bound with woven strands of gold. With my sword I slit it open.

Within was a brief personal note from al-Kamil:

> To the august Caesar, Roman Emperor Fridericus, King of Germania and Lombardia, Toscana and Italia, and Apulia and Calabria and Sicilia, King of Jerusalem, sustainer of the Roman Pontificate, and champion of the Christian faith: Greeting, and in the name of Allah, peace! The enclosed letter from the Christian Knights Templar will surely prove of interest to you; we ourselves are disgusted by such low treachery. We wish for you: good health, and the mercy and benediction of God. . . .

The enclosed letter was indeed of interest. My veins swelled and my fists clenched as I read it. It informed the Sultan where and when I would bathe in the Jordan, how many armed men were in my party, and what route I would take on leaving. It suggested that an ambush would be simple, and my capture or death might be accomplished with ease.

Ecco! Such was the chivalry of the Christian knights who swelled my ranks. For such crusaders I had won victories enough.

13

NEWS reaching me from Sicily became increasingly grievous. The Pope had released all my subjects from their oaths of fealty; many believed the rumors that I was dead. Jean de Brienne, in the Church's campaign to "liberate the oppressed," was pushing steadily southward with an army raised and paid for by the Pope—the first avowed "Soldiers of the Keys." And I, stranded in the Holy Land, was impotent. My galleys were being made ready at breakneck speed, but another month was needed—and in any case, to sail before the end of April when the spring tempests abated, was a hazard in itself.

I curbed my impatience as best I could. To alleviate my anxieties, and sorrow at the loss of Balian, I launched a campaign of minor activities. Every day a rabbi came to teach me Hebrew. Every day I had discussions with the Arab astrologers and philosophers. I studied Arabic architecture, with its rhythmical precision, and made excursions to examine the crusader castles, which seemed to have combined the most effective elements of Roman military architecture with certain features developed by the Arabs. I visited the castle of Baniyas, which stands on a brown deforested hill guarding the Syrian coast, the castle in the harbor of ancient Sidon, and the castles at Byblos and Tripoli. I journeyed inland to see the enormous castle, the *Krak des Chevaliers,* which guarded the desert flank and was certainly the most splendid of all the crusader fortifications. Without these castles, garrisoned by soldier-monks, the Christians would never for a moment have been able to maintain a foothold in this land.

I tired quickly of military architecture, however, for I was thoroughly sick of crusaders and all their works, and sought other diversions. I found the Arabic *harīm* not uncongenial, and certainly productive of a certain forgetfulness. I found myself reveling more than was usual with me; and more unusual still were the bevies of girls and boys I chose to play with. It was whispered among the monks, who licked their lips licentiously, that orgies went on day and night in my apartments, and I was said to have gone mad with lust. But I was neither so mad nor so enfeebled that I had not the strength to pursue my favorite sport of hawking almost every day.

I had noted, in spite of the serious deforestation, many birds I recognized—the black and white jay, starlings, cliff-living martins, ravens, sprightly desert chats, and falcons. The falcons trained in hunting were well trained, and I liked particularly the Arab method of temporarily blinding the birds with a cap, rather than seeling the eyes with thread. I ordered a large quantity of the falcon caps, and resolved to introduce their use in Europe. They were made of soft black leather, and, with a pompom on the top, looked not unlike a priest's *biretta.* Some I had tooled with intricate designs in red and blue and gold; these I intended to send as gifts to other falcon fanciers. I made a collection of the finest falcons, sent half to al-Kamil, and saved half to take home.

But for once, even hawking bored me. I yearned for some other excitement—something more unusual than hunting, something more bizarre than amorous orgies with youths and maidens. I found it in the "Assassins," when I made a visit to the "Old Man of the Mountain" on a lofty crag. Hassan i Sabbah, the "Old Man," was the leader of a sect so fanatical that I was reluctant to credit its existence until with my own eyes I saw its followers. These were the hashish eaters, the Assassins. (The Latin *assassinus* is derived from the Arabic *hashshāshīn.*) Their daggers had let out the life of more than one leading crusader, for they were dedicated to killing for Islam. Their fame had spread far and wide, and the fear of them was equally extensive.

In visiting the Assassins some risk was involved, for even the Sultan could not guarantee a safe conduct. When my desire became known, word came to me that Hassan i Sabbah would welcome me as a guest and would send a guide in whom I could have confidence. Exhilarated at the prospect of an adventure, I took only my elite guard for protection and Piero for a companion. I was pleased that he seemed as excited as I—for I had been so involved with Fakhr ad-Din and Balian that I had seen little of Piero of late, and I sensed a hidden resentment.

We were comrades in arms once more, engaged in a mutual sharing—as so often in composing poems or writing the documents of state. In fact, this was becoming a pattern between us: after diversion, reconciliation. With Piero I was constant in my inconstancy; but about his private life he never spoke—so it was easy to forgive one another. I took it for granted that I could do as I liked.

To reach the aerie of the Old Man we crossed a repellent desert strewn with black stones small and large, many grotesque in shape. Here and there were clefts and valleys, covered in the bottoms with masses of bright red poppies, or dotted with scraggly sheep led by Arab shepherds swathed to the eyes in woolen robes. Twice we saw Bedouin tents, clinging to the earth like long black caterpillars. Then from a rift the path led upward into mountains barren of all life, except conies and occasional gazelles, where lions once roamed. Long, long ago, said the guide, these mountains had been covered by gigantic cedars, and he quoted King Solomon: "Now therefore, command them that they hew me cedar trees out of Lebanon." But I found more interesting the guide's remark that the farthest reaches of the mountains were inhabited by a group of Christians, called Maronites, who supported mixed monasteries of monks and nuns. Long since they had been cast out of the Roman Church as heretics—not for mixing, but for believing in the single nature of Christ. To the guide, they—like all Christians—were merely eccentrics.

The Old Man inhabited a stone tower on the top of a mountain, bounded on one side by a chasm. The vast view was one of undulating mountain tops, of sunlight and shadow like gigantic brown waves, but more desolate than the sea because the only motion was derived from wind-blown shrubbery and cloud. The Old Man himself was not at all what I had expected. He was slight, bird-boned, nervous—but sharp-nosed, hard, and tough. His thin black beard made his cheeks seem blue, and he scratched continually the backs of his hands. His only distinction in dress was his *argal*. This rope, bound around the head to hold the *kaffiyeh*, is normally woven of camel's hair; but his was woven of gold.

He welcomed us with bows, salutations, and many a *salām*, bowing low, with his left hand on his heart and his right hand on his forehead. He asserted repeatedly the great recognition we had brought him by our visit. In our honor he gave a banquet, offering bowls heaped with rice, mutton, varied cakes and patties, and a pistachio paste formed in the shape of antelope's horns. The food was held and eaten with a thin paper-like bread. The Old Man was surrounded with a bevy of his young men, the Assassins; they were all physically superb specimens, with nothing vicious in their faces to mark them as killers. Rather, I noted a vagueness in their eyes and an air of unreality about their movements. This pricked my curiosity.

The answer was provided by the Old Man himself. The next day, after we had rested, Hassan i Sabbah took us through a secret tunnel in the rock, which opened after some distance into a narrow ravine. We followed a tortuous trail until, suddenly, through a slit in the walls of the gorge, we saw a flowering sunlit valley. It was, the Old Man said, rather like a Petra in miniature; in the center was a small but elegant palace with two beautiful round towers guarding the entrance.

"This palace," said the Old Man, smirking and speaking in Latin, "is our facsimile of Paradise."

We entered through a side door, not the main gate, and climbed a short stairway to a balcony completely hidden by elaborate stone grillwork. Below was a central courtyard girded by a colonnade rich in Arabic mosaics. It was a lush oasis. Flowers bloomed; birds sang among palm trees; fountains splashed precious water into the air; and two fountains—reminiscent in design of Palermo—trickled goat's milk in thin streams down exquisite mosaic ramps. All about were silver pitchers at the fountains and golden bowls of honey.

In this setting, a group of young Assassins lounged on over-sized cushions, dressed in elegant robes of the finest materials. They were attended by *hauris* (the women of Paradise) whose bodies were concealed only by thin veils, by handsome nearly naked boys (the Arabs seem almost as fond of boys as of women), and by many obedient slaves.

Thus literally was the Koran's promise of Paradise fulfilled.

The Old Man's explanation was very simple. The future Assassins were carefully selected at an early age, and brought up by him on a frugal military discipline while being drilled in the Koran. With discreet quantities of hashish they were taught to have no fear. Just before their services were needed as killers, they were heavily drugged with hashish and finally awakened in "Paradise." All to them seemed like an ecstatic, erotic dream, and they indulged themselves to the utmost. Then more hashish, and the cruel awakening in the Old Man's barren tower. They were told that with their own deaths they would recline forever in another such Paradise. So believing, they followed implicitly the directives of the Old Man.

When we returned to the tower, the Old Man ordered two of his young men to climb to the top. Then, at a given signal, they plunged into the chasm—so eager were they to attain Paradise. Piero was sickened; I was intrigued. It was an impressive and astonishing demonstration of the way men could be trained (as we trained falcons) to behave against their own interests. But surely the obverse might be true . . . someday . . . ?

With gifts of hashish and jeweled Assassins' daggers, we parted from the Old Man of the Mountain. Thoughtfully and somewhat sadly we made our way over the desolate purple-brown landscape to the coast. At first sight of the sea, my mood changed. I was as eager to attain Sicily as the Assassin Paradise. Yet I was hardly prepared for the Christian Hell awaiting me.

14

In my absence, the Patriarch Gerold had managed to stir up a sizable proportion of the crusaders against me. It was being said that I had enlisted the Assassins to dispose of my enemies; so that all tepid crusaders who felt guilt also felt fear, and immediately turned against me. Many were angry because a truce meant no plunder. Further, the Patriarch had the audacity to recruit troops in the Kingdom of Jerusalem—against whom? Not the Muslims, but against the Christian Emperor!

Like a true eagle, I swooped. I confined to quarters, under guard, Gerold and all his supporters—the Templars and their leaders—and a number of monks who had denounced me from the pulpit (these last for their own safety, for my supporters in their congregations had beaten them and threatened worse). I cut off my enemies' supplies and let them pray for manna. I was pleased to note the good Lord God made no response to their prayers.

The Patriarch's reaction was to reiterate my excommunication and place all Acre under the ban. It mattered little. In a few days, on the first of May, I sailed. We embarked at dawn, and as the galleys cast off we were pelted from the shore with stones and filth—Gerold's proponents, who then raised their voices in a Te Deum. I was thankful when I could no longer hear the notes over the widening gap of water. Some of my hotheads wished to shower them with arrows. . . .

I had the sleekest, fastest galley, manned by a hundred oarsmen. To the slaves I promised freedom and to the sailors special rewards for a swift journey. Quickly we outdistanced the other ships of my fleet, and with the first light on the tenth of June I saw the long flat coastline of Apulia, with the hazy blue rampart of the mountains far behind. It was another longed-for homecoming, and my heart leaped. I would be, forever, a child of Sicily, the boy of Apulia. To von Salza I remarked: "Had Jehovah ever seen the island of Sicily or Apulia, never would He have called Palestine the Promised Land!" But von Salza was shocked by what he thought was blasphemy.

It was difficult to believe that my own ports might now be closed against me. I had been informed that Jean de Brienne had given secret orders to Papal agents to take me prisoner at the moment of landing; but it occurred to me they would be watching for a fleet, not for a single galley. Accordingly, the Imperial flags were furled and an ensign of the Teutonic Knights substituted.

We put into Brindisi without incident, and garbed as an ordinary knight, I went ashore. Not until we reached the castle and security did I declare myself. The news of my arrival sped with the speed of falcon flight, but many refused to believe its truth. Back to the streets I went on horseback, clad now in splendid armor and wearing no helm but a crown. At once I was recognized, and the people screamed with joy. Indeed it was almost as if I had risen from the dead, for loudest of all were the shouts of "Saviour, Saviour . . . !" Yes, from the clutches of a Vicar of Christ they cried for me to save them.

With the Vicar of Christ I now launched into verbal battle. He had called for all the princes of Europe to rise in a campaign against me, "the Emperor who has betrayed Christianity." In Germany he had gone so far as to set up a pretender to the Empire, a Welf; but his efforts were without success. Only in Lombardy did his appeals fall on willing ears, and Gregory found himself in the curious position of recruiting heretics for a Papal army. I repeated my charge that "the Pope has used sanctified money, subscribed for the Crusade, for the purpose of harrassing us." The world was now treated to the astounding spectacle of a Christian army, commanded by the Pope, killing the Christian soldiers of a Christian Emperor who had just returned from liberating Jerusalem from the Infidel.

My success, in spite of the Pope's thunders against me, had made a profound impression throughout Europe. No one could dispute the fact that Christian pilgrims could now visit the most holy of all Christian sanctuaries, and all Europe was deeply moved and grateful. It was common talk that the Pope's obstinacy was an evil thing. "The Pope's head is ailing," people said; or, "the Pope seems to be possessed by a Devil"; and, "Christians will suffer from the deeds of this Pope until the Judgment Day." Conscious of such unrest, I issued a manifesto (penned by Piero) announcing my return and appealing for peace. To the Pope I sent, in haste, a special embassy. It was ignored.

Once again, with open talons, I swooped. I exhorted all towns resisting the Papal armies to hold out—soon I would come to their rescue. Within the Realm, those who had sought elevation by treachery, I elevated on gallows of extra height. Those who had proved loyal (and Manfredo Lancia was among the most steadfast), I rewarded with new honors. I appealed to the people to come to my aid, and almost overnight I found nobles and commoners flocking to my standard. From my all-Saracen town, Lucera, I drew a corps of lancers and archers. From German crusaders homeward bound I drew a contingent of fully armed knights. I sent trumpeters and criers to announce far and wide that I rode in person at the head of my forces. At the end of August I marched toward Capua against the Soldiers of the Keys.

Then occurred an extraordinary thing—as some said, "a miracle." The Pope's army melted. They were afraid of my very name. With hardly a show of resistance, they ran for the border; but when they resisted, I was merciless. Let Gregory test the loyalty of his mercenaries, I said; even seizure of the Church treasures of San Germano by the Papal Legate to pay his troops did nothing to stem their rout. Within two days I was in full possession of Capua. Jean de Brienne escaped to Rome; Count Walter had disappeared. The invasion was over.

With banners flying and to the thump-thump of drums I marched northward, and the news threw the Curia into panic. At the river Garigliano, the border of the Papal states, I stopped. It was the Pope who was an aggressor, not I.

The military campaign of General Gregory was a defeat, a disaster, a debacle. Yet Pope Gregory insisted that I, not he, should sue for peace. So I, the victor, begged Gregory, the loser, for peace. Such was the chilling power of the Papacy; such was the strength of the Church; such was the blight of excommunication unabsolved. Peace was a necessity for us both; but Gregory shut himself up and hardly deigned to talk to my ambassadors. For one entire year I negotiated patiently with this man, sending alternately von Salza, Berardo, Pier della Vigna. At last, yielding to pressure within the College of Cardinals, the Pope made known his demands. They were staggering in their audacity.

I was contrite, humble, penitent. It was not I who was responsible for dissension within the Church, for I gave way on every point (though in fact I gagged almost to death). I declared an amnesty for all who had supported the Pope, I restored all confiscated Church property (including even the Templars), I gave the Pope a free hand in all episcopal appointments, I exempted the clergy from secular law and from taxes. But—all these provisions were to be annulled in the event of war. This was my way of saying to the Pope that he had best keep his strange bedfellows, the Lombard League, at peace. On the success of my campaign against the Pope's army, the Lombard towns, with enthusiasm, had declared themselves loyal to the Empire. It was my hope that their loyalty would remain well burnished—that they would leave me at peace. It was, alas, too much to hope.

I wrote to al-Kamil frequently, explaining the intricacies of my position, that he might be well informed vis-á-vis developments in the Holy See and any future Crusade—for already the fire eaters were preaching against my truce. Whatever his religion, he was a kindred spirit; we talked the same language, not Latin, not Arabic, but the language of brothers. This was, I thought, a very Christian thing, but the Vicar of Christ bitterly held the letters against me.

During the campaign I had cherished the hope that I might lay hands on Jean de Brienne and his son Count Walter. I wanted to give those red beards a twirk! Not only was this pleasure denied me, but I was placed in the difficult position of welcoming Jean to the ranks of emperors—something I certainly did not enjoy. With the Holy Father in the usual role of marriage broker, Jean managed to palm off one of his daughters on the child Baldwin II, Emperor of Constantinople—also adroitly acquiring for himself the title of Emperor. The title (he wrote in the contract) was to be retained until his death. He must have believed firmly that happy is the head which wears a crown. But, in truth, he was a better acrobat than king. As for Count Walter—he fled to France and became a mercenary at the royal court, where eventually he attached himself to Charles, Count of Anjou, the rapacious and bigoted younger brother of Louis IX. Word came to me more than once that Walter had sworn publicly to settle a score with me. Since the past had buried its dead, I decided to await his pleasure.

At length the Pope grudgingly acceded to my request to lift the ban of excommunication. Not in the basilica of San Pietro but in the little chapel of Santa Giusta in Ceprano, in the presence of various dignitaries, he solemnly revoked the interdict. Joyful news to me, joyful news to Christendom, for it meant that peace had been sealed between Emperor and Pope and all men could draw breaths of relief. My mind leaped to the pious works ahead.

A few days later I rode to see the Pope in his own town of Anagni, where he was staying. Scrupulously I encamped my guard outside the moldy gray walls and entered the town with but one man—Hermann von Salza. The three of us dined together in private: I, on my best behavior; von Salza, in ecstasy at having achieved the highest aim of his life—the reuniting of Emperor and Pope; and Pope Gregory, now at eighty-three not a drop mellower than when I had taken the Cross from his mottled hand in Rome, chewing still on the cud of his anger against me. He was, I think, in spite of his age and his anger a little awed at my presence, for he came of the lesser nobility; not every country palazzo could write on its walls that an Emperor had dined there. No doubt in Rome he would have felt otherwise.

Our dinner was a great success. It ended in perfect accord because I challenged nothing the Pope chose to say. It was interesting to note, too, that of the three of us, Hermann von Salza was by far the most voluble—a big man chattering like a child. And since he was a man who preserved his silences, he must have felt that he was making a sacrificial plunge into a void. I was grateful to him—for the less I said, the less I was accountable.

So it came to pass that, filled with good viands and good wine, the old Pope placed an arm about my shoulders and led me to a balcony. There, before the cheering crowd below, the man who had but lately scorched me with his own fiery breath —calling me a "reptile," a "basilisk," and a "parricide"—now blessed me and called me "the most beloved son of the Church."

Then he drew me close, and before the eyes of the world, loudly implanted the Kiss of Peace.

IV

STUPOR MUNDI

I

ON A SUN-BRILLIANT May morning, my vanguard of Saracen lancers, wearing turbans and flowing trousers, rode their Arabian horses briskly up the long, wide ramp which led to the old Norman castle at Melfi. They were followed by a procession of beasts slowly mounting the ramp.

An elephant led, bearing on its back a tower with the mahout and two Saracen trumpeters. No one was certain that the drawbridge over the moat was strong enough to support the elephant; and the entrance gates, flanked by two polygonal stone towers, seemed too small to permit entrance of the giraffe—an animal then unknown in Europe. The camels, bearing curtained palanquins wherein rode Arab dancing girls, tended to balk at the ascent. The guards, giant halfnude eunuchs carrying scimitars, prodded the camels and cursed in their own mysterious tongues. Only the cheetahs and leopards, despite their chains, moved effortlessly. The bears grumbled to their keepers. The apes scolded like fishwives. African ostriches fluttered their wings. The acrobats and conjurers, further to impress the amazed and gaping townsfolk, did cartwheels and tricks, while the dwarfs scurried in and out. Then falconers in multi-colored stripes, with their birds, and masters of the hounds with their dogs. The dusty air reeked of horse sweat, camel piss, and elephant dung—so that the court, as always, found it expedient to travel a little behind.

Shortly came trumpeters on horseback, blowing flourishes, and crying aloud that the Emperor was about to pass. Next another band of Saracens, archers bearing the eastern short bow, which is almost like the figure 3, painted in gaudy colors. Then knights, carrying the Emperor's standard—the Imperial Eagle—and banners. And at last, the court itself, following a horse's length or two behind the Emperor and his chosen companions. Finally, a rearguard of lancers, protecting the baggage train of horses, carts, and asini—for with every movement of the court went tents, clothing, arms, traveling equipment; and also current records of the judiciary, the treasury, the chancery, and necessary supplies; and treasure of gold, silver, jewels, and purple cloth; and, invariably, a library of hundreds of books. It was not surprising that people came from far afield to view the Imperial train.

The court itself was no mean sight. Usually I chose to ride my spirited black stallion, "Dragone," who pranced and snorted and whistled and never seemed to tire. For convenience in traveling, I often wore the short green tunic and hose of a huntsman; but others, even on the march, preferred finery (and Piero was one of these). The courtiers were clothed in capes and hose of clear bright reds and blues and yellows, in feathered caps or shining helmets, and soft leather boots. The young pages, white or black (I did not discriminate), wore tunics cut higher than their buttocks and genitals, long tights often with each leg of a different color, hair bobbed short, and caps with visors rolled into a point. My scholars dressed in academic caps and gowns. The clerics traveled in robes of black or brown, wide flat hats, and wore crucifix or ring to mark their rank. Women wore subdued colors, long sweeping gowns over an inner dress, long sleeves, veils and hoods; they rode side-saddle or were borne in litters. Small children (among them my own) were cared for by nurses in wagons; others rode ponies or mares not in heat (Enzo was already big enough to ride an Arab stallion). The astrologers and wizards wore capes marked with the signs of the zodiac, and peaked hats painted with magic symbols. The jesters' uniform was motley and bells—though I rarely found their antics amusing, I kept fools for the entertainment of others. Since I particularly enjoyed music, I organized a band of young *servitelli negri* to blow silver trumpets; I dressed them richly and all alike.

The new palace at Foggia, with its gardens and fountains and pools and marbles and sculptures, was unfinished. The castle at Melfi I had already extended and refurbished. I had chosen to move on to Melfi because of its central location and coolness in summer. I was preparing to issue a complete new codification of laws on the model of Justinian—the first since ancient times. It would, I hoped, mark a date in history. The compilation, under the direction of Pier della Vigna, was not yet completed, but its contents already had leaked to the Pope, so publication was planned for August. I had summoned a great gathering at Melfi of officials from all parts of the Realm—a show of strength to offset papal truculence.

For almost a year I had been continually in the saddle. I had made a circuit of the Realm, visiting the royal estates, overseeing excavation of antiquities, and repairing or constructing new fortresses. High in the mountains at Castrogiovanni, near the center of Sicily, I built a castle as a retreat in case of future invasions. At two of the most important towns, Catania and Siracusa, I built fortresses anew. I had evolved a standard plan which yielded little to ground sites: a rectangle or square, cornered with square or round towers—the whole built of smooth close-fitting stone. Surveillance and defense of such a construction was easy. All, incidentally, without chapels and with plumbing.

Only in ornamentation did I veer from functional simplicity. For example, at the Castello Maniace in Siracusa, I placed two handsome bronze rams over the entrance. They were ancient Greek castings. In Lucera, I finally finished the massive fortress which dominated the Adriatic coast, decorated it with ancient marbles, and garrisoned it with my Saracens. At Capua, I thought to build a great gate to the bridge over the Volturno River, as a symbol of the difference between the realm of the Church and my own Realm. My gate—on the ancient Via Appia—would be of purest white marble. It would be embellished with human likenesses, both antique and so recent that my own and Pier della Vigna's would be included. Over the gate itself would be carved: ENTER WITH CONFIDENCE ALL YE WHO COME WITHOUT AGGRESSION. And under my statue would be carved: IN WRATH WILL I DESTROY THE MAN WHO PROVES FAITHLESS. Nowhere would be cross or crucifix. It would be, I thought, a triumphal arch—celebrating the triumph of the Kingdom of Man.

From the peace which now reigned over all the land, I had derived a new infusion of creative force for useful works. All our enterprises seemed to blossom and bear fruit. I felt an exhilaration such as I had not experienced since I first flexed my wits as a boy-king in Palermo. A sense of continual excitement overhung the court. Debates raged. Activity was intense. Day and night, messengers arrived and departed. Lawyers, jurists, scholars, architects, engineers, philosophers, doctors, sculptors, poets, astrologers, Cistercian monks (those experts in agriculture) sought consultation or assignment. Because the clergy was rarely invited or included, priests hinted darkly that I planned to overturn the world. But of this I was heedless; I was the new luminary around whom new constellations were to revolve in harmony. We would not, with our wonder-working, overturn the world; but we would, if we could, fashion much of it anew. If I seemed to be driven by a frenzy, there was a reason: how long might the tenuous peace endure? I dared not waste a day or an hour or a minute of this so precious time.

Happily, the coming summer months at Melfi were to be of a richness and texture which I could not possibly have imagined, even in my dreams—because, for once, the reality surpassed the dreams. I gulped down life as if famished. I was in my mid-thirties; though my strength was the strength of youth, my body had reached a perfect mastery of itself, a peak of virility and vigor. My energy was inexhaustible; at the end of each day I turned enthusiastically to fresh diversions in the night. Conversation, song, dalliance.

Sex I had in plenty, of all varieties. Two more daughters, Blanche (by a French woman), and Caterina (by a Sicilian) were sired by me. Three or four of the dancing girls became my favorites; garbed only in paint and jewels, their private performances were not untouched by the ancient frenzy of maenads. And by two Moorish page boys, Marzukh and Muska, I was amused in the eastern manner. But in this period my chief affection (aside from Piero) centered on one Johannes Marus, a boy of about fifteen. He was the son of an Ethiopian slave woman, father unknown. He had come to my attention before the Crusade, when I had noticed his extraordinary quickness of intellect. I had ordered his education, and I returned to find that my efforts had not been wasted. At once I made him a page at court, and then guardian of my bedchamber.

Piero, I found, reacted to my attentions to Johannes with a touch of ill grace. It was not, actually, that he felt he was being supplanted in my affections by this boy, or that he considered Johannes any threat to his official position. True, the boy was handsome, warm and affectionate, and certainly with his intelligence and education was likely to rise high in the world. (He was, after all, only repeating on a lower level the remarkable accomplishments of Piero himself.) Rather, Piero seemed to feel that it was he who possessed me, and he would share me with no one. I do not mean physically; from the first day of our relationship Piero fully understood that I indulged myself sexually when and where and how I liked. He wished no intrusion on our rapport, nor did he wish anyone else to become equally valuable to me. But I simply could not see our relationship with his eyes; I saw it only with mine.

Just at the time I announced the appointment of Johannes as guardian of my bedchamber, Piero became ill. I greatly missed his presence in the chancery, his advice on judicial matters, his adroit pen, his conversation when we relaxed at meals or in the evenings with lute or viol. I had not, in truth, fully realized the extent of his participation in my official and nonofficial life until he was so abruptly removed.

With anxiety over his health, I called to see him in his chambers; I found him lying in bed, moodily reading, by a smoky candle, the orations of Cicero. "*Allora*, dear Piero—what ails you?" I said, permitting all my concern to burden my voice.

He shrugged. "Nothing in particular, Imperatore. I suffer chiefly from a general malaise. I ache everywhere and my spirits fail me."

"You work too hard without rest or relaxation. Look—why this heavy stuff, *Cicero's Orations*, when you are sick? Why not Catullus? You need a little cheer!"

"I read Cicero because I endeavor to improve my Latin style," he said quietly. "For you, dear Federico, the best is not good enough—"

"I am touched, Piero, by your devotion," I said, "but I am not a demon to consume you wholly. You need a life apart from your work and me. Sometimes I think you are a monk at heart, for all your love of elegance. Never do I see you with girl or boy. Why, how long has it been since you warmed these bedsheets with some body other than your own? Come now, a confession!"

He stared into his *Cicero* with obvious embarrassment. "Some months, perhaps—I do not make attachments with much ease."

"Attachments! To play with a boy or a dancing girl, your souls must first be *simpatico!* Piero! In spite of the closeness of our association, and the unnumbered hours we spend together, I do believe you are lonely. For your ailment you have need of a wife. And what could be easier to arrange—why not one of those pretty and agreeable girls from the Aquino family? You have but to say the word. . . ."

Suddenly he became very formal. "My Lord," he said stiffly, "you forget that I am not of noble blood."

"Oh, come come! If you like, I will give you a title—make you a duke—"

He frowned. "A title would resolve nothing. My Lordship would only be mocked behind my back by those who are born with a *stemma*."

"You are so difficult! Madonna! Then why not a good-looking girl who is frisky in bed and will bear you a whole litter of puppies?"

"In my present position," he said sternly, "to marry a woman not noble would be out of the question. I could not bear the insulting and satirical remarks which would be openly heaped upon her!"

"You are only saying, my dear Piero, that you do not wish to marry. Very well—but don't brood. Have at least a little pleasure! Indeed I love you, but I cannot confine my affections solely to your bed. You will, I fear, waste the capacity God has given you—when your bird wants to fly, let it go. Someday it will be too old to take wing. . . ."

He flushed. "My Lord Federico—I wait only for a falcon!"

Though I treasured the intensity of his love and loyalty, I felt anger with him for his obdurate loneliness, which I could not understand. I had no hesitation whatever in going straight from his bedside to another's arms; and the boyish vigor of Johannes made it easy to forget the querulous possessiveness in Piero's voice.

But if everyone at court took it for granted that I should amuse myself as I saw fit, the Pope did not. News of my appointment of Johannes came at once to Gregory's ears. Thereupon he took it upon himself not only to protest the youthfulness of pages at my court, but to condemn my behavior as "scarcely veiled sodomy." I wrathfully dismissed his charges as unwarranted interference in my affairs, and advised him to look to his own acolytes. He would have been less crude (and more accurate) had he used the term παιδεραστής—in the ancient Greek sense of lover of youth.

As for Johannes, however deep or prolonged was such an affection, it could not properly—for me at least—be called love. I felt the lack of one thing only: not a wife, but the love of a woman I myself could love.

For, alas, even an Emperor cannot command love.

2

IN THESE DAYS a man came to court wearing an iron hat. The hat was not a helmet, but truly a hat, with crown and brim, crudely made of iron. When queried, the man said that he had predicted his own death from a falling stone, and he wore the hat as a precaution while traveling. His name, he said, was Michael the Scott, and he bore letters of introduction from the University of Bologna to the Emperor. When he spoke his name, many people in the castle trembled with fear, and he was announced to me at once.

I received him in a small audience chamber off the great Hall of the Three Domes. I was well aware of his work, and I wished to talk with him privately before loosing him on the court. He had, I found, removed the iron hat, though he carried it in his hand as he bowed. He was a man of about fifty, totally white of hair and grizzled beard, and, though wrinkled, very ruddy and fresh in complexion. His eyes were lively, curious, mischievous—his own twinkling stars in a blue firmament, for he was far-famed as astrologer and wizard.

"Milord, I bring you good augury," he said, his Latin marred by a burr in certain sounds. "The stars say the times are propitious for any works you undertake. Just last night I had a bit of a look at your horoscope, your Majesty, and you've great victories ahead. But while the number three and its combinations bring great good fortune to most men, your Highness should beware of the number nine—nine could prove very dangerous for you. This is but a feeble warning from your most humble servant, Michael the Scott."

He was referring, of course, to Innocent III and Gregory IX. I smiled a bitter smile at the inference. "Today we are innocent of all concern about the number three," I said, "and the number nine is troublesome only when the monks sing the Gregorian chant. We prefer to contemplate the beauty of the number 100, which is perfect according to our understanding, and represents Heaven."

"It is said that Milord the Emperor wishes to bring Heaven to earth, with peace and justice. But let the Emperor not forget that 100 is perfect only because it is the square of ten—and ten itself the perfect number because it represents the square of the Trinity plus one: the Unity of God. Therefore let the Emperor beware the number nine—for should nine unite with one, ten is the product. This, Milford, is a simple problem fraught with gravest consequences. Let the Emperor ponder the matter. . . ."

"Ponder it we shall," I said, "but with, we hope, aid and comfort from yourself, most learned doctor. We know you not for astrology but for your excellent translation of Aristotle's *De Caelo* and *De Anima*, with the commentary of Averroes. Why not let the stars rest in their accustomed orbits and continue this great work? We offer you the title and the post of Philosopher of the Court—does this please you?"

"O Milord, it pleases me mightily!" he cried. "I would continue the labor I began when I studied in Toledo—translations of Aristotle's zoological works, those assembled by Avicenna and called the *Liber Animalium*. How willingly would I dedicate these volumes to your serene and glorious Highness!"

"For such a dedication, we would be very grateful," I answered, "indeed, nothing could please us more. We would distribute copies to various universities, and thus introduce the thoughts of the great Greek philosopher to all Europe. Under the third Innocent, this was a project fraught with peril, for the works were banned; but the ninth Gregory cannot now prevent us from carrying out this purpose. So Maestro Michael—on with your work! You will find at our court all that you need for the good life—both of body and of mind. We will, when we have leisure, summon you frequently; but be not perturbed. You are to speak your thoughts as you think them, beholden to none, pleasing or unpleasing. And write them, too—for your pen must be as free as your tongue.

"If you wish—on the side—to continue the work of a wizard, we will not object. We are not averse to frightening our enemies a little! We know how men shudder at the very mention of your magic: it is said that you have read the forbidden *Liber Auguriorum* and know the names and hiding-places of all the demons. But we ourselves are more interested in the secrets of nature than in the secrets of magic—so look you to this! We are aware of the enormous resources of your knowledge. We would ply you with certain questions we have prepared about the structure of the earth—for we are sick to death of such current nonsense as the solemn debate on whether the toothless will grow teeth and the bald grow hair upon the day of Resurrection! We have heard nothing of those secrets which delight the mind truly wedded to wisdom—about Purgatory, Hell, the foundations and the wonders of the world. So, learned doctor, we shall beg of you the explanations."

Michael the Scott tucked the iron hat right under one arm and bowed low once more. "I am most greatly flattered by your revered Highness," he said, "for you yourself are well known to all men as a wonder of the world—some call you *Stupor Mundi*. My slender resources are at your disposal. You have judged me right, for I am chiefly a scholar at heart. Though as a wizard I advise you to consult a wise man only during a waxing moon, as a scholar I advise you to consult him whenever he may be at hand. But let us note that just now the moon is waxing; and if you think me wise, I shall do my utmost to justify your faith—for the times are propitious."

"Let us hope that the wizard will prove a wise man," I said, "and the wise man a wizard. For in truth we have need of both wizardry and wisdom!"

Thus we began with mutual respect.

Here is a transcript of the questions I put to him—in secret, because of their dangerous nature:

How is the earth fastened above the abyss of space? And how is this abyss fastened beneath the earth?

What else beside air and water might bear the earth? Or does the earth stand firm of itself? Or does it rest on the heavens below it?

How many heavens exist, who governs them, and who inhabits them?

How far distant is one heaven from another by our measure? Is one larger than another?

If many heavens exist, what fills the space beyond the last?

In which heaven is God Substance—that is, His divine majesty; and in what manner does He sit upon the throne of Heaven; and how is He accompanied by the angels and the saints?

And what do the angels and the saints do unceasingly in the presence of God?

In addition tell us: How many hells are there? Who are the spirits dwelling therein and what are their names?

Where is Hell? And where is Purgatory?

And where is the heavenly Paradise? Under or over the earth, or in the earth?

What is the difference between the souls which go to Hell, and the spirits said to have fallen from Heaven?

Hell has how many torments?

Does one soul know another in the next life? Can a soul return to this life or reveal itself to anyone?

And what of this: when the soul of a living man passes over into that other life, can nothing give it power to return—neither first love nor even hate? Or does the soul care nothing for what is left behind, whether the soul was blessed or damned . . . ?"

In spite of the seriousness (and apostasy) of these questions, I could not resist teasing Michael the wizard and astrologer, trying to show him up as a charlatan and fake—yet all the while praising to the very skies his scholarship, for he had made a brilliant record at the universities of Oxford and Paris. Indeed, as he wandered from land to land he had for a long time lived off his predictions and horoscopes, for these things were potboilers—and who was at hand to pay for philosophy or science? He had become so accustomed to using his magic wand that he could not leave off. I gave a banquet to introduce him to his colleagues at court, and thereupon played him a trick.

My scholars were serious and skeptical men, most of whom placed little faith in necromancy. I was curious to see whether, in their company, my wizard Michael would take a new tack. Though his face was grave, his eyes never lost that mischievous sparkle as one by one he greeted the wise men of my court. Chief among them were these: the Arab al-Hanifi, distinguished mathematician and astronomer, sent me by the Sultan al-Kamil; Maestro Teodoro, of Antioch, who had studied at Mosul and Baghdad, charted the heavens, translated the *Secretum Secretorum*, and could concoct a most exotic violet sweetmeat (I ordered some for Pier della Vigna when he was ill); Juda ben Salomon Cohen, a very young man who already had produced an encyclopedia of the works of Aristotle, Euclid, Ptolemy, and Alpetronius; Jacob ben Abbamari, who had translated not only much of Aristotle's *Logic* into Latin, but several important works into Hebrew, including the *Elements of Astronomy* of al-Fargani; Moses ben Salomon of Salerno, who had written learnedly on the *Guide for the Perplexed* by Maimonides; Petrus Hispanus, who compiled a long treatise on hygiene; and finally, Peter of Ireland, who was so famed in logic and mathematics that I had imported him at great expense to teach at my University of Napoli. At table they were an impressive gathering, and their conversation was stimulating to the mind.

For this occasion, the introduction of Michael the Scott among them, I constructed a special dais with a false floor which could be raised or lowered the thickness of one terra cotta tile. The work was done quickly and in the utmost secrecy, for I wanted neither the courtiers nor scholars to get wind of it. Then an elaborate banquet was prepared and the entire court invited to sit in attendance. I myself sat upon the dais among the scholars, at the center of the table, with Michael upon my right hand.

At a certain point in the merrymaking I called upon my new Maestro for a demonstration of his prowess. "Learned doctor Michael," I said, "often we have puzzled over the height of the sky. Can you tell us precisely, in Roman miles, the distance from the floor of this dais to the lowest level of Heaven?"

He rose and gravely bowed. "That may be possible to determine, Milord, if you will bear me a little patience."

Thereupon he called for string, chalk, ruler and slate and moved away from the table. Upon the pavement he made elaborate geometrical designs with the string, chalk and ruler, and to the eye of the uninitiated they were truly impressive. Upon the slate he made elaborate algebraic calculations requiring many minutes and a certain mumbling to himself. The whole court hung breathless with attention. At last he smoothed his forehead and turned with a bow to me.

"If it pleases your Majesty I will announce the result?" And upon my nod he continued. "The height of the sky from the floor is exactly 4,991 miles; by curious coincidence the same number as the years in the Hebrew calendar, as has been reported to me."

"A curious coincidence indeed, *indeed*," I said, "and, Maestro, we are greatly impressed. But we would have you climb the highest tower of this castle and there take sights to confirm your calculation."

I clapped my hands and a chamberlain appeared to guide him.

In an awed hush all stared as he donned his iron hat and departed. Then I clapped my hands again. Mechanics appeared, windlasses were revealed, and with one loud creak the floor of the dais was lowered. The court, bewildered, watched with more than a hint of apprehension; but I bade all to drink wine and be gay.

At length Michael the Scott returned, and announced in a firm voice, "My calculations were exact, your Majesty. They could not be otherwise, for I used a formula known only to me."

"Nevertheless, some among us have doubted the accuracy of your result, Maestro," I answered. "Would you once again, with the facility of your intellect, and for the enlightenment of our court, repeat your calculation of the distance of this floor from Heaven?"

"Indeed, Milord," he said, "*indeed!*"

And once again the diagrams and calculations were repeated, but slowly, slowly, so that the sand in the hourglass ran out. But at last the final report was ready.

"Your most learned Highness was well advised to ask for a second calculation," he said in a dry voice, but the blue eyes star-twinkled with a hinted smile. "It does seem that in the interval either the sky has receded or the earth has fallen a distance precisely equal to the thickness of one terra cotta tile—for surely, Milord, this formula could not be wrong . . . ?"

I burst into laughter, and the scholars and then the court joined in. How neatly he had trapped me!

"You are a canny Scott," I said, "a very wise man and a great astrologer. Your are gifted either with incredible eyesight or amazing insight—not to say, of course, mathematical genius—for the distance is *indeed* increased by the thickness of one tile. Come now, Michael, and take your place among us, and permit us to honor you for your brilliance which is like unto the very stars."

"Milord the Emperor, in his greatness of spirit, understands many things," he replied sweetly, "and not least, the magical way in which numbers behave for a magician. Let us rejoice and be glad that neither the sky nor tyranny presses upon our heads. . . ."

3

I TURNED NOW to scientific experiment, for I marveled much about many things. I wished to see "things which are, as they are." This was one of my favorite phrases, along with another of my maxims: "no certainty comes by hearsay." I wanted to observe, analyze, and record. And my interests extended from the stars to the egg in the nest.

I was fascinated by one of the Sultan's gifts to me: a planetarium of silver, in which tiny gears and springs moved the planets in unison (I have been told that a similar machine can be constructed to mark the time of day). Equally I was fascinated by the strange chick I found in a *praeneus* nest. It had an immense mouth and was covered with long, thick hair-like down over its whole head. It developed into a cuckoo; and the mystery of the cuckoo's nesting habits—which had so long puzzled me—was solved.

As for the Sultan, I was able to repay him with a truly astonishing gift. I had sent agents to Norway to investigate a spring which was reputed to petrify wood; in response to my command to buy the unusual, my agents returned with a polar bear. The beast created a sensation in Egypt because it ate nothing but fish. (I sent the animal to Alexandria in the newest and largest galley of my fleet—the *Half World*. It, too, created a sensation because it carried a crew of three hundred men.)

For years I had been planning some of the experiments I now undertook—for at last the necessary leisure was available. Diligently I had kept lists of questions which bothered me, such as, for example: Why does Canopus appear larger when rising than at zenith? Why does a lance inserted in still water appear broken? Why do eyes suffering from cataract see streaks and black spots? Why does quicksilver make a man deaf if dropped into his ear? Why do different crops grow best in different soils . . . ?

In an effort to find answers to some of my questions about the human body, I made great changes in the medical school in Salerno. I equipped it with laboratories, and—in defiance of the Church—human cadavers. Remembering my beloved Guglielmo, I thought it better for doctors to experiment on the dead than on the living. I banned magic rites; required that no student study medicine without first having studied logic for three years; required the study of Hippocrates and Galen for five years concurrently with the study of anatomy and surgery; required that students pass all examinations successfully, and thereafter serve at least a full year at the side of an experienced physician before practicing. In due course the Salerno medical school became famous, and students enrolled from everywhere. I myself paid it visits whenever possible; I watched dissection and observed in detail the skeletons. I was impressed by the resemblance of the human skeleton to those of many animals.

I had long wondered about the mysterious processes of the human stomach, in which so many different foods were completely transformed. I resolved to see, if I could, whether physical activity had any effect on digestion. I therefore took two slaves who were twin brothers, fed them well, and sent one to rest in bed and the other on a rigorous run up a mountain path. Some hours later they defecated in my presence, and the court doctors, who were used to examining feces, gave the opinion that the man who had rested after eating had enjoyed the better digestion. The point seemed to be proved by the fact that the man who had taken violent exercise had also experienced violent cramps.

I was interested, too, in the question of heredity. Since I could not study the human fetus, I turned to the chick embryo. With the aid of the Cistercian monks (who were as interested in bringing blessings from the earth as from Heaven), I constructed artificial incubators, after a method I had learned from Egyptians. Thus it was possible to examine eggs in all stages of development. I studied the breeding of poultry and pigeons, and went so far as to try to hatch ostrich eggs. In artificial ponds I observed the breeding habits of fish. I set up model breeding farms for dogs and horses, and developed strains of outstanding beauty and stamina. I also tried cattle and camels. In the process of these investigations I discovered that inbreeding was not necessarily bad. It would have been interesting to attempt an experiment with humans—but one lifetime was not enough.

Another type of experiment was possible with humans. Many theologians were of the opinion that the natural language of man was Hebrew, the language of Jehovah. In an effort to determine the truth or falsity of this opinion, I acquired ten newborn illegitimate infants who had been abandoned by their mothers. They were of most diverse origins—Sicilian, German, Lombard, Tuscan, Saracen, Greek, Spanish, French, Turkish, Ethiopian. Deliberately I excluded Hebrew, though in another nursery I placed three babies of Jewish parents. I gave orders that not one word of any tongue should be spoken or sung in the infants' presence; then, as they grew older, we should hear what language they might speak. Alas, we heard nothing—before the end of a month they had all perished from an epidemic of diarrhea. Some people said that the babies had died from lack of mother love; but the priests said I had deliberately sent infant souls down to Hell, unbaptized, for I myself was in league with the Devil.

I was curious, too, about the fulfillment of prophecy, or ill-omens. It occurred to me that knowledge of the prophecy or omen was itself suggestive of the fulfillment, through fear or even unacknowledged wish. On one occasion when Berardo was not feeling well, he requested a doctor. But Michael the Scott, who liked to stick a finger into every bowl of *pasta,* warned against blood-letting when the moon was in the sign of the Twins. Notwithstanding the warning, I summoned a doctor. All went well with the blood-letting. When the doctor had finished, I remarked casually that my astrologer had said the day was ill-omened. Thereupon the doctor became very nervous, dropped his knife and cut my foot—a deep and painful cut. He seemed compelled to fulfillment. Michael the Scott was effusive with apology when he learned what had happened.

Omens and oracles are, of course, closely related to wishes ill wishes and good wishes, which in turn seem to be related to dreams. Sometimes my dreams seem a continuation of reality; sometimes they assume an unintelligible disorder and distortion. When I am grealty disturbed or filled with anxiety which I have swallowed or concealed, my nights are restless and dreams haunted. From my reading, I would say that the Greeks understood more of the nature of dreams than perhaps any other people, for they write candidly of deep and dark dream wishes which most men keep secret. The now prevailing explanation of nightmares I cannot accept: that in sleep a female demon, a succubus, rides men; and a male demon, an incubus, rides women —both seeking evil forms of sexual intercourse.

I discovered that when I asked metaphysical questions, many theologians were eager to attempt answers. It occurred to me to constrast Mohammedian exegesis with Christian, and I prepared a set of questions which I dispatched to Muslims in countries ranging from Yemen to Morocco. I was eager for whatever specific, rational evidence might be obtained. Among my questions were the following:

> ARISTOTLE in all his works expressly says that the world exists in eternity—and it is clear that he so believed. If he demonstrated such eternal existence, what were his proofs—or, how does he discuss it?
>
> What is the scope of theology; what are its primary postulates, if postulates it has?
>
> What are the categories of sciences? How can they be proved?
>
> What is the proof—if any—of the immortality of the soul? Is the soul's existence—if it exists—eternal?

The replies I received were, in most cases, no better and no worse than the replies received from Christians in response to similar questions. That is, all tended to be strictly orthodox—though, in the case of Ibn Sab'in, even a little insulting. It was absurd, he said, that anyone should fail to accept Mohammedanism as the one true religion—though he would have liked to speak to me about the matter "mouth to mouth." Since I knew in fact he was not orthdox on many matters, I could only conclude that the pressure for religious conformity (and persecution) was as strong among the Muslims as among the Christians. This I could easily understand—for I myself, as Emperor of the faithful, buttressed the very institution which could not tolerate divergence. But in an age of faith, when most men were shocked —no, horrified—by religious nonconformity, what else was a Christian, most-Catholic prince to do?

Left to myself, I continued to hold my private views, make my private remarks, and pursue my private experiments for myself alone. When I asked a question about the existence of the soul, I tried to find ways and means to demonstrate an answer

—not merely to state an hypothesis based on faith or wishful thinking. I therefore undertook an experiment, which, as it happened, aroused far more controversy than I had expected.

I remembered how I had crouched in the jar in the gardeners' storeroom that night when murderers sought me. My body was in that jar, and my soul too. We entered and left the jar together. But suppose I had died of fright? My soul would have left, while my body remained. I could speak certainly about the fate of my body; but the fate of my soul would have been truly a mystery. So I resolved to put a dying man in a jar.

But first I performed a preliminary experiment with a hunting dog about the weight and size of a man. Michael the Scott prepared a sleeping potion for the dog, enough to keep him long unconscious. Once the potion had taken hold, we sealed the dog in a jar—airtight. Nowhere was crack or crevice. Not a creature could pass, not so much as one breath of air. We waited and watched for three hours. Nothing was to be seen, nothing heard. We broke the seal. The dog was dead. The Church taught that animals have no soul: indeed, I thought the proposition proved.

For my human subject I took a cook who had run amuck. In a rage one night he had butchered his wife and two girl children, and hence had been condemned to the gallows. But in the dungeon he sickened and was very near to death. He was given last rites, at my instruction. Then he fell into a coma. Nonetheless his heart beat and he breathed audibly when we put him in the jar. The soul allegedly departed at the actual moment of death, not with the loss of consciousness—so the soul went with him. Solemnly we sealed the jar, and surrounded it with watchers: Piero, Berardo, Michael, others of the court and the doctors. I sat on a specially made high chair, that I might watch from above. For twelve long hours we kept vigil. Never a sound from the jar, never a movement, not a break in the seal, not a crack of a hair's breadth anywhere. All was exactly as before.

How had the soul escaped from the jar? But—perhaps this man had no soul—no soul, in the sense that the Church taught. Heavenward had winged no doves, no celestial music played. All was silence in the jar. All was exactly as before.

We broke the seals. The man was dead. Like any dead man, anywhere. The news, as it spread through the castle, was shattering. People were apprehensive and afraid. I was avoided. Priests said that I had used witchcraft to frighten the soul—so that it remained in hiding in the man's body. But, as with the dog, I thought the proposition proved.

When I returned from questions in metaphysics to questions in physics, I found few scholars eager to attempt answers. In my mind were many questions about the earth; in fact, I was far more curious about its structure and composition than about the makeup of Heaven. The earth was at hand for observation and study. I could feel it under my feet, smell its odors, touch its stones, drink its waters, taste the growing things which sprang from its ancient womb. On the island of Stromboli I had climbed to the very edge of a living volcano, and I had looked down into an awesome pit of fire; but it was only livid fire and ash and lava—not Hell. Off Messina I had thrown a golden cup into the sea and commanded Niccola the fisherman, who was himself almost fish, to dive into the depths to retrieve the cup—and, returning, tell me in detail what he had seen. The cup was to be his, but I tossed it again and then again into deeper water, and finally neither man nor cup came up. I had come to believe only in the testimony of the senses.

Passing one day a field of wheat and a vineyard, I remarked, "How can this grain be transformed into the body of Christ, and the wine from these grapes into His blood?" As I ate bread and sipped wine at Communion, the bread to me tasted like bread and the wine like wine. I could not imagine "transubstantiation." What a vast amount of flesh would be derived from the field, what a vast amount of blood from the vineyard . . . !

Despite all this searching, all this wondering, I could find no answers to my questions:

How does it happen that sea water is so salty?

Has the earth a hole in its center, or has it a solid core like a stone?

Whence comes the fire which the earth vomits out of plains and mountain tops?

Whence comes the wind which blows from different parts of the circle of the earth . . . ?

On one occasion, when Michael the Scott was away on a mission, he wrote me as follows: "O fortunate Emperor! I verily believe that if ever a man in this world could escape death by his learning, you would be the one . . . ?"

To escape death is not possible. For me it is not death, but life, which is the ultimate mystery.

4

As so often, I grew tired of court routine, and sought surcease with my falcons. I liked alternate periods of activity and repose, investigation and thought, companionship and loneliness. What singer could make a melody with a single string to his lute?

I escaped from the petty jealousies of courtiers, the sentimental love songs of the *trovatori,* the too willing submission of mistresses, the tiresome jokes of the fools, the metallic clatter at the armorer's, the curses of the saddle-makers, the continual bray of *asini,* the skreek of quill pens in the chancery, the complaints of Pier della Vigna, the Ave Marias of the priests and the Paternosters of the nuns. I sought, in their place, the solace of sky and earth and forest. In the not distant mountains I moved under hoary giants—pine, beech, laurel, lime, maple, yew, ash, and cedar. I listened to the wind in their branches and delighted in the sunlit patterns of their leaves.

As I despised the crude practice of hunting with snares, and had no emotional need for the violence of the chase against stag or boar, I restricted myself solely to hawking. I saw it as an exciting game of skill, a test of the trainer more than test of bird. Never did I cease to marvel than man could induce a bird of prey not to seek its freedom, and, on the contrary, respond directly to command. That moment of exhilaration when the falcon, bearing prey, turns homeward . . . ! But the hunt also, by repetition, loses zest; and once again I too would turn homeward, seeking my greatest delight: intellectual companions, the pitting of minds, the play of words and ideas.

Once, on the night of my return to the castle I found a festa in full progress. Already at dusk the polygonal towers were illuminated with oil lamps, and the gates with torches. I felt surprise, but was pleased when Piero came to meet me and I learned that he had arranged the affair to welcome me. I was greeted with blasts from silver trumpets, a barrage of flowers from the parapets, and glad cries of "*Benvenuto Imperatore . . . !*" It is always flattering to be missed.

Dancing was already in progress in the Hall of the Three Domes. Later in the evening would come a great banquet, with diversion of all varieties—jugglers, acrobats, dancing girls. I thought of the food with relish, for I ate but little during hawking. I answered all greetings with pleasure, and hurried to my apartment to change my clothing from hunting green. I decided to dispense with kingly robes and vestments of state, and dress simply in a style suitable to youth—for I enjoyed the dance. I chose, therefore, long hose—tights—with one leg dyed scarlet and the other azure blue, and a short tunic of magenta silk worked with gold. (I was not averse, now and then, to displaying how generously I had been endowed by nature.) For my dagger I chose a curved Saracen blade, with a belt inset with rubies and pearls. My only concession to kingship was a light golden crown. My body was thus unweighted and unhampered, and my spirits soared with my senses. I was ready for some new game, some great adventure, some enormous excitement to possess me. From the sheer exuberance of life I felt a need to leap into the air, to sing, to make love. . . .

Piero had assembled an admirable band of musicians—players of lute, viol, harp, gittern, trumpet, citole, horn, flute, pipe, nakers, bagpipe, tabor, cimbals, bells and timbrels. They were grouped at one end of the hall; the throne was at the other. At my approach, the music stopped and a trumpet sounded. I entered from the main door, and while the dancers paused and bowed, I walked in silence to the throne. Once seated, I gave a signal for the music to continue; it was my custom to watch the dancers before I danced. For affairs of state I preferred the utmost pomp and ceremony; for social affairs at court I preferred to be informal. Though I sat above my people on a throne, I also liked to mingle with them—to laugh with them, to sing and dance.

Assembled this night, too, were some of my favorite poets. All chose to express themselves in the common tongue. Percivalle Doria, who traveled back and forth to the court almost as much as a courier; Rinaldo D'Aquino, who had written the famed, "Lament on Leaving for the Crusade," and had now become my most prized falconer; Giacomino Pugliese, who composed nothing but songs of love; and Jacopo da Lentini, an Imperial notary and lawyer, who of all the poets, wrote with the most spontaneous grace. Jacopo was a volatile young man, always in motion, always in conversation or debate. He carried on with Piero a running argument as to who had invented the *sonetto*—he or Piero—for he claimed to have first discovered the beauty of the form. They produced poems and dates; but never came to any resolution. Notwithstanding his hawklike face, Jacopo had a way with women—he spoke his poems in a certain tone of voice which added an extra dimension to himself. He was known less by his name than simply as *il Notaro*, though I myself always addressed him otherwise. He paused from dancing to sit on a cushion near Piero at the foot of the throne.

"Ser Jacopo," I said, "in the heat of the dance, what thoughts have you on the nature of love?"

"The same thoughts, my Lord, that I have at other times. Love is desire, generated by the eyes, rising by consent of the imagination, and nurtured by the heart."

"Love," said Piero, "is universally a sentiment of the heart and not necessarily a physical thing."

"Ah no!" Jacopo said. "Such a sentiment is merely affection. A true and strong love can never be born without physical aspect! The faraway love, when the person is not seen, is not love—never, never can it arouse the heart to frenzy. In remembrance nothing remains but a pleasant warmth. . . ."

"Bravo, bravo! Well spoken by both of you," I said. "To me it seems that a true and strong love requires both the touch of two hearts and the touch of two bodies. Affection does not necessarily include or exclude passion. Passion brings true love to its complete fulfillment. Love adds frenzy to passion—passion adds frenzy to love. Is it not so . . . ?" I sighed, touched by a curious loneliness. Some part of my life, in spite of its fullness, remained unfilled. Nor did words about love requite my need. But I turned away from myself.

"Ser Jacopo," I said, "we beg you to sing us a song about love. . . ."

"It is my joy to please your Highness," he replied, and took up the lute which was always at hand.

Piero stood and gestured the musicians to silence; the dancers came abruptly to pause. "Our Lord the Imperatore has asked for a song," he announced, "and il Notaro has offered to sing."

Ser Jacopo mounted one step and stood to my left. He drew back his long sleeves and cradled the lute. Gradually the murmur of voices and shuffle of feet gave way to stillness. Jacopo tilted his head, half closed his eyes, and hoarsely whispered his song:

> *"Canzonetta novella*
> *va, e canta nova cosa;*
> *lèvati da maitino*
> *davanti a la più bella,*
> *fiore d'ogni amorosa,*
> *bionda più ch'auro fino:*
> *'Lo vostro amor, ch'è caro,*
> *donatelo al Notaro.'"*

The response was laughter, roaring applause, and cries of "Bravissimo! Encore! Encore!"

"With the permission of your Highness?" Ser Jacopo said.

I nodded assent, and once more the evocative voice stirred misty memories half-forgotten. I felt anew an old melancholia. How could I yet experience disturbance at the mystery of love . . . ? I repeated to myself the words of the song as if it were my own:

> *"Quella c'ha bionda testa e chiaro viso*
> *E lo bel viso e 'l morbido sguardare . . ."*

But I heard no more than these two lines, for I was transfixed, enraptured. The imaginary and fascinating blond woman of Jacopo's song had been summoned into life. She stood not far off, smiling softly, and regarding not Ser Jacopo but my own face. In spite of the flickering candlelight, I recognized her at once. She was Bianca Lancia.

Almost twenty years had passed. Now I was thirty-six; she, thirty-one. I had forgotten, but I could never forget. As I was now a man, not a youth, so too she was a woman, not a girl. And the change had not decreased but enhanced her beauty. Where before she had been thin-faced and almost breastless, now she had come fully into the natural endowments of a woman. Yet she had not lost the aura of golden paleness, not spoiled the delicate pensive face. I would have known her, I think, had she reached the age of a hundred. And when she caught my stare, she smiled but looked aside. Her partner was her brother, Manfredo.

When Ser Jacopo had finished and the applause had ceased, I stretched out my hand. "The lute—" I said, "I too will sing."

And I sang the song I had composed one night, half-dreaming; it was a dialogue between lover and beloved, faced by a long parting:

"'*Dolze meo drudo, e vatene:*
meo sire, a Dio t'accomanno;
che ti diparti da mene,
ed io, tapina, rimanno . . .'
'*Dolze mia donna, lo gire*
non è per mia volontate;
che me convene ubidire
quelli che m'à 'n potestate . . .'"

Before the applause could finish, I gave the signal for the music to resume. I stepped down from the throne and mingled with the dancers. In a moment I stood at Bianca's side.

"Monna Bianca, welcome to our court," I said, and kissed her hand. "How astonishing to compress the years! But how does it happen you have come here without herald and without presentation. When I urged the noble Manfredo to settle with us, I had no intimation that you too might join us—a good fortune not to be surpassed."

"This good fortune, alas, my Lord," Manfredo said, "is derived from ill fortune. My wife is dead a year now, as you will recall; Bianca has come here to be mother to my smallest children. We arrived today, with all our baggage, and found you hawking—"

"My sorrow joins your sorrow," I said. "But Monna Bianca is not mother to her own . . . ?"

"No, my Lord," Bianca murmured, "I am not wife to any man."

The sound of her voice, even more than her words, awoke in me new and strange emotions. We appraised one another directly, boldly, as we had done that brief moment in the Doria garden when I first found her sitting by the dolphin fountain. The appraisal now was equally brief, but its content had another meaning.

"May we dance?" I said. "This is the night to be gay."

When my hand touched hers, I understood what I had long forgotten: I was in love, both then and now. "You will come to me tonight?" I whispered.

She smiled shyly. "I will come."

I squeezed her hand, then whispered close to her ear, "Go,

heavily veiled, Bianca, with a serving woman, to the stable. Ask the groom to see my horse Dragone. The groom will take you to a secret door. A secret stairway ascends the tower to an alcove in my bedroom. Except your woman and my groom, none will know of your coming or your going. We will keep our secret between us as long as you like. . . ."

"My Lord—I am not afraid for your love to be known."

"But if someday you choose to marry—"

"No, Lord Federico. No—"

"And why, no?"

"Had I wished to marry, I would have done so long since. I had not that wish—"

"Because—?"

"Because I could marry only with love."

I breathed deeply. "*It was not of my own will, Dido, I left your land . . . I did not, could not imagine my going would ever bring such terrible agony on you . . . Thus did Aeneas speak. . . .*"

And once again, as nineteen years before, I put my arm around her, oblivious of the throng.

5

A MESSENGER, streaked with the dust and sweat of August, arrived in Melfi from Rome. From his saddlebags he took packets sealed with the Papal seal. Thus an ominous silence of many weeks was broken, and I felt certain that some new trouble was ahead. The Pope's letter was a warning:

> IT has reached our ears that you are minded to promulgate new laws—either of your own impulse, or led astray by the pernicious councils of abandoned men. Thus it follows that you may be called a persecutor of the Church. . . . If you, of your own intention, contemplate this, then we must gravely fear that God has withdrawn from you His grace—since you so openly undermine your own good name and your own salvation.

Even had I so desired, it was much too late to draw back from my own intention. Already I had summoned the officials, the lawyers, the notaries, the lay princes and the ecclesiastical princes, and even the common people to assemble in Melfi for the issuing of my new Constitution. I had, in fact, gone so far as to plan semi-annual meetings of representatives of commoners to discuss the formulation and application of the laws, that the State might be continually on the alert against injustices. The administration of law was to be placed solely in the hands of the laity. In the draft I had contemplated, the Church was hardly mentioned; and no doubt Pope Gregory knew all the details. My new secular state was to be based on Law, Nature, and Reason; nevertheless the Church was to have its place.

Much of the work of organization was done by Taddeo da Suessa, a high court justice who recently had come into prominence. Suessa is not far from Capua, and Taddeo was well known to Piero. Taddeo was older than Piero, younger than Berardo;

and in character a serious man—a kind of Italian equivalent to Hermann von Salza. I found, both then and later, that the portly Taddeo was admirably equipped to deal with the clergy without ruffling ecclesiastical feathers.

In advance of the general assembly, I undertook a number of steps to strengthen the popular image of secular authority. I decreed my own birthday as a general *festa*, thus giving to Christian, Muslim, and Jew alike a common feast day. I issued the golden coins known as *augustales;* and upon these coins was stamped a portrait likeness of myself, my hair cut short, wearing the toga and laurel wreath of Caesar. On the reverse side was an Imperial Eagle. Nowhere was cross or lamb or other Christian symbol, common to all other coins of these days. I had great difficulty in finding truly artful goldsmiths, as the mints usually produce crude or even brutish work. My coins at least can be compared with the Greek and Roman. And they are gold—a metal now hardly used for specie. None can doubt their value.

At last the great day came when the first edicts of the new Book of Laws were to be read aloud to the assemblage. Of all these who had worked on the codification, I chose Pier della Vigna to speak in the name of the Emperor. In the Hall of the Three Domes I was seated on a great gem-encrusted throne, under a gigantic crown suspended above me. At my right hand stood Piero, richly dressed in robes of state, for now he held the royal post of *Logethetes*, which I had especially created for him. Before him was a carved and gilded lectern bearing the parchment folios of the Constitution. Had I known, I might have commented that in almost these same moments Pope Gregory was initiating a new Inquisition in Rome; more and more heretics were being burned alive.

Piero began with my titles, as the Emperor Justinian's titles had been listed in the beginning of his own code:

IMPERATOR FRIDERICUS SECUNDUS
ROMANORUM CAESAR SEMPER AUGUSTUS
ITALICUS SICULUS HIEROSOLYMITANUS
ARELATENSIS
FELIX VICTOR AC TRIUMPHATOR

The reading required many hours, indeed, days, as the codification traced the origins of human law from the fall of Adam and

Eve, who had violated divine law, to the rise of secular rulers—for, as I myself phrased it, "necessity created kings." My rights were based upon "the grace of Heaven." The laws themselves had been collected from the legal efforts of a thousand years, and now refined into a coherent whole. And here and there I had dictated the precise phraseology I wished to be used:

> IN no sense do we detract from the reverence due earlier rulers when we beget new laws to meet the peculiar needs of the new time, or find new medicines for new ills. The Imperial dignity carries this illustrious privilege as an inevitable condition of rendering service: daily to conceive new methods to reward the virtuous and to restrain the vicious. . . .
>
> We who hold the balance of justice for the rights of all, do not wish to make distinctions but to achieve equality in our judgments. Be plaintiff or defendant Frank, Roman, or Lombard, we wish that he be awarded justice. Nor is anything more odious than the oppression of the poor by the rich. . . . Although the supreme Imperial dignity is free of the law, we shall take care that in the observation of laws, and in the inflexibility of justice, we also will follow the law common to others. We consider damage to our faithful subjects damage to ourselves, and their gains our gains.
>
> May our people welcome, to the glory and honor of God, this work begun in the hope of Divine favor, and completed under the guidance of Divine grace. Receive these laws with thankfulness, O ye peoples, make them your own. . . . Posterity must believe of us in centuries to come that we collected this Book of Laws not merely to serve our own renown, but rather to wipe out in our day the injustice of earlier times—for the voice of justice has long been silent . . .

For practical reasons the code began with edicts against heretics—as had Justinian's. For his beliefs no man was to be persecuted, but schismatics against the Church and rebels against the State were declared guilty of heresy. While these edicts were a concession to the Pope, they were also intended to demonstrate to the Church its reliance on the State for defense, and further, implied the sanctity of the State itself. Since I abhor anarchy and respect order, I felt no reluctance in including these provisions.

But of more interest to me were the essential innovations—those modifications of old forms or outright creation of new. The most important was a complete overhaul of the administration of government. Officials called justiciars were appointed as governors of provinces, were paid by the crown and were responsible directly to the crown in the equitable application of the laws. They might not possess money or land in their official district, or take part in any commercial transaction. They were to have no relatives in the district, and might not even bring their wives. Districts were to be yearly exchanged. Feudal courts were almost wholly superseded. The new courts were required to sit daily (except holidays), and no case might extend more than two months. Twice yearly, citizens could present complaints. Only men of culture, with university educations, were to be selected as judges; and the penalty for bribery or unjust sentences ranged from confiscation of property to death. For the first time, bail was permitted. False accusers were fined one-sixth of all their possessions. Widows, orphans, and the impoverished were to receive free legal assistance at the expense of the State. Lawyers' fees were to be fixed by the judges.

The use of torture was severely limited; it was reserved as a last resort in charges of murder against persons of known evil repute. Nor was it ever to apply to children. Trial by ordeal was completely abolished. Of this I chose to write: "How could a man believe that the natural heat of glowing iron will become cool or cold without an adequate cause . . . or that, because of a seared conscience, the element of cold water will refuse to accept the accused? These judgments of God by ordeal which men call 'truth-revealing,' might better be styled 'truth-concealing.' "

Arms were limited to courtiers, knights, and merchants on their travels. Treason was assessed as the gravest of crimes. The intelligence service was instructed to be alert for conspiracy with Pope or Curia; a special police, the *comestabuli,* was assigned to watch suspected persons. Once reasonable grounds for suspicion were established, the suspected person was to be given a small black book listing the accusations against him, together with names of his accusers.

Severe limitations were imposed on the rights of churches, monasteries or the religious military orders to acquire freehold land or fiefs. Serfdom as such was abolished on the royal estates.

Model farms were established. Persons who owned no land, but seriously wished to work the land were to be awarded required amounts for sustenance from estates lying idle. Closed hunting seasons were inaugurated, to protect the breeding of animals and birds.

The old law which barred women from succession to estates was annulled. The persons of women were given every protection, even the persons of prostitutes. Anyone who heard the cries of a woman for help, and failed to respond, was to be severely fined. For rape, a man might be sentenced to death or to mutilation. But for false charges of rape, the woman herself might be condemned to death. Pimps were to be sentenced to forced labor or slavery; a woman who prostituted her daughter faced prison unless she could prove she was so forced by poverty. The procuress was to have her nose cut off. A man who abetted the adultery of his wife was to be scourged.

Miracles were banned outright. The compounding of love potions was forbidden. Pharmacies might not sell one product for another; prohibited on pain of death was the sale of toxic substances which cause death or loss of the senses. Doctors, if so demanded, were to make at least two visits per day or one per night to the sick person, nor were they to charge more than one-half gold taren per day; for visits outside a city, the rate was increased to three tarens. For public hygiene, the accumulations of pools of stagnant water were prohibited; dead animals and rubbish might not be thrown into streams; the sale of bad food was subject to fine; and all butchering of animals was to take place outside city walls. Public baths were to be operated by the State.

All weights and measures were controlled by the State. Internal tariffs were largely abolished, and a strict control of customs instituted. The State assumed a monopoly of the production and sale of salt, hemp, iron, silk, and dyeing. A quasi-monopoly was set up for the sale and transport of grain. New industries were encouraged, such as the refining of sugar. State warehouses were to be built in every major city.

No case might be made against a minor or a homicidal maniac. Failure to help victims of shipwreck was punishable by heavy fines. Perjurers and robbers of corpses were to be punished by amputation of hands.

Such were many of the new laws and the penalties prescribed for those who failed to obey. But I felt a word of caution was in order: "Unjust sentences cannot be too severely punished, since otherwise the path of truth will be darkened and the oppression of the just will prevail. We condemn to death those judges who have given unjust sentences from any motive. Their goods are confiscated. If any have erred through ignorance, they may thank their own folly in assuming the office of judge."

Hardly had the last word of the last folio been read, before a new letter arrived from Gregory. Its contents created a certain consternation among some of the weaker reeds. Only the edicts against heresy were approved by the Curia; the other laws, said the Pope, the Church "will by no means calmly tolerate."

For these laws, the Pope wrote, "have renounced salvation and will conjure up immeasurable ill."

6

THE SHADOW of a shadow crossed my happiness. Rumors reached me that my son Heinrich, the King of the Germans, was behaving in a frivolous manner unsuited to the responsibilities of kingship. It was not so much that he wined and dined excessively, or that his companions were brutes, or that he was capricious, or even that he wished to divorce his Queen though she had borne him a son. More disturbing was the fact that he seemed not to understand the role of a king. He could not command the respect of the princes if he placed himself beneath them; he could not rule without insight and firmness; he could not hope to maintain an Austrian alliance if he disposed of his Austrian Queen merely to marry some youthful flame.

Now he was twenty-one. For eleven years I had not seen him, and I decided the time had come for a father-son reunion. I called a Diet for All Souls' Day in Ravenna, and bade Heinrich make haste to cross the Alps to meet me halfway. I was concerned, too, about the constant strife in Lombardy. I therefore announced that my mission was for the "honor of God, of the Church and of the Empire, and the prosperity of Lombardy"—and invited the Lombard towns to send representatives.

Of all my children, Heinrich was the one I knew least. Twice I had parted from him when he was a child; it was I who was responsible for ordering him to Germany against his mother's wishes; I who had permitted him to be educated strictly as a German prince without ameliorating foreign influences. Surely in the last years I must have become a vague and unreal figure to him, no more than some distorted memory from earliest childhood. It was easy for me to visualize him; he could not, I was sure, visualize me.

I now took care, whenever possible, to see my children every day. In those years the nursery at Melfi was rather overflowing, and happily Bianca took on its supervision as if she had been the mother of all my brood. To fasten their clothing she used the new invention of "buttons"—well adapted to children, she explained. The oldest girls were Selvaggia, Violante, and Margherita, who ranged in age from eight to eleven. All were demure, bright and very pretty, though Selvaggia showed signs of becoming truly a beauty. The youngest girls, Blanche and Caterina, were hardly more than toddlers. As for the boys—most were the very cockerels that boys should be. The youngest was Corrado, three—aside from Heinrich, my only legitimate heir. Fortunately he bore no marked resemblance either to his mother Yolanda or his grandfather Jean de Brienne. Little older was my Federico of Antioch, who at five so reminded me of his beautiful mother Balian that at times he gave me intense pain. His limp had worsened, and with it my concern for him; I devised corrective exercises, but nothing seemed to help. Next came Riccardo di Theate, at eleven a desultory sort of boy, shy, too remote, often ill, always too deeply concerned with his own thoughts. I was glad that he loved books, but he balanced them with nothing else, and for his health also I was concerned. But the joy of them all was Enzo, aged thirteen. Though his was the only German mother among them, he was the most Italian of Italians in temperament, in gesture, in song. He was quick-witted, happy, and in physical characteristics most amazingly reflected me. Constantly he was laughing, exercising, reading, and he so loved hawking and dressed so often in green that people called him "Falconello." I suppose he had hungered for a mother all his life, so he took at once to Bianca; I was more than gratified at the deep affection which sprang up between them.

Bianca herself was to present me with another child. Already we knew that she was pregnant. At once we decided on names: if a boy, Manfredo, in honor of her father and brother; if a girl, Costanza, in honor of my mother. Bianca had moved boldly and without shame into an open relationship with me. I chose apartments for her near mine, and assigned to her one of my two most trusted body servants—those Saracens "Pietro" and "Paolo." Manfredo acquiesced graciously in these arrangements. It was, in truth, Bianca who prevailed upon him—not I. It was not unfitting, however, that he should receive a new post, new lands, and a new title of Marquis; but I was careful not to make the awards too rapidly, lest it be said I had bought his sister outright.

Bianca was, of course, the wonder of the court, for she seemed to hold me as no other woman ever could; and she was treated with more than the respect due a queen.

Only with Pier della Vigna was there any hint of difficulty. Bianca herself was much too astute to make any allusion to Piero, knowing that the relationships of men among men are wholly apart from women. She seemed content to accept her role for what it was, and leave others quite alone. Not so, Piero. He was, I think, profoundly jealous of my absorption with Bianca—not of the physical, but of the intellectual rapport. This was his own chief province, and he disliked the thought of intruders. One day soon after the reading of the Book of Laws he spoke to me in a casual tone so forced that he betrayed at once his concern.

"Imperatore," he said, "what was the Nobildonna Bianca's opinion of the new laws affecting women?"

"She endorses them heartily," I answered. "She thinks them long overdue."

"Ah, so?" he said. "Splendid! And did you discuss them with her in advance, to ask her advice?"

"I did indeed. I thought the judgment of an intelligent woman might be useful in such matters."

"And on which provisions, Imperatore, was she best informed?"

I stiffened. This was dangerous ground. "About the problems of estate inheritance," I said, "since thus far in her life none of the other provisions has directly affected her. And I shall see that none does. . . ."

He flushed and cast down his eyes. "I had not consciously intended an affront," he said. "You know me too well—" Then he made the gesture of prayer.

"You err, dear Piero, from an excess of zeal," I said. "In your love for your Emperor you forget sometimes that he is also a man; and in your love for the man you forget sometimes that he is also an Emperor. And who but Pier della Vigna could have achieved such a synthesis of love for both? But have no fear—both Emperor and man return your love: you will never lose it . . . to whatever heights or whatever depths the path of fortune leads us. . . ." I put my arm around him, to assuage the *dolore* in his face.

Even so, when I departed for Ravenna, I left him behind. I took with me Count Tommaso d'Aquino, with whom my relationship was excellent but impersonal; and Berardo, who at sixty-five was white of beard and suddenly a little old; and Bianca Lancia. . . .

7

My son Heinrich failed to appear in Ravenna. Representatives of the Lombard towns failed to appear. Apparently I was to be left to talk to myself at the Diet, or twiddle my thumbs. I did neither. Politely I asked the Pope to send mediators to the Lombard rebels (I expected no results); less politely I did not ask, but ordered, my son to meet me the coming Easter at Aquileia. This town, not far from Trieste, was accessible from Germany. Meanwhile I contented myself with a number of other activities.

I undertook some excavations which interested me. I uncovered the mausoleum of Galla Placidia, long since buried under earth and rubble. For the first time in centuries the extraordinary blue and gold mosaics of this structure were again seen by human eyes; both Bianca and I took great delight as each day's work yielded new surprises. But I was torn between my admiration for its beauty and the beauty of Bianca, as she stood in the central vault, bundled to the ears in furs, examining the winged lion which flew across the blue star-spangled heaven. The translucent alabaster windows cast so soft an aura about her golden hair that she herself seemed almost divine. Certainly she had proved the good angel of my life.

In the early spring I sailed to Venezia, ostensibly to worship at the shrine of San Marco, but more particularly to improve my relations with that lagoon power. The Doge received me with mingled trepidation and hauteur—they were afraid of me in spite of their own vast holdings in the Levante, their fleets and riches. I was much impressed with the shrewdness of these traders: one example will suffice. I brought presents of great value—gold, silver, jewels. In return, with great pomp and solemnity, they presented me a splinter of the True Cross. I saved it, and shortly thereafter passed it on to von Salza when he arrived in Aquileia from Thuringia; he was almost overcome with joy. As for the merchants of Venezia, they were glad to see me go, in spite of their good bargain.

At Eastertime a reluctant Heinrich arrived in Italy. I declined to see him, but assigned him quarters in the not far distant town of Cividale, close to the Austrian border. The divorce problem had resolved itself: the unhappy Agnes of Bohemia, who had been the object of Heinrich's desire, took the veil to avoid further attention. But nothing could undo the disastrous effect of Heinrich's enforced gift to the German lay princes of almost unlimited sovereignty over their towns and lands—including the rights to coin money, collect customs and tolls; and all fortifications. He had unwisely provoked the princes, and all this they had wrung from him. True, I had given away much to the ecclesiastical princes in Germany; but with lay princes, and the principle of hereditary succession, such gifts were another matter. In effect my son had carved up Germany into a series of petty kingdoms even more absolute than those already existing; he had weakened the Empire to a shadow. Worse still, rumors abounded that he had prepared secretly for revolt; but the facts of this situation I preferred to remain undisclosed—unless I should be forced to disclosure by Heinrich himself.

I therefore prepared to deal with Heinrich first as an insubordinate king, and second as my son—though our blood relationship made the situation for me monstrous and untenable. Had he been merely stupid, I could easily have forgiven him; but his failure to come to Ravenna had been willful disobedience, and even now he appeared only because he had been placed under heavy pressure by certain princes and bishops. Obviously he wished to escape completely from my authority: but volition was not statesmanship, and this he sadly lacked.

I sent negotiators to Cividale to deal with him, refusing to permit him to enter my presence until he had agreed to all my demands. I required that he swear publicly, in the presence of the princes, to obey all my future commands; that he no further provoke the German princes against himself and the Empire; that he write a release of the princes' oath of fealty to himself should he fail to obey my commands; that he write to the Pope of the oaths he had sworn, and beg for excommunication should he break his promises to his father and Emperor. To all this he agreed verbally, though with what reservations in his heart I do not know. Then I invited him to come to see me in private.

What can a father say to a son who has failed to fulfill expectations . . . has dashed high hopes to the ground . . . has nullified the advantages so painfully created for him . . . ? Perhaps the expectations were too onerous? The hopes too high? Perhaps advantage for one is a disadvantage to another? Can a father speak of the weight in his heart, or pretend to dismiss it as nothing? How I had counted on being proud of him! Pride: that was a factor. I recalled my pride at having sired my first-born son. If only he had felt a similar pride at birth! But perhaps his dominant feeling from then till now had been resentment? But had he no pride in his father, his lineage, his inheritance? No pride in accomplishment? Had he no sense of responsibility to his father, himself, or to the opportunities opened to him? What now were his emotions—his reactions to the past, his aspirations for the future? My own emotions writhed and lashed inside me. My sense of disappointment was boundless. I considered his failure an adjunct of some failure of my own. My head ached. I was irascible, angry. I felt nausea, and during the exhausting hours of a sleepless night, longed to vomit up the phlegm which somehow had poisoned us both.

I removed from my person all kingly symbols of authority—my signet ring, the massive gold chain and medallion I often wore about my neck, my crown. The orb and scepter I concealed. I wished to receive my son not as a king but solely as a father. But why so agonizingly difficult to bridge the gap between father and son . . . ?

I was sitting with a book on my lap when he came in. I would never have recognized him had not the memory of Costanza's Spanish face remained with me. His was not so dark, but he had a dissipated, haggard look; he had not the glow which comes with health and happiness. His mouth revealed a tightness which distressed me, but was less distressing than the air of sullen hostility which radiated from him. I put aside my book and stood up. He was both thinner and taller than I, but much less muscular. In his gauntness he was like my father. He bowed, and sought to kiss my hand; but I brushed him aside.

"Come, my son," I said in Italian, "let us sit together on the couch."

"As you wish it, Kaiser," he replied in German, as we sat down.

"Shall we speak together in the ordinary tongue of Italy?" I said.

"My Italian is rusty," he said.

"And my German. Latin, then."

"As you wish it, Sire."

But his Latin had so guttural a German accent that it was difficult to understand. Even language was a barrier between us! But for this I could blame only myself. I spoke slowly and carefully, that he might not misunderstand any of my words. But the Latin itself was so formal, so much a language of state, that we lapsed almost at once into the stylized phrases of two hostile princes, not father and son. I tried again to communicate.

"I am deeply grieved that our first meeting, after so many years, should not be one of rejoicing," I said in a tone of conciliation.

"You could have come to Germany had you wished," he said.

"I could not come—you do not understand."

"You could have sent for me."

"I might have sent for you—but many political considerations were against it. The Pope, the Crusade—" He had forced me, curiously, to the defensive.

"I might have joined you on the Crusade. I would have liked killing infidels."

I breathed heavily. "We killed no infidels. We negotiated peace."

He shrugged his shoulders. "A negotiated peace is no peace. Only force has value."

I had no wish to debate with him, but I said, "My policy, always, has been to use force as a last resort." I paused, then added, "This policy I also apply to you not because you are my son, but because its worth is proved. If you fail to fulfill your obligations toward me, as your overlord, then of necessity I shall try another policy. I wanted to be sure you understand this, because I place the welfare of the Empire above all else. I cannot let ties of blood weaken my resolution as an Emperor. But I have not forgotten that you are my son, however much you may think that I have forgotten you. . . ."

"I understand you clearly," he said with the cold arrogance I recalled from his boyhood. "I am on probation, and I can expect exactly the same treatment as anyone else. So in effect I am not your son!"

My heart was beginning to thud, and anger to suffuse me. Why could I not tell him how desperately I wanted him to succeed, to be honored and beloved. . . . But I said, instead, formally, "You have not behaved well—"

"Revered Father," he said with a hint of sarcasm, "I am not a child—shall we continue to talk of policy and not of bad behavior? My personal errors are indeed my own, and for them I feel little inclination to apologize. But my public errors, perhaps with guidance, can be corrected. Really I never know which way to turn. . . ."

At last I understood: I had expected too much. He could not see a crow in a bowlful of milk. I had allowed others to train him for the tasks I had expected of him, and his own weakness was in part a reflection of the weakness of others. How could I have expected lesser men than myself to rear my son equal to myself? But now it was too late. . . .

"I am sorry," I said, "if you have been bewildered and confused. Try to follow my instructions. Do not listen to the advice of men who wish to use you for their own ends against me. If you allow yourself to fall into conspiracy you will gain nothing but sorrow—and you will lose the crown which, God knows, I pray will remain yours. Remember that I hold no animosity for you, but only prayers for our reconciliation and your success. . . ."

"Is that all, Sire?"

"From me, all. And you—what have you to say, Enrico?"

He ignored my use of the Italian form of his name. "Only that I wish permission to visit my mother's tomb in Palermo."

I hesitated, then shook my head. "That would be inadvisable for a while. Perhaps in a year or two or three—"

"I thought it would be inadvisable," he said bitterly. "Everything I wish to do is always 'inadvisable'! I am no more than a puppet for you to pull the strings! Sire, may I be excused . . . ?"

"You may go," I said, my voice choking. It was well that he left when he did; I could not tolerate much more.

That afternoon the jousting began, with Heinrich entered in the lists. And that night, the drinking and feasting. At midnight, Bianca was delivered of a male child, to be called Manfredo. I was the father of another son.

8

NOTHING was resolved; everything was only in suspension. Heinrich, the Lombards, the Pope—in effect with each I was in a stage of uneasy truce. My judgment of Heinrich I held in abeyance; I wanted to give him every opportunity to reinstate himself in my eyes and the eyes of the world. The Lombard towns continued their fratricidal warfare, their intrigues against the Empire. The Pope ceased not for a moment his little games with the Lombards, trying slyly to play the middle of Italy against both ends. The outlook in each case was not sanguine; the best I could look forward to was an interlude of nonbelligerance. How long? How long could the crisis with each be postponed? This was the basic question; but it was not a simple question, because all were interlinked. I exercised extreme caution to avoid giving any of the hostile parties a legitimate excuse to break the eggshell of peace.

I did not, however, draw back from the programs I had inaugurated. I continued with the organization and consolidation of a new State, seeking to fuse its economic and cultural life into a new force. Indeed, our measures were the talk of men everywhere, and a steady stream of visitors came to court to investigate, discuss and report to their sovereigns.

Many were the ambassadors who arrived from the East; my old friend Fakhr ad-Din, for the Sultan of Egypt; another for the Sultan of Damascus; and still another for the Old Man of the Mountain. This last caused some uneasiness and much whispering; but I assured the Christian envoys that they were safe. Indeed, for the Muslim feast of the Hegira, we all sat down together: French and English ambassadors, German princes, Italian nobles, Sicilian ecclesiastics. It was, all said, a big success. But the Pope was scandalized.

Among the ambassadors was a special envoy from that Louis IX, King of France, whom people spoke of as so pious and devout a Christian that he was likely to become a saint (certainly no one ever suggested the same of me!). I found this Louis an interesting figure. He was reputed to be an ascetic, and the most kindhearted of men; yet he did not flinch to advise: "The layman, when he hears any speak ill of the Christian faith, should defend it not with words but with the sword—thrusting it into the other's belly as far as it will go." At court, a tale was told of how Louis, riding out of town one morning at dawn, was doused with offal thrown from a chamber pot above. Cleaning off the mess, Louis stamped with his guards up the stairs of the house and burst in upon a frightened young man. Charged with the deed, the fellow admitted it; but King Louis paused to ask what he was doing up at such an hour. "Studying for the university," the young man said. "Ah," said the King, "would that we had more earnest students like you!" and forgave the boy upon the spot.

For so serious a student, I too would be willing to forgive much. So great were the demands of my new State for enlightened, educated, and efficient administrators, that I felt very keenly the need for improvement in education. My University of Napoli itself was not enough; its training program required many years, and was meant for relatively few at only the highest levels.

When I investigated the lower schools, I discovered to my surprise that a sizable number of grammar schools had survived from Roman times. But education, especially at the elementary level, had fallen almost completely into the hands of the Church. Teachers were priests, or nuns, or schoolmasters who were ecclesiastical officers. The first question asked of little children was: "*Vultis flagellari in discendo?*"—"Are you ready to be flogged while you learn?" I took steps to increase the number of schools and encourage teachers who were not directly under the control of the Church. And, so that children would not have to "learn their ABC's on an apple"—as the saying goes—I provided large numbers of hornbooks, those bits of parchment protected by a transparent layer of horn, on which was written the alphabet and perhaps the Lord's Prayer.

My interest in education extended equally to my own children, and I resolved, in training the youngest, to try to avoid some of the mistakes of the past. When, in time, Bianca bore the girl child we named Costanza, I gave her over completely to Bianca herself—for I wished the girl to be both as seemly and accomplished as her mother. To little Manfredo I paid great attention. He was a delightful child: warm, curious, extremely quick to learn—in appearance a masculine edition of his mother. I taught him to study nature, to speak many languages, to relish hawking, to sing, to handle arms, and to understand what someone (a Greek, I think) called "the grave and beautiful games" numbers play with each other—as, for example, the law that the difference between the square of a number and the product of its next-door neighbors must always be one less than the square.

Trouble, as ever, was not absent. A revolt broke out in Messina, and I myself rushed to crush it. I found abuses, and some discontent was justified—but certain conspirators, opposed to my new regime, had made much of little. I thought it wise to apply the edicts against heresy. As the Pope chose to conduct his heresy hunts in Lombardia chiefly through Domenicans without the presence of an Imperial official, I chose in Sicily to eliminate the presence of an ecclesiastic. Thus we were able to concentrate on activities rather than beliefs—though the Pope was infuriated and made representations on the matter. I foresaw a time when dangers might well arise from looseness in the definition of heresy. How easy for the Pope to declare that supporters of the Emperor were heretics! Indeed, the time was not long in coming.

The winter of 1233-34 in Italy, as it happened, was one of the severest in the annals of history. In Venezia, the lagoons froze solid, and an army could have marched from the mainland. Rome was buried in snow, and even the streets of Napoli were covered with ice and slush. Sleet fell in Sicily. All mountain passes were blocked by snow; gigantic waves and bitter winds halted all travel by sea. Italy was marooned. Food grew short in the major towns. In Rome, riots broke out against the Pope.

And in all Italy, wandering friars preached the "Great Hallelujah"—a peace and penance movement which became a madness, and men were said to be "drunk with heavenly love." No—not all Italy, for these howling preachers were not allowed to cross the borders into my Kingdom of Sicily; elsewhere they roamed at will. They praised the Holy Trinity and performed miracles. I saw one such preacher myself: he wore a heavy black beard, and was dressed in sackcloth adorned front and back with a bright red cross. On his head was a peaked fur cap. He played a tiny copper trumpet, which produced strange squealing sounds—like the cries, some said, of souls in misery. People followed him with burning branches chanting, "Hallelujah! Hallelujah, hallelujah!" Where the frenzy spread, all work stopped. Peasants left the fields, cooks abandoned their pots, men-at-arms laid aside their weapons. The warfare of town against town abruptly ceased, and men fell on each other's necks as brothers. Then, like the plague, as quickly as it had come, the madness vanished. On the return of spring and warmth, work and all the old quarrels were resumed.

As the Laterano had been sacked, and the palaces of many cardinals plundered, the Pope had been forced to flee to Rieti for safety. With the passing of the Great Hallelujah, the Roman people took up active hostilities against him. As his situation became increasingly desperate, Gregory dispatched frantic letters urging all Christendom to come to his rescue.

This was a situation made to my order. Rieti was on the Via Salaria, not far from Aquila, a town I had founded for the defense of my borders. With my seven-year-old legitimate son and heir Corrado, I marched to aid the Pope. Corrado I intended to send ahead as a hostage, so that the Pope would believe I came to help, not to attack. How strange, I thought, that I should rush to succor my bitterest enemy.

It was well that I did so—for at almost the same moment in Germany, Heinrich raised the standard of insurrection against me.

9

Secret information reached me that my unfortunate son had fallen for the blandishments of the Milanese and the Lombard League—though as yet I did not know the full extent of his treachery. To ease the situation as much as possible, I issued a public statement which implied nothing more serious than a misunderstanding between father and son—that Heinrich was guilty only of "boyish defiance." Privately, I proceeded with the grim business which had actuated my rapid rescue of the Pope.

Gregory received me cordially; he could hardly do otherwise, as I was the only Christian ruler who had rushed to his relief. Graciously he declined to hold Corrado as hostage. But a man of eighty-seven does not take much trouble to dissemble, and under the surface cordiality it was easy to detect the querulous distrust, the acid hate. Actually, he seemed genuinely pleased with the difficulties which beset me in Germany, though he did not relish publishing the ban of excommunication against my son. He had sought to catch me, but he himself had been caught in a trap. Heinrich secretly had negotiated an outright offensive and defensive alliance with the Pope's Lombard friends; and now Gregory was forced to excommunicate his friends' ally.

As more details came to me, I discovered that Heinrich's negotiations with the Lombards had been conducted by none other than Anselm von Justingen—that bearded, booming envoy who had brought to me in Palermo the German princes' summons to their kingship. After twenty-three years, I still remembered well the echoes of his voice in the cathedral. Precisely why he shifted his allegiance I never learned; but it was a cunningly defiant move on Heinrich's part to use him for a messenger. Eagerly Heinrich took the Milanese bait on a hook disguised as the Iron Crown of Lombardy—which the Milanese, despite my power, had consistently denied to me. Heinrich thought to split the Empire in half; the Milanese thought that war between the two parts would destroy the whole. Both were wrong.

When Heinrich's Lombard alliance became known to the world, the Pope was infuriated. He could not support the Lombards against me; he would not support me. Yet I had but lately saved the tiara by the sword of Empire. Unhappy man! Ever so delicately I demanded that he punish the Lombards for their treachery.

Meanwhile I prepared to handle Heinrich's insurrection in my own way. To indicate that my patience was at an end, I issued another statement; King Heinrich VII, I said, is "a madman who imagines he can hold the northern throne against us." And though he is my son, I added, "the power of the Empire takes no account of individuals." To Heinrich I sent Hermann von Salza with my demand for unconditional surrender; to the German nobles I announced my imminent arrival in Germany.

At the earliest possible date in the spring I set out, not with an immense army, as everyone expected, but with a few retainers, a full exchequer, and my menagerie. I was well aware that north of the Alps gold and glamour would be far more useful to me than hordes of men-at-arms. I returned to Germany not as the impoverished boy from Apulia, but as a glittering monarch of world fame, surrounded by exotic animals, Saracens, Arabian dancing girls, Ethiopians, eunuchs, astrologers and wizards. I came from the mysterious southland. I came as a German Emperor. I was a dazzling legend. My mightiest weapon was my name.

Among the members of my party was my heir Corrado; the time had come for him to play a role in Germany. But Enzo, little Federico, Manfredo and the others I left behind, in the care of dear Berardo. Only if Berardo stayed would Bianca consent to come, and I had no intention of leaving her—though her presence might complicate a plan I had in mind. Piero was not among us, for he had been sent to England to have a look at the Princess Isabella, sister to King Henry III, with the thought that I might take on a new bride. This had been the suggestion of the Pope when I saw him at Rieti; he was anxious to tie England closer to Italy, for he was discontented with the slowness of collections. For my part, I saw advantages in England's restlessness with Pope and Curia—though certainly an English marriage would require careful explanations to the French. And—perhaps it would be necessary to make careful explanations to Bianca, too. In a sudden burst of cowardice, I postponed this problem. . . .

We sailed from Rimini, a regular Noah's Ark, to Aquileia of unhappy memories, and disembarking, pressed on to Udine and the north—for the Lombards had closed the Brenner. At the border I dismissed all officials of the Kingdom of Sicily, retaining only those who served the Empire. I had no need of them, for as we progressed my retinue grew by tens and hundreds and finally into thousands. I was followed not only by my supporters, but by a marveling populace which gaped at the elephant and giraffe, the leopards, apes and camels. They told one another that the elephant would copulate only if fed the magical mandragora root. Their amazement grew when I spoke to the keepers in Arabic, and they stared at my Saracens with the awe due a bodyguard of angels. Of the curtained palanquins which concealed the dancing girls, they whispered in excitement; and from the wizards and astrologers they drew back in fear—though Michael the Scott, for one, politely tipped his iron hat to them. All came running from far and near to see us pass.

When we arrived at Ratisbon the news flew ahead by carrier pigeons—and the news did its work. As I had hoped, the rebellion collapsed. Moreover, the spreading anarchy suddenly gave way to order. It was as though princes and bishops and all the people had responded intuitively to an unspoken command. The insurrectionists themselves were paralyzed, as if frozen in action. Heinrich attempted flight, but to aid him no one would lift a finger. At the castle of Trifels (where Richard Coeur de Lion had been held prisoner and the crown jewels were now kept), he gave orders for defense, countermanded them. He could not decide which way to turn. Suddenly, to Hermann von Salza he offered his unconditional surrender. His life was forfeit, for the son had raised his hand against the father. I commanded that he be held until I should sit in judgment.

In Worms, I was welcomed in the streets by a multitude, and at the cathedral by twelve bishops standing as rigid as if portrayed in a mosaic. Among them I recognized the face of Landulf of Worms, one of the secret instigators of Heinrich's rebellion. Choler rose within me; before a word of greeting was spoken I ordered the wretched cleric to be seized and stripped of his vestments on the spot. All were aghast at my vehemence; but when I saw him humbled, my anger cooled, and the ceremony proceeded. And I thought: the Pope will protest—but let him scratch where it itches!

Deliberately I delayed the judgment of my son for some days, for fear that in my wrath I might act to excess. My anger against him had hardened; and the very fact that he was my son made my anger more violent. I told myself that I must take care to act as if he were only an ordinary traitor and not my son. And yet, while I thought of him aside from his treachery, my heart softened; for I remembered how as a tiny child he had clutched me when we rode horseback on the same saddle. So I was torn between two emotions, which bled me within.

At last I sat in solemn judgment. The hall was jammed with nobles and ecclesiastics, all charged with the nervous excitement of expectation. At a trumpet blast, I entered and took my place up on the throne; I was dressed in the full regalia of Empire. Then at the cry of a herald and the clank of armor, a door opened and King Heinrich, in chains and shorn of crown and sword, was escorted before me. He flung himself at my feet, bowing his head to the floor in abject submission.

I tightened my lips and said nothing; inwardly I fought for control. The silence became protracted, oppressive. All waited, but I spoke not a word. My glance did not change, but my heart struggled between fury, scorn and compassion. Finally Hermann von Salza from native goodness implored, "My Lord, I pray you —let him stand.

I drew breath. "Rise," I said.

As Heinrich stood, he burst into sobs, muttering brokenly, "*O gravenvolle Stunde! O Gott, was harret mein . . . !*"

I spoke in a clear, sharp voice. "For such a crime as has been committed, no defense is possible. Yet mercy must ever temper justice. The Bishop Landulf and Anselm von Justingen we restore to our Imperial favor, as having been misguided. The Lombard emissaries taken as captives, we release. The King Heinrich VII, alas our son and firstborn, we banish forever from our sight, and condemn him to prison for the rest of his life.

"For him we mourn. Thus we pronounce our sentence upon those who would have destroyed us. We pray that God in his infinite mercy will forgive them all."

Weeping and collapsed, Heinrich was dragged away.

Beside me I heard von Salza murmur: "It is written: 'And Abraham stretched forth his hand and took the knife to slay his son.' "

10

At first Heinrich was imprisoned in Heidelberg; then shortly transferred to Apulia. I placed him in the custody of Manfredo Lancia—I wanted to be certain he would have good treatment. I chose for him the lonely and inaccessible Rocca San Felice, which in everything belied its name. From its grim windows he could see the dominating height of Monte Vulture, and recall that on the other side lay Melfi and the life he had forsworn. I ordered for him every comfort and many books; but he paced the floor and rarely chose to read. I wondered if time and thought would change him.

My hands were full in Germany, and I found little opportunity for regrets. Much that was done could not be undone, but I made some effort to bring some order out of the chaos of existing laws. I hoped the day might come when I could issue a single Constitution for all the jealous principalities of Germany. I issued the Proclamation of the Landpeace of Mainz, a substitute, and published it in the German language—the first time the common tongue, not Latin, had been so used for an official document.

I ended the Welf-Waibling blood feud in Germany; though in Italy the Guelf-Ghibelline contest was to rage on and on. I chose to call to me in peace Otto von Lüneburg, the nephew of that Otto the Welf whom I had vanquished. This new Otto was the Welf heir. Him I confirmed in his lands as an Imperial fief, and created for him the new Dukedom of Brunswick. In return he placed his hands in mine, and on the crucifix swore perpetual allegiance. He was pleased and relieved, I saw, for he was a man who disliked animosities.

I sat in judgment of many cases of importance. Fortunately the heresy hunting against the Luciferians (who worshiped Satan as the Creator) had declined. Under Heinrich it had reached such a peak that even burghers and nobles had been accused, and every denunciation was accepted as a proof of guilt. No man could sleep well in his bed. The Pope's Inquisitor, Konrad von Marburg, a gloomy, fanatical, nightmare-haunted man, was finally murdered as a reward for having fed the flames too well with human flesh. So all my efforts now were directed toward calming the population, striving for order and a respect for the processes of law.

This hoped-for calm was badly shattered by a massacre of Jews in Fulda, in which hundreds were rounded up and burned on specially erected platforms in their cemetery. Happily some of the children were snatched from the fire and baptized upon the spot, else the toll would have been much worse. All this horror was occasioned by the death of a Christian boy, whom some mad friar (himself no doubt guilty of the rape and strangulation) claimed had been killed in a Jewish ritual murder. Now both parties, Christians and Jews, came to me clamoring for a decision, for the Jews denied what the Christians affirmed.

I lost no time in the hearing, for the Christians came bearing the pathetically mangled and stinking corpse of the boy as *prima-facie* evidence. "Bury him at once," I said, pointing to the body; "the dead are fit for nothing else."

Then came the wild charges and vehement denials, and I was hard put to prevent another riot. But the majesty of my presence prevailed, and I was able to hear all parties to the end. It was perfectly evident that the Jews were not guilty; and I so stated. However, to end the Christian muttering and to keep the peace, I imposed a heavy fine on the Jews as contributors to disorder. But I did not stop there.

"We do not believe," I declared, "that ritual murder is anywhere practiced under the tenets of Judaism. Nevertheless, we shall undertake a world-wide enquiry to establish the truth, and report to the people the results. For if ritual murders are possible, we shall slay every Jew in the Empire."

Thereupon, with the help of Michael the Scott, I wrote to leading churchmen, nobles, and scholars asking their opinions in the matter. Their replies were meaningless, and I decided on another step. I dictated the following statement:

"THESE men, being of different minds, have expressed different opinions, and have shown themselves incompetent to give an adequate judgment in the case. We, therefore, out of the secret depths of our own knowledge, have perceived that the simplest method of procedure against the Jews—allegedly guilty of the said crime—would be through the testimony of Jews converted to the Christian faith. They, now being opponents of Judaism, would have no reason to conceal what they might know against Judaism or against the laws of Moses or the books of the Old Testament.

"We ourselves in our wisdom, acquired from many books which our Majesty has studied, reasonably consider these Jews to have been proved innocent. Nevertheless we are anxious to satisfy the law and to calm the unlettered populace: hence we have decided in concurrence with the princes, nobles, wise men, abbots and Church dignitaries, to dispatch special messengers to all the kings of the western lands, requesting that they send us from their realms representatives of the newly-baptized who are learned in Jewish law."

The kings responded promptly, and a remarkable commission of learned men assembled at Hagenau. They deliberated for days, keeping detailed minutes of their proceedings. In due course they announced their conclusion that the Hebrew Scriptures forbade all blood sacrifices, that the Talmud and the Bereshith set forth severe penalties on animal sacrifices involving blood. On the basis of these findings, I issued an edict which forbade the accusation of ritual murder against Jews anywhere within the confines of the Empire. The results of this method of work, I am happy to say, created a profound impression.

But my happiness, as so often, was transitory. On the same day as the decision, when riding out of the Castle of Hagenau, I lost Michael the Scott. He died, as he had predicted, from a falling stone. But he had thought a mountain would slide, or a cliff topple upon him. Instead, a guard leaned far out on a tower to cheer us, and a loose stone slipped from under his hand. It caught Michael cleanly on the iron hat, which proved no protection at all. My anger at the guard gave way to sorrow, for this was clearly an act of fate.

I missed my Scott enormously; he had become for me not only a useful prognosticator of the things I wished to prognosticate, but a vast encyclopedia of knowledge always at hand. He himself, I think, would have been not only surprised but amazed at the accurate fulfillment of his prediction. But certainly pleased. Therefore I solemnly affirmed at his grave that he had known all in advance—the day, the hour, the moment.

Would that he had! Would that he could have foreseen for me the future . . . !

II

FROM PIERO in London came word of Isabella. This daughter of King John had been proposed only a few years before as a bride for my son Heinrich. Now, Piero wrote, she was twenty (I was forty), comely of face and figure, modest and charming in manner. She was not too tall, even in her slippers, and she moved with such grace that she was a delight to the eye. Her cheeks were pink as appleblossoms, colored thus by nature, for she used no paint. Her breasts were well formed, neither too small nor too large, with the paps well marked. She had no hair on her upper lip, and her breath was sweet. She loved music and song.

Piero had not, however, been able to arrange to have her seen naked by trustworthy ladies—a usage I had decided to adopt from the Kings of France. The English, Piero wrote, have a strange attitude toward exposure of the human body—the climate being so raw and damp that people rarely see each other naked—and nude statuary does not exist at all. King Henry had been shocked and aghast when such a suggestion had been made; and promptly produced the sworn statements of five doctors that the girl was healthy and without blemish.

There was much resentment in England, too, that so many nobles on the Continent thought it degrading for an Emperor to marry the sister of an English King. It was being pointed out in England with considerable feeling that the Princess Isabella could trace her descent through a long line of kings to Alfred the Great, and through him, probably, to Adam and Eve. A Roman Emperor need no longer consider the people of Britain as savages. Besides, her proposed dowry was thirty thousand marks sterling: a record sum.

At once I gave Piero full authority to act in my behalf, and he concluded all arrangements. The Princess Isabella was brought from the Tower of London, her residence, to Westminster Court, where Piero and my other envoys waited upon her. There, solemnly, Piero placed a ring upon her finger in token of betrothal, and hailed her as Empress of the Romans. Poor Piero!—this was the only betrothal in which he had ever participated; my demands on him were so great that for all practical purposes he was married to me. He had neither time nor inclination to serve a mistress in addition to his master. Year after year I had drawn from him all the strength of his body and his mind. . . .

As for Isabella's appearance at court—of this I need have no fear, Piero wrote, for he had been shown her trousseau. It was the talk of all London. She had green and blue dresses of the finest French stuffs, trimmed with ermine. She had scarlet robes furred with doeskin and embroidered with gold. She had a glittering necklace of mixed jewels, and caskets of other jewels to choose as she wished. Her crown was of solid gold, worked with the images of four English kings. For the bridal bed she brought silken counterpanes and the softest cushions, and her cooking pots were of unalloyed silver. It had been arranged for three thousand knights to escort her to Canterbury Cathedral for her prayers; and thence to Sandwich where a ship awaited, provisioned with fine wines, grain and bacon.

I thought it wise, at this point, to send Bianca back to Italy—more for her sake than for mine. Because I had released the Lombard captives, she could safely return to her ancestral home in the Piemonte—Vercelli. "Take heart," I said, "this parting will not be for long."

She smiled wryly. "I hope my Lord speaks with greater accuracy than his astrologers," she said.

She left that night, shrouded in veils, and guarded by my most trustworthy men. I think—but I am not sure—that she was crying. At her departure I felt a deep loneliness, and recalled the words of the poet Abu t-Tayyib.

When you part from a person
Who could have retained you,
And did not—
In reality, that person
Has parted from you. . . .

But from Bianca Lancia I had no intention of parting. She was the only woman in my life who had stimulated such an emotion.

Just now, I felt no eagerness to receive my new bride. It was Pier della Vigna I was anxious to see: momentous plans were afoot, and I had the utmost need of him. I was in fact so busy that when Isabella proceeded from Antwerp to Köln I kept her waiting for six whole weeks before the wedding. I kept her occupied, however, with pageants and feasting, and she took no umbrage.

She was met by riders on Spanish horses who performed the symbolic nuptial breaking of lances. She was beguiled by ships sailing on dry land over silken waves. She was entertained by singers and players of instruments unknown to her. She so intrigued the women of Köln that they begged to see her face; and as she rode through the town she dropped her veil and hood, to the people's utmost delight. She was indeed lovely, and all praised her.

It was a cool English beauty, as I realized at once when I met her, wholly unlike the beauty to which I had become accustomed. Her reserve was more than good manners, more than the submissiveness of women. It was almost as though she had no sex, but only beauty. She also had a certain naïve charm, for she sang to me at once her favorite song in English: "Sumer Is Icumen In." Her sweet, clear notes quite touched my heart; and I felt a certain regret that she had not run away with some fine young prince to live happily ever after in an enchanted castle. She managed bravely, too, to express herself in Latin.

"I would that my Lord the Emperor some day will visit my brother King Henry in England," she said. "England is a fair land of green fields and small fowls that make much melody."

"Perhaps," I said, as to a child, "perhaps some day, Princess."

We were married in the Cathedral of Worms, in midsummer.

Four kings, twelve dukes (including a representative of the Russian Grand Duke), thirty counts and margraves, uncounted prelates, knights in the thousands—all attended the ceremony. Banners, blooded horses, crucifixes, armor, jewels, drums, trumpets, robes of the rainbow, merged and mingled into a panoramic whole. Jousting and feasting continued for four days and nights. Minnesingers and *trovatori* held contests of song. My menagerie was constantly on view. Never had Germany tasted such glory of Empire. Men become drunk on my name.

After the wedding, I arranged for a court astrologer to announce that the first night was not auspicious for consummation of the marriage, and the Emperor therefore would defer entering his bride's bed. Actually I was so tired physically that I wished nothing but sleep, and I cared not a whistle for the amazed discussion which would occupy the court. Certainly continence on my part had never been heard of before. On the second night I went quietly to the chamber earlier than expected, and found a frightened and lonely Isabella just beginning her Rosary: "*Salve Regina. Mater Misericordiae. . . .*"

She paused and said, "I bid welcome to my Lord the Emperor." Then she added in a whisper, so that her two English ladies-in-waiting might not hear: "My Lord—must I always be surrounded by black eunuchs whose faces look like hideous old masks . . . must I . . . ?"

"You must—always," I said gently. "You must—to assure that you have only royal issue."

She turned her head quickly, and I thought that she was about to cry.

"This is the price you must pay for being a Queen and Empress," I went on, with a note of weariness—for being a King and Emperor also had its price. And part of the price was *fornicatus* with Queens . . . even young and beautiful queens . . . for in the truest sense we certainly were never married. . . .

Next morning the court astrologer announced that the Empress had been made pregnant and would bear a son. The astrologer did not say, and he did not know, that the Emperor had performed his function only with considerable effort. Nor was the reason the bride's essential coldness. The Emperor's mind was not occupied with thoughts of the flesh; he was no longer interested in the Song of Songs.

The Emperor's mind was occupied with thoughts of war.

V

CAESAR

I

"ITALY is my heritage, and all the world knows it," I wrote to the Pope. And to the people of Rome I sent a manifesto: "Behold, ye have a King and Caesar who has offered his person for the greater glory of the Roman Empire—a King who has spared neither his treasure nor his labors—a Caesar who with his constant calling stirs you from your slumbers . . .!"

The time had come for the Romans to recall their ancient role in world affairs. And the time was soon to come when Rome herself once again would become the capital of the Empire, center of the world. This was my dream. To the role of Caesar Augustus as lawgiver must be added the triumph of arms: *arma et leges.* Not military action or warfare for itself, but the force of arms to be used against disturbers of peace. The goal is peace, I wrote: "The Roman Empire must strive earnestly for peace, urgently devote itself to the establishment of justice among the peoples of the world. It stands as a mirror before the world."

I thought of the Empire as one state out of many states. I wanted the unity of the Empire, and peace. I wanted the unity of Italy, and peace. I could have neither so long as the petty nobles of the Lombard towns maintained their oppressive laws, continued blood-letting among themselves, or turned in concert against the Empire. I could have neither so long as a militant Papacy followed the temporal policy of dividing the world to rule the world, dividing Italy to rule Italy. I would have preferred the Lombards as allies, not enemies; I would have preferred the Pope as an ally, not an enemy. But military conflict was inevitable; they were irreconcilable. We all knew the truth and prepared for the worst.

I had shown, I thought, great patience, great forbearance. Had the Pope made an honest effort to mediate the Lombard crisis, some reasonable compromise might have been reached. But in fact he intensified his efforts to aid the rebellion, sending money, and lending clerics as secret agents of discord. On my part, I charged the Pope with winking at heresy among his Lombard friends.

In Milano, heretics had invaded the churches and hung crucifixes upside down; in Mantova, the Paterenes had risen, seized the bishop and crucified him above the altar in the cathedral. So long as the nobles successfully turned the selfsame rabble also against me, the Pope took little or no action. I made one last effort to urge the Pope to intervention, but I received no reply to my letter. I sent Pier della Vigna to Rome to appeal to the Curia. At last the Pope wrote; he had failed to answer, he said, "out of a kind of dreamy forgetfulness, one might say." As for the rebellion in Lombardy, he had no comment; instead he was greatly vexed with the state of affairs in Sicily, under the heretical laws I had promulgated. Moreover, I seemed to have forgotten the Donation of Constantine:

> CONSTANTINE had found it seemly that the Viceregent of the Prince of the Apostles . . . should possess supreme power over the affairs and persons of the entire world. Christian Emperors must subject their actions not to the Roman Pontiff alone . . . but the necks of kings and princes must be bent under the knee of the humblest priest. . . .

So, according to Gregory (interpreting Constantine), every priest was omnipotent.

Two, however, could play at the game of divide from within. I had not forgotten that His Holiness the Bishop of Rome was loved by neither nobles nor plebians. I had not forgotten the number of times Gregory had been forced to flee for his life. I recalled, too, that the majestic buildings of antiquity now served as fortresses within Rome itself. These structures I quietly bought, one by one, and returned each as an Imperial fief to the noble family who occupied it—thus making the fortress my own, and the nobles my vassals.

The common people I planned to win both by largesse and the reawakening of their sense of destiny. I would become for them a true Caesar, triumphant, messianic, godlike, almost divine. I would arouse the Roman people, I said, "to scale once more the peaks of their ancient greatness." Bread, peace, glory—these would be the rewards.

Nevertheless, like some barbarian, I was forced to cross the

Alps to invade Italy and my own Empire. It was only a probing expedition because I was not yet ready for a massive effort. While the German princes at Mainz had enthusiastically agreed to support all efforts to maintain the unity of Empire, they now suddenly found themselves occupied with other cares. So the German knights who accompanied me were very, very few. I relied chiefly on infantry levies from the loyal towns, volunteer knights from all parts of Italy, Sicilian cavalry, Saracen archers, and the mercenary troops of Ezzelino da Romano.

This Ezzelino da Romano had come to my attention some years before. He was a ferocious man—ferocious in everything: hunger, ambition, activity, cruelty, loyalty. He was short, hairy over all his body, and quivered constantly with rage. He was feared by his enemies "like the Devil." If he was ravenous, he was also strong; if cruel, also audacious; if ambitious, also fearless; if loyal, also tractable. While most men saw only his vices, which were an exaggeration of the vices of lesser men, I saw also his virtues—and for all the evil in him, I trusted him more than the publicly virtuous. He was what he was. For my estimation of his character, and the promised reward of my daughter Selvaggia (who was of a wild temperament herself) in marriage, he repaid me with astonishing devotion. Would that I could say the same of many of the "good" men who surrounded me!

When I came down from the Brenner I found Ezzelino fully in control of Verona. He had lived day and night in armor, and his hands were calloused from wielding sword and lance. I hastened on, to secure the route to Cremona, a loyal town and my projected headquarters for the campaigns to come. With my departure Ezzelino was attacked in force by troops of the Lombard League, headed by the Lord of Vicenza; urgently Ezzelino called me to his aid.

I responded with a forced march of my heavy cavalry and archers, covering the seventy miles from Cremona in one day and two nights—not, as my enemies supposed, to take them in the rear, but to veer suddenly eastward toward the town of Vicenza itself. When the news reached Ezzelino's attackers, they decamped in haste, leaving baggage and tents in an effort to reach Vicenza before me. They were too late. I had "flown through the air," people said: a miracle. I demanded the town's surrender. The Pope's agents urged refusal. So I took the town, and allowed Ezzelino to give it over to plunder—as was his custom. But on second thought, I ordered him to restore the property of those who had not opposed me, and to punish only the rebels. I observed that Ezzelino's men were more than thorough in stripping naked all and sundry, seizing for themselves everything movable.

Ezzelino himself was a true tyrant: his rule was based entirely on guile and force. Reason and justice were meaningless concepts to him. He felt concern only with the maintenance of his own authority, his own wishes, his own will. Yet, in the midst of all the uproar, the looting and burning, I myself saw Ezzelino with his sword kill a mercenary who was raping the wife of a noble on the street.

"You surprise us, Ezzelino," I said. "You will ruin your reputation by such acts of charity."

His dark face lighted, the hard mouth unbent. "My Lord, I would have struck down you, had you—in public—been guilty of so great a scandal."

I laughed; I thought it well that Ezzelino was not my enemy. Later, when calm had been restored, we walked together in the garden of the bishop's palace, where I had taken up residence, as the bishop, in his guilt, had hidden.

"Ser Ezzelino," I said, "we have very little advice to give you, as obviously you are an able soldier and a determined administrator. We would recommend but one virtue: discretion."

So speaking, I drew my dagger and loped off the heads of the tallest flowers (chrysanthemums—the flower of the dead) we happened to be passing.

"I understand you prefectly, my Lord," Ezzelino said, "and I will behave accordingly."

Within a few days I prepared to leave Vicenza. It was now mid-November, and I had no wish to battle winter snows. Yet, even in my haste, I could not resist my usual game with the astrologers. On the death of Michael the Scott I had elevated Maestro Teodoro to the post of Court Philosopher. Nevertheless I called on him from time to time to provide me a useful forecast —as, in the popular mind, philosopher, astrologer, and wizard were one. Now I chose to tease him.

"By what gate, Maestro, will we leave Vicenza?" I said. "We wish a written answer, delivered in advance, but not to be opened until we have quit the town."

"As your Majesty wishes," he answered, bowing so gravely

that I felt more than a twinge of regret for the humorous nonsense of Michael the Scott.

I underestimated my man. To thwart him completely I had ordered secretly a breach to be made in the walls for my passage. Consider my astonishment when, on the road, I opened his envelope and read this cryptic phrase: "By the new gate."

By old gate or new gate, I was glad to escape from the miasma of warfare. I could, for a while, put these problems behind me. I rode, like a swallow cutting the air, to a rendezvous with Bianca. And thereafter, refreshed and happy again, on to new responsibilities in Austria.

I was concerned about the succession. Not only had the prediction that Isabella was pregnant of a son proved an error, but seventeen months passed before she had issue at all. The child was a girl, a serious blow to my hopes. I had wanted a son by an English queen to rule the Germans. As I had no choice, I turned now to the son of Yolanda.

I called a Diet of German princes in Wien, and requested that nine-year-old Corrado be chosen the King of the Germans. He was elected as Konrad IV without concessions on my part, and without the slightest opposition—so powerful had I become. Further, he was designated the future Emperor. I chose, however, to delay the announcement of his election, and to postpone his coronation until some indefinite date in the future. I had learned my lesson. He was to rule, not independently, but as my deputy. His tutors and advisers I selected with utmost care—not German knights and bishops, but scholars of diverse origins and points of view. Also, he was to be taught with other boys. I placed him under the special care of the Neapolitan Landolfo Caraccioli, a page, a responsible and sympathetic youth. (I had not forgotten my own Guglielmo.)

The official posts, of necessity, were filled by German princes. Among these was a man about whom I held grave doubts, but who was chosen Regent on recommendation of the bishops. His name was Heinrich Raspe—a name I disliked on intuition. He was, I thought, too big an eater: his jowls were puffed like two loaves of bread, and he could scarcely bow for his belly. No doubt his moneybags looked similar.

The princes who had proved so coy about my initial campaign against the Lombards, now lured by my successes, flocked to my standard. They proved troublesome allies, because they could not understand why I continued negotiating, negotiating, instead of striking, striking. I did not give up hope, even at this eleventh hour, that some accommodation might be worked out between Pope and Lombards. I was distressed by the cost of war, the heavy taxes, and the waste of funds.

I sent, once more, Hermann von Salza to plead my cause—though by now I felt no positive results were possible. In actual fact, the Lombards were frightened and wished to compromise; but the Pope, backed by a suddenly alarmed Venezia, made no serious effort to advance peace.

Thus I accepted the inevitable. After a winter in Wien I returned to Italy, accompanied by two thousand heavily armed knights and their retainers. Once again the wide boots and long staves of Germans were to be seen in Italy. At the moment we crossed the divide I seized a standard, an Imperial Eagle, raised it aloft, and shouted for the world to hear: "*Roma caput mundi* . . .!"

Such was the beginning . . . of the end.

2

DETAILS of battles do not much beguile me. I find much more interesting the consideration of results—the way the course of history may be changed by the slaughter of so-many-thousand men, as though the very weight of corpses counted in the scales of fate. Another factor, too, is the element of chance: how astonishing that an army superior in numbers, arms and generalship may be defeated or even routed by some single stroke of ill luck, such as a sudden thunderstorm out of season or the unexpected flooding of a river.

To defeat the rebel Lombards, but two courses were open to me: smash their armies in open combat, or besiege and destroy their towns. Though their armies were certainly equal to mine in numbers and armament, I preferred to meet them in open combat. Warfare of strategy had almost ceased to exist since the final shattering of the ancient Roman legions, and battles had become haphazard affairs in which two groups of armored men lined up opposite each other, then rushed together hewing and hacking. As I had studied Roman history with much care, I hoped to reintroduce the element of surprise.

It was evident, however, that the Lombard armies would be reluctant to meet me in open combat because of my aura of invincibility; so of necessity I assembled my siege engines—mangonels, battering rams, catapults, trebuchets—and sulfur and crude oil, the ingredients of Greek fire. The walls of the towns were thick and well-defended; sieges were long, difficult, and costly. I resolved in advance to negotiate surrenders whenever possible—with the exception of Milano.

Milano was to me what Carthage had been to ancient Rome. I could never be secure as Emperor, the city of Rome itself could never be secure as the seat of Empire, so long as the military power of Milano dominated all of northern Italy. Thus a union of north and south was not possible. The arrogance of Milano, from its riches and its strength, was not new. At one point my grandfather Barbarossa had felt himself forced to burn the city and reduce it to rubble; but straightway it had risen again, for it lies at a strategic crossroad of the Lombard plain. What could I accomplish that my grandfather could not? As part of a united Italy, Milano would become a part of the whole; and with a strong central authority in Rome, would be governed accordingly. Actually, in winter the climate was raw and damp—foggy for months on end; the site was suited only for a military garrison. Why not a new city in a more favorable location? The idea, to me, was not audacious. Had I not built Lucera from nothing on the Apulian plain. . . ?

I turned now to my first task of attempting to lure the Lombard armies into the open. My forces comprised about fifteen thousand men—the largest army assembled since my grandfather's time. The Lombard's force was somewhat smaller than mine; but nearby they had the walled city of Brescia for support. After a series of feints it became clear that under no circumstances would the Lombard army accept open battle, and I found myself in the ambiguous position of striking at an enemy who was not there. We mutually came to pause no great distance from one another, but they so encamped as to be fully protected by the marshy banks of the river Oglio, a stream which flows from Lake Iseo into the Po. A fleet of barges—not armored men and horses—was needed. My only hope was stratagem.

Suddenly I broke camp and marched southward toward Cremona, my headquarters. As the time was late November, the Lombards assumed that I had given up all fighting for the winter; so they themselves broke camp and set off for Milano. When I learned of this, I ordered the foot soldiers and baggage train to keep their course, but under cover of darkness and fog I split off with my archers and heavy cavalry, and turned about to the north. As the Lombards marched up the left branch of the Oglio, I followed on the right, and by a forced march outdistanced them. Near the little town of Cortenuova I waited in ambush, well hidden by groves of poplar trees, for them to cross the river. The only sounds were the quacking of ducks, the hissing of geese, the creak of peasants' cart wheels hidden in the river fog.

The Lombards' first knowledge of my presence was a knight

on a white horse, bearing the Imperial Eagle, who seemed to materialize before their eyes from the swirling mists of early morning. "Prepare for combat with your Emperor!" the knight cried. Trumpets sounded. Flights of arrows darkened the air. The mounted knights charged to the battle cry, "*Miles Roma! Miles Imperator*!" Taken was the Lombard leader, Pietro Tiepolo, *podestà* and son of the Doge of Venezia; taken was their standard and its chariot—utmost humiliation—the *carroccio*. Its cross was found mired in mud under a heap of overturned wagons.

In these words, Pier della Vigna hurried to impart the news to a waiting world:

> WHO can describe the heaps of corpses or the number of captives? God, a just judge, at last regarded the rights of the Emperor and overthrew the pride of the Lombards: they lost the *carroccio* and their *podestà*. Each of our men slew as many as he would and took as many as he would. Caesar himself smote the foe with his own hands. The Germans dyed their swords in blood; the happy knights of the Kingdom fought with ardor by the side of their Prince; the warriors of Pavia avenged themselves completely on the Milanese; the loyal Cremonese satiated their axes with blood; the Saracens emptied their quivers. Never in any war were so many corpses piled up; had not night come on suddenly, none of the enemy would have fled from Caesar's hands.

I made an entry into Cremona by the Porta Romana, after the manner of the ancient Romans—a true triumphal procession. First came trumpeters and my guard. Then Caesar. I rode my black horse, "Dragone," wore a crown of laurel, and carried an upraised sword. Behind me came wagons and carts heaped with captured arms and booty; after that, the prisoners, limping and stumbling and gazing apprehensively at the cheering people along the streets; and finally, my elephant with Saracen trumpeters in a wooden tower, pulling the Milanese *carroccio* with their *podestà*, in fetters, bound upon his back. The crowds pulsated with excitement at thus seeing their bitter enemy Milano humbled in the dust, and taunted the prisoners without mercy. But I myself used another tactic: some of the prisoners I sent to my palace in Foggia—then I released them, that they might return to Milano and tell of the wonders they had seen in Apulia.

The Lombard League seemed to dissolve at a single defeat;

Milano was left with but five supporting towns. Nonetheless, I was not deceived. The walls of Milano were impregnable; the wealth of Milano, enormous. The amputation of a limb does not necessarily destroy the body. Yet, if Milano was not finally defeated, at least the Pope by the battle of Cortenuova was reduced to desperation. At Gregory's age, only a man whose life forces burned with the intense flame of hatred could survive such a blow. Gregory, I knew, was just such a man.

So I resolved to provide for him the utmost in provocation: I dispatched the captured *carroccio* to Rome, that it might be carried in triumph along the way of the Caesars to the heights of the Campidoglio. It was dedicated to the Senate and People of Rome. Bitterly the Pope opposed its entry; but he was impotent to enforce his wishes. And ultimate horror of horrors: it was escorted by an honor guard of cardinals. Some among them claimed to see my handwriting on the walls of Rome.

While Gregory, in fury, isolated himself in his palace, the *carroccio* was erected like a holy relic on five marble columns, and dedicated to my victory.

3

MILANO sued for peace. The city sent a friar, a Francescan, to arrange terms. They offered to give money indemnity, troops for a crusade, and to burn their banners. I replied that I wanted unconditional surrender. Everyone—including me—believed that the Milanese rulers were "slippery as eels." Riots took place in the city; churches were desecrated and God blasphemed for the defeat. The friar came to ask, if Milano surrendered unconditionally, what would I do to the city? I gave him an oracle: "I will do only what I must."

The Milanese decided to strengthen the walls and fight on. A secret deputation from a group of nobles urged me to attack the city, declaring they would open the gates; I did not believe them. The Pope dispensed with his covert aid, and openly took over the task of defense. As Papal Legate he appointed Gregorio da Montelungo, one of my most implacable enemies. This man was a general disguised as a prelate, though in Milano he openly wore armor over his stocky body as he supervised the city's defenses. He was, in fact, a gifted organizer, shrewd and untiring, as I well knew, and his purpose was to provide a rallying point for all my enemies of every class and station. In fact it was he who finally established this fusion under the single name "Guelf" for all opponents of the "Ghibelline" Emperor. I was more uneasy over his presence in Milano than at the presence of ten thousand knights.

With the new year came all sorts of recruits to my cause. First and foremost, a son from Isabella. Thus I had another heir to replace the one I had lost, and I named him Enrico. By now the story of my struggle against the Lombards was well known to the world, and help came from the four corners of the earth. Besides my soldiers from all of Italy and much of Germany, came knights from Burgundy and Provence; troops from the Kings of England, France, Hungary, and Castile; Greek lancers from the Emperor of Nicaea; Arab horsemen from the Sultan of Egypt. It was a vast army, polyglot, colorful, costly, and difficult to control. (Alas—not many people spoke so many languages as I.) I seemed to all invincible.

In Cremona I held a council of war to decide which of the five rebel towns to attack. Said Ezzelino da Romano: "Strike the snake on the head—I advise my Lord to begin with Brescia. . . ." He meant that the fall of Brescia, Milano's closest and strongest ally, would in effect isolate Milano, protect our flank, and fear would dominate the hearts of the Milanese. So, early in August I deployed all my troops around Brescia, and my menagerie as well—which the wondering Brescians could see from the heights of their well-fortified towers. We drew deep breaths, and hurled ourselves upon the walls.

From the very first hours the whole undertaking was ill-omened. Ezzelino had dispatched to me the famed Spanish military engineer, Calamandrinus. He was taken captive en route by a roaming party of Brescians, and sent to serve the town instead. He was offered the alternative of death or a beautiful wife and riches in their service; willingly he turned all his inventiveness against me. His missiles were exceptionally effective against my engines of war, and my siege towers he managed consistently to burn. We were never able to get close enough to mount the walls. The siege increased in fury and in savagery: each side tied prisoners in exposed positions to ward off assault (a favorite device of my grandfather Barbarossa), but nothing was accomplished save butchery. I found, too, a lack of vigilance among my multilingual forces, and the Brescians in sorties took prisoners at will.

After an inconclusive fortnight, I thought it well to negotiate. I sent as my representative the well-known Bernardo di Rossi of Parma. He was a big, impressive man, famed for his ability to lay about him with a battle-ax; and equally famed for his powers of persuasion in negotiation. He returned to say that he could get nowhere with the Brescians. I believed him—and much time was to pass before I learned the truth about the noble Bernardo di Rossi of Parma.

Next we were harassed by a plague which broke out among the animals of our camp. The knights' horses died, our cattle sickened, all food ran short. It was said that the Brescians by night had driven infected animals among us. The disease itself was new to me, and I had no methods of control. Attempts at isolation of the sick proved ineffective, and the knights grumbled more about the loss of their horses than about the death of comrades-in-arms. Each day at our camp seemed worse than the last. Freshets and torrents of rain began to fall. Never have I seen such a deluge! We wallowed and slithered in mud, slipping and tripping over dead beasts, while the fire balls of Calamandrinus fell among us.

At the end of two months, we attempted a massive attack; it failed. In less than a week I broke off the siege, more disgusted than discouraged. This was, in retrospect, one of the gravest mistakes of my life. At whatever cost, I should have held on to the bitter end; I should have taken Brescia. For, in the end, the cost of failure was far greater than the cost of success.

The legend of my invincibility was, at last, seriously shaken. The Pope publicly rejoiced. The Lombard League took on new life. Like an affronted lion, I retired to Cremona to lick the wounds which I preferred to consider hardly more than scratches. I dismissed the foreign auxiliaries of my cosmopolitan army, and regrouped the most reliable of my Imperial forces. I thought to adopt new tactics the following spring, when war and weather went hand in hand.

Temporarily I forgot my military woes as I planned the knighting of my beloved son Enzo, "in face and figure our very image," as I described him. *Falconello*: lithe, strong, gay-hearted and amusing, a maker of poems and singer of songs . . . long golden curls . . . smiling blue eyes. Such was the charm of his person that he was the talk of all Italy by the time he was twenty. He was desired by all the girls who met him, desired by all the mothers and fathers for their daughters. But most of all he was desired by Pope Gregory for his niece.

In the weeks after the failure of my assault on Brescia I moved politically with great caution. I waited for secret information from the Curia, to know whether the wind blew toward peace or war. I thought the Pope might now be willing seriously to arbitrate, since his own position was so greatly enhanced. But he was a wolf on the trail—he scented blood. There would be no peace. So I threw caution aside, and married Enzo to Adelasia, the heiress of Sardegna. Thus Enzo became King of Sardegna and the island itself was attached to the Empire.

To Gregory this was a double insult. He considered Sardegna a fief of the Church; but about the loss of Enzo to his family he began to brood. He considered this an insult to his blood.

And now to all else was added his private, personal, vituperative hatred.

4

STRANGE and unsavory rumors about me began to circulate through the land. So luridly painted was my personal life that I began to wonder if I was not, as alleged, an insatiable monster of lust. The tales about the orgies of the Emperor Tiberius were as nothing compared to the orgies ascribed to me. Every conceivable form of sexual relation was described as my favorite. Lascivious were my tastes, not unlike the Muslims in Paradise. I was bathed in milk by scores of naked Arab dancing girls; I paddled in fountains of wine while nude youths filled my cup. All about were bare *servitelli negri* who made music, but paused now and then at my bidding to demonstrate their prowess at intercourse. Polished mirrors reflected everything. And on the walls, where I reveled, was painted the phallus flying with wings.

Such emphasis on the nude human body when nothing but the soul was supposed to be of interest to men! I wondered if, in the end, such rumors might not be self-defeating—stirring unanticipated thoughts and passions in pious people. But for me the rumors were a warning signal; I sensed at once their import.

As I could not return to Sicilia, I moved to winter quarters near Padova—into the monastery of Santa Giustina. The Empress, with her children Margherita and Enrico, I installed not far distant, at Noventa; Bianca, with Manfredo and Costanza, I housed in Padova in a palazzo whose arcade formed a street. As my guests I had Ezzelino da Romano and the Marquis d'Este—the latter no more than lukewarm in my cause. The good monks were hard put to maintain my menagerie, and at first were frightened of the elephant. But the beast proved so docile that even the Abbot, Fra Arnaldo, ended by feeding it hay. So honored was the Abbot by my presence that he unlocked his treasure chest and presented me with magnificent tapestries and a superbly decorated throne and footstool. Then, for good measure, he threw in thirty baskets of barley, twenty-four wainloads of hay, a fresh catch of sturgeon, and two huge casks of the best wine. I found it very pleasant to receive gifts *from* the Church for a change.

At this time a plump young Francescan, Fra Salimbene, came to me, through Piero, asking aid. He wished me to write my friend Fra Elias, the Minister-General in Assisi, requesting that the young friar be sent home to his father in Parma. The youth was very homesick and had not adjusted as yet to the rigors of his Order. I agreed to write the letter. Fra Salimbene overwhelmed me with gratitude, in a Latin oddly interlaced with the dialects of Toscana and Lombardia.

"Always I will love your Highness for this," he exclaimed, "and when I pen my chronicle I will speak of you with greatest favor!"

"We are astonished that so holy a youth as you comes for help to a King of such wicked repute," I said with gentle irony, for I was perfectly aware of the role of the friars—in spite of Fra Elias—in defaming my character.

"Oh no—it may be that your Highness is not a good Catholic," he answered in all simplicity, "but surely you love God and your own soul and are not so wicked as we are told to say!"

I thought he protested overmuch, and when he came to write his chronicle with those fingers of his like sausages, I would not shine too brightly in his pages.

In spite of the import of all the rumors, I thought it worthwhile to try one last time to bridge the ever-widening chasm which separated me from the Pope. For this mission I much preferred Hermann von Salza, but, as he was ailing, I dispatched him not to Rome but to my most learned doctors in Salerno. To Rome I sent Taddeo da Suessa, on whom I more and more relied; Count Tommaso D'Aquino; and dear Berardo, in his seventies, who stroked thoughtfully his all-white beard and declared it useless to try to reach an understanding with a man so old as the Pope—who was now approaching his one-hundredth year.

The results of this mission were indeed slight. I was informed in detail of Gregory's destruction of the palaces of my supporters—mosaics, marbles and ancient frescoes along with the defenses (later I attempted to have these monuments repaired). And shortly I was visited by a delegation of four prelates sent by the

Pope to inquire in detail as to my beliefs. To this latter I submitted in good grace—though with a host of witnesses.

Then I myself wrote, not to the Pope, but to the cardinals, pointing out that they were the successors of the Apostles, and that San Pietro himself had been equal among them and was only their spokesman. Such should be the role of the Pope. And now the cardinals should avert the imminent disaster which threatened the Church because of the impetuous actions of the present Pope. I myself was willing to bear patiently injustice inflicted by the Holy Father; but at a certain point I would requite violence with such measures as Caesars would use. It was not a threat, but a warning.

I settled down in Padova to wait. I lived each day for itself alone, and waited. Outwardly I was wholly absorbed in hawking, dancing, and the usual gay life of court. On Palm Sunday I appeared at the festa of the people of Padova; I ascended a dais erected in a meadow that I might watch their sports and merrymaking. I smiled and waved from my rustic throne. I wore a purple robe and the Imperial crown, and was attended by Pier della Vigna in his robes of state. It was a crystalline spring day, warm and sun-splashed, for the time was the end of March. Piero spoke to the people in my behalf, telling them how close they were to my heart.

Theirs was an ancient festa, probably far outdating the Christian calendar, and its climax was music and dancing. At the very peak of the merriment, a shadow passed over the edge of the sun. The shadow grew, and gradually the earth was darkened. It was an eclipse; but my astrologers had made no forecast. Slowly the face of the sun was consumed.

In panic, people ran from the meadow, screaming and crying aloud to God for mercy. Piero attempted to calm them, to explain what was happening, but no one could stem the rout. I sat calmly, unmoving, shading my eyes with my hand and studying the corona around the sun. For me it was a phenomenon of extraordinary interest; for the people it was a terrible omen.

In the next few days it was interpreted as a terrible omen for me. It was said that God no longer could bear to allow the sun to shine upon me.

For in those same black moments, in faraway Salerno, my trusted and honored Hermann von Salza lay dying.

And in Rome, the fiery madman Pope Gregory IX had assembled his cardinals in the Basilica of San Pietro, and, in a voice quavering with fury, read aloud to them the following words:

> "In the name of the Father, Son, and Holy Ghost, and of the blessed Apostles Petrus and Paulus, we excommunicate and anathematise the Imperator Fridericus."

The year was 1239 of our blessed Lord, Christ Jesus.

5

A SHUDDER of horror and apprehension swept the whole of Christendom. The dream of universal peace was shattered. All must suffer, great and small, when the lords of the world strive to annihilate one another. On nine counts the excommunication was pronounced against me. Not one was new; not one was truly related to the conflict over Lombardy. The Pope had but one objective: to destroy me and all my works.

Now the waiting was finished, the murky atmosphere was cleared. I was almost joyous in the release from tension. To the world I could show my resilience, my exuberance. And I would strike back until my strength failed. I suffered no illusion that to defeat this Pope would be an easy task. All the Christian world was too intricately involved with the mechanism of the Church to be suddenly cut loose. And all the Christians were too deeply concerned with life beyond the grave to stand up boldly for life before the grave. Even my most dependable supporters—all but a few—would have in their hearts a chamber of reserve, of anxiety, of fear. To ignore the scorching fires of Hell meant the reversal of a thousand years of indoctrination. In how many men can be found the strength to set the spirit free . . . ?

Outwardly I recovered quickly from the Pope's interdict. I remained dignified, calm. I restrained my anger, though openly I expressed regret at the Pope's intemperance. I called a meeting of the people of Padova. Piero addressed them, using as his text this phrase from Ovid, who suffered the tragedy of exile: "Punishment when merited is to be borne with patience, but when undeserved, with sorrow."

"No Emperor," said Piero in a voice ringing with emotion, "—no Emperor since the days of Charlemagne has been more just, gentle, and magnanimous—or has given so little cause for the hostility of the Church . . . !"

This, then, was the theme: that I was being persecuted unjustly, not by the Church itself but by the intransigence of one man who happened to have been chosen Vicar of Christ. I resolved to expose to all peoples the unfitness of this man for his post. I held a secret council with my most intimate advisers, and we decided step by step on the action I would take. When Berardo arrived for this meeting, I kissed him, then wiped the tears from my eyes—for he had been personally singled out by Gregory for excommunication.

"Oh Berardo," I cried, "what miseries I have brought down on your head . . . !"

"You may weep, my son," he answered, "only if the head has not strength enough to bear them. You are approaching a time when you yourself must have the strength of many, for many will falter. The strength of steel is determined in the forge; the strength of a man is determined by adversity. Soon you will see that some you considered weak will prove strong; and some you considered strong will prove weak. As for me, I could not do other than follow you, even if I wished—for that is the course and chief aim of my life. . . ."

I kissed him again, humbly; for he was more to me than any father to a son.

On Berardo's advice I sent word to the Pope that I would be willing to appear before an impartial council to answer the charges against me; but the Pope ignored my message. As news came of the vigor and violence with which the interdict was being pursued against me in all the churches of Christendom, I issued the first document in a war of words, a battle of manifestoes. It expressed the same sense of outraged indignation what had characterized that ingenuous "Appeal to the Princes" I had written as a child. Now I talked; Piero composed:

> Lift up your eyes, prick up your ears, O sons of men! Mourn for the woe of the world, the dissension of peoples, the extinction of justice. Wickedness has gone out from the elders of Babylon, who hitherto appeared to rule the people, while judgment is turned into bitterness, the fruits of justice into wormwood. Sit in judgment, ye Princes—ye People take cognizance of our cause!
>
> We hold Pope Gregory an unworthy Vicar of Christ, an unworthy successor of Petrus; not in disrespect to his office,

but of his person—he who sits in his court like a merchant weighing out dispensations for gold, himself signing, writing the bulls, and doubtless counting the money. He is unworthy of his place; we therefore appeal to a Council. He has but one real cause of enmity against us—that we refused to marry our son to his niece.

But ye, O Kings and Princes of the earth, lament not only for us but for the whole Church. Her head is sick. In the midst of her sits a frantic prophet, a man of falsehood, a polluted priest! He wishes to overthrow Caesar first; he will then tread down the rest of the Princes of the earth.

Thus it began. I detailed all the charges against me, with answers. I struck sympathetic chords. As I had in my first duel with Gregory, I tried to speak with the voice of reason, but I struck harder blows. Gregory's reply was a masterpiece of vituperation. He wrote:

Out of the sea a beast is risen, whose name is "Blasphemy." He has the feet of a bear, the jaws of a ravening lion, the mottled limbs of the pard. He opens his mouth to blaspheme the name of God; and shoots his poisoned arrows against the tabernacle of the Lord and the Saints who dwell therein. This Beast is striving to grind all to pieces with its iron claws and teeth. . . . Look carefully into the head, the middle, and the lower parts of this Beast Fridericus, called Imperator, and consider the truth. . . . Weigh in the scales the benefits which the Church has heaped upon this Dragon. . . . Yet this staff of the impious, this hammer of the earth, has robbed, banished and imprisoned the Sicilian clergy and has given the Churches over to adulterous embraces. He has built mosques on the ruins of churches and has forbidden the preaching of the Crusade. He has taken from the nobles their castles and forced those brought up in crimson to lie in the mire. He has built schools for the perdition of souls!

This man who delights in being called the forerunner of Antichrist has now openly thrown aside the mask. . . . This pestilent King maintains, to use his own words, that the world has been deceived by three imposters: Jesus Christ, Moses, and Mohammed; that two of these died in honor and the third was hanged upon a tree. He has asserted even more loudly that only fools aver that God, the Omnipotent Creator of the World, could be born of a virgin. This heresy he has aggravated by the mad assertion that no one can be born except when the intercourse of man and wife preceded the conception. He even maintains that men should believe only what may be proved by the power and reason of nature!

Cease to wonder that he has drawn against us the dagger of calumny, for he seeks to extinguish from the earth the name of the Lord. Rather, to repel him by simple truth, to refute his sophisms by the argument of holiness, we exorcise the head, the body, and the extremities of this Beast, who is none other than Fridericus Imperator.

I was hard put to control myself, for I knew that such accusations would strike fear and dread as well as astonishment into the hearts of those of true faith. Horrifying would be the charge that I had called Christ an impostor, and confusing the charge that I had lumped Mohammed with Him—for in earlier years Gregory had alleged that I was more Mohammedan than Christian. But I swept aside such intricacies, and denied outright that such statements were mine. In point of fact, the "Impostor" phraseology had circulated throughout Christendom for many years; and Maestro Teodoro unearthed proof that decades earlier a Parisian Doctor of Theology, one Simon de Tournai, had stated the thesis in a monograph—to demonstrate the skill of his dialectic in disproof. As a faithful prince of the Church, I went to great pains to declare Gregory a heretic, and I itemized his dealings with the heretics of Milano. But I went further than this. For the first time, using the first person, I uttered a hint of direct military action against the Pope:

Because I will not recognize the Pope's sole unlimited power and honor him more than God, he, himself the Antichrist, brands me, the truest friend of the Church, as a heretic. Who can wish more than I that the Christian community should resume its majesty, simplicity and peace? But this cannot be until the fundamental evil—the ambition, the pride and prodigality of the Bishop of Rome—be rooted up. I am no enemy of the priesthood; I honor the priest, the humblest priest, as a father, if he will keep aloof from secular affairs.

The Pope cries out that I would root out Christianity, with force and by the sword. Folly—as if the Kingdom of God could be rooted out by force and the sword! It is by evil lusts, by avarice and rapacity that it is weakened, polluted, corrupted. Against these evils it is my mission of God to contend with the sword.

I will give back to the sheep their shepherd, to the people their bishop, to the world its spiritual father. I will tear the mask from the face of this wolfish tyrant, and force him to lay aside worldly affairs and earthly pomp, and tread in the holy footsteps of Christ.

It was perfectly clear, I thought, that I was close to the limit of endurance. Let all who were concerned take notice.

I was not surprised—though others were—when an oracle was found one morning in the bedchamber of the Pope. Written on a scrap of parchment, it read:

Rome totters, through a maze of errors led,
And of the world shall cease to be the head.

By stars, by flights of birds, by fate we see
Of all the world one man shall hammer be.

6

Like sudden bursts of flame in a spreading forest fire, revolts sprang up all about me. The rebels everywhere blazoned upon their arms the red cross of crusaders, for now they were engaged (heretics, too) in a holy war against an excommunicant. They fought with the Pope's blessing against one who had been damned by the Pope. As the excommunication expressly applied to all who aided or supported me in any way, I found myself in the curious position of being head of the infidels. I wondered idly if I ought to change my title from Emperor to Sultan, and call Islam to my succor. That would have been a shock to the Pope!

Even Ezzelino's brother, Alberico da Romano, turned against me and led an attack on loyal Treviso. The Marquis d'Este suddenly decamped one day when we were enroute to Verona, and holed up in a Rocca more or less impregnable. On these men, and others like them, I pronounced the ban of Empire—proclaimed by Piero on horseback in the piazza in Verona—and seized such relatives as I could for hostages.

I acted as though the Pope's ban had not the slightest significance for me, and deployed my armies about the whole of Lombardy—taunting my enemies and attempting to provoke them into open combat. I had no wish for another such siege as Brescia, though I made feints at Milano as if I intended to settle down before the walls. At this point the Pope's Legate, Gregorio da Montelungo, urged all monks and priests to gird on armor, and I thought we might be battered with crucifix and relics instead of ax and fireballs. In any case, this metamorphosis of prayers into fighters was premature, as the Milanese engineers flooded my camp with waters diverted from the Olona—then dug ditches in such a way as to create an impassible water barrier. I veered southward to attack a Lombard bridgehead on the Po near Piacenza, but the heavens emptied and the Po rose—so that after interminable days of autumn rain and fog and mud we found ourselves growing web feet and cackling like geese. I contented myself with laying waste as much of the enemy's lands and possessions as possible, and turned my attention to a plan which was maturing in my head.

I was well informed of activities at the Papal Court in Rome. As the word-battle for men's minds progressed, the Pope turned beseechingly to all Europe for support. "Support" included, of course, large sums of money to prosecute his campaigns against me, for all armies except angels cost and cost and cost. The responses he received were not anticipated:

"We know," wrote the English prelates, "that the Emperor faithfully set out to war for our Lord Jesus Christ, and exposed himself to the perils of the sea and of the fight. We have not, up to now, observed an equal piety in the Pope. . . . The greedy avarice of Rome has exhausted the English Church; we can submit to no further exactions."

The Germans were blunt. Said the Archbishop of Salzburg: "He who is the servant of servants would be the Lord of Lords. This accursed man, on whose haughty forehead is written, *I am God, I cannot err*, sits in the temple of God and pretends to universal dominion."

The French reply, in answer to Gregory's proposal to depose me in favor of King Louis' brother Robert, was closely reasoned. "Whence this pride and audacity of the Pope," wrote Louis IX, "who thus presumes to disinherit and depose a King who has no superior, nor even an equal, among Christians? A King neither convicted by others, nor by his own confession, of the crimes laid to his charge. Even if those crimes were proved, no power could depose him but a General Council. On his transgressions the judgment of his enemies is of no weight, and his deadliest enemy is the Pope. To us thus far, he has not only appeared guiltless, he has been a good neighbor. . . . If Gregory should conquer him by our means, or with the help of others, the Pope would trample on all the Princes of the world—assuming the horns of boasting and pride, since he had conquered the great Imperator Fridericus."

Sorely disappointed, Pope Gregory turned for support nearer home. Some months before, he had negotiated a secret alliance between Genova and Venezia, with the object of eventually attacking my Kingdom of Sicily. The division of spoils had been carefully worked out in advance—which power was to receive which harbors, which persons were to receive which lands, and all the rest—like thieves plotting before a robbery. Now, abruptly, the Pope revealed the adherence of the Lombard towns and the Papal States to this alliance, and to its program of imminent invasion. With the powerful fleets of Genova and Venezia, this was no idle threat; and I knew that I must make great haste to circumvent it.

The first step was to prepare to repel the attack. How could I, stationed with a field army in northern Italy, both direct the affairs of Empire and organize the south against invasion? It was thinkable at all only because of the centralized and efficient system of government I had set up in Sicily. But this alone was not enough. The time had come to establish a uniform administration for all of Italy, tightly controlled and administered by the corps of men I had been training all these years. (Only two Germans played any part—the Hohenburg brothers.) True, I had promised Pope Honorious before my coronation that Sicily would not be integrated; but the promise was no longer valid. With a single decree I established in effect a new Italian state.

The burdens I placed on my people were enormous. The Imperial camp, wherever we happened to stop, was like a beehive—no, more like a hornet's nest, which never ceased activity. Over all was the sound of an angry buzzing; flights of arrival and departure took place at every moment of the day and night. Edicts, orders, manifestoes, directives—sometimes thirty or forty from the chancery alone in a single day, with innumerable copies and often artful devices for maintaining secrecy (like letters hidden in wax loaves of bread). I had reorganized the chancery under the able direction of Pier della Vigna and Taddeo da Suessa, and I encouraged them from time to time to inform me of the minutest details, that I might breathe air less rarefied than that surrounding the throne.

Piero came in one night (looking very tired) to read me a letter from a scribe, one of the young officials: "I am, as you might say, of one body with my pen—my own person is so coördinated with my register. I am so often hot, so often cold, and hard work so often overwhelms me—as this register, the companion of my martyrdom, will testify. . . . And to the pains of personal fatigue is added the slightness of my salary, which you well know bears no relation to my work."

"He dares to complain?" I said.

"Yes, Imperatore," Piero answered. "Our staff is not afraid of reprisals. Hence they work so well."

"If this, then, is the general situation with all the scribes, increase their salaries—but by no means decrease their work. And certainly see the they have braziers when the days and nights are cold!" I paused, then added: "And Piero—try to rest a little more. . . ."

Taddeo came, mumbling under his breath, "This priest is a *porco*!" Himself as plump as any pig (for he was a great eater of *pasta*), Taddeo had, however, a hooked nose and a fat bird's face. He was noted for the delicacy of his hands. Though he was a most serious man, he smiled and laughed continually, and could not speak without the use of gestures—his hands, his shoulders, his head, even his nose. In the courtroom his mind cut clean, like a curved Saracen blade, and he excelled at debate. Now he waved a letter in exasperation, fanning the air.

"Listen to this, my Lord. This priest craved a rescript from your gracious Majesty to legitimize his bastard sons. In line with your policy of clemency for the foibles of priests, we granted it. And now he writes to complain that your excommunication invalidates the document . . . !"

"*Hòi*!" I said, laughing. "Confiscate his property and banish him for his shameless impudence. Let him seek a rescript from the Pope, if he has gold enough . . . !"

So it went, without surcease. I wrote to Bianca that I was "ever ware and waking, dozed not, and never slept." This seemed to me, at the time, the literal truth. Under such pressures it was difficult to be always serene, always understanding, always just. Once to Andrea da Cicala, one of my cherished bright young men, I exploded with words hot as volcanic lapilli. I wrote him this apology:

> THE unfortunate words which caused you pain and so suddenly upset the calm of your firm mind, sprang from a mood of wrath and irritation. We are all the more rejoiced that your well-tested uprightness and good faith remained unshaken by such mistaken words. The more strongly you feel such unjust phrases, the more steadfast and sure is your constancy . . . your incorruptible loyalty. Need we say more?

> Can you still find room to doubt . . . ? Apart from the subtle signs of affection which the eyes cannot see, you must be conscious of our trust—for we leave our cares in your hands and rely on you as on a second self.

Peninsular Sicily I gave over entirely to the direction of Andrea, and island Sicily to the direction of Ruggero di Amicis, one of the rising young poets. I trusted their intelligence as other men trust simplicity, or venality. Though my demands are great, I offer great rewards. Are such men corruptible? I hope not . . . I like to believe not. . . .

The pace of activity did not for a moment cease. My objective was to seal Sicily and ring it with arms. Frontiers were closed: passports were needed to enter. All border castles were equipped with missile-throwing engines and garrisoned with crossbowmen. All coastal watchtowers (chiefly built against the Saracens in the ninth and tenth centuries) were repaired and activated. The Sicilian and Imperial fleets were joined under a single command. Chains were renewed and harbor defenses refurbished. Ships entering port were searched. And all communications with Rome, of whatever sort, were strictly forbidden. Even to have a letter from Rome in one's possession made the holder subject to imprisonment and confiscation of property.

All taxes in arrears were collected, and new taxes levied. Already I was in debt to the sum of 24,653 ounces of gold—and was borrowing wherever I could find lenders, at whatever interest rates. I preferred, however, to borrow from the wealthiest men of Rome—as this gave them a vested interest in my victory. I controlled trade with great care, using my monopolies to produce large profits. I even went so far as to permit trade with the enemy, selling of grain—"but prudently," I declared to my factors, "so that it may not appear a general permission." How it pained me to stuff all this wealth down the bloated gullet of the god Mars!

Now—what of the Church in an excommunicate land? The Archbishop Berardo, himself excommunicated, became head of the Church. The authority of the Vatican was terminated. Priests who failed to conduct services faced forfeit of property. All bishops who had supported the Pope were expelled. No new appointments were made without the approval of the Archbishop Berardo. Entry of all Domenicans and Francescans to the realm was barred. All other suspect clergy were carefully watched. So services for births and confirmations, and marriages and deaths, went on just as before—and it was clear to the people that the Emperor was not against God.

At last, when all defenses were in order, I wrote an open letter to the Archbishop of Messina:

> We have long had confidence in the justice of our cause; but now we recognize that, far from remembering our services, the Papal Curia has pronounced itself against us on all occasions. Hence we believe it necessary to adopt a new course of action: We shall renounce the amity of which we have given so many proofs. We shall now resort to force. . . .

I had decided to invade the States of the Church before the Papal armies could invade Sicily. It was my intention to relieve the Pope of his temporal power.

7

A COMET APPEARED in the heavens shortly after we crossed the Apennines and began our march toward Rome. By friend and foe alike it was interpreted as an omen of my victory. I saw it from the open top of the stark and lofty tower of San Miniato, which dominates the undulating valley of the river Arno and the road to Pisa. We had stopped at the Rocca for a needed rest. The December night was moonless, crisp, and starry. Piero and I had climbed the tower together in an effort to find a few moments of tranquillity, a little surcease from the endless cares of day. We leaned against one of the four round columns of brick which support the roof, and, swathed in long woolen cloaks, breathed thirstily of the clean cold wind. Standing close for warmth, we surveyed the shadowed valley, the dreamlike Tuscan hills with olive, pine, and cypress, and then the sweep of heaven. We came close, I think, to the sensation of birds in flight. We were as we had been, not youths, but alive and young once more. I put my arm about him; as always, he sighed, content.

It was Piero who saw it first, for his eyes were sharper than mine. "Madonna!" he cried, "Look, oh look toward Rome—a comet!"

I saw it then, streaking across the black sky, suddenly brilliant, flaring and flaming and leaving behind a sparkling tail, soon to fade and die. "Ah—*Dio!*" I breathed, deeply. "How petty is man . . . !"

"No, Imperatore," Piero whispered, "now it is like you."

"And after . . . ?" I said.

He hesitated. "Darkness. Only darkness, darkness, darkness—such brilliance will not be seen again. . . ."

We descended the tower arm in arm, but completely in silence. There was nothing to be said.

Next morning we rode on toward Pisa. An unaccountably somber mood was upon me. It was not relieved until, toward noon, our royal party acquired an astonishing recruit—none other than Fra Elias, the Minister-General of the Francescan Order, who had ridden from Assisi.

Or, I should say, *ex*-Minister-General, for soon after my excommunication he had been deposed—though his deposition was not related to my quarrels. Ever since, he had remained in Assisi doing penance and pondering whether to join me.

He was a fine-looking man, imposing of figure and voice, sternly pious. He was one of San Francesco's oldest friends and earliest converts and had been named by the Saint as his successor. He was a friend of Gregory, too, and for years had directed the affairs of the Order. He was a man of culture and taste, and it was he who built the beautiful Lower Church at Assisi. But ascetism, he thought, could be carried too far; he liked good food, good wine, and had written a treatise on alchemy. He traveled everywhere by horseback, even the shortest distances, and was always followed by an elegantly dressed handsome young page.

Now, after he saluted me, I kissed him on both cheeks and bade him welcome. I thought that we only happened to be traveling the same road; but he said no, in truth, he had come to join my court. I warned him of the inevitable, for the Pope would pierce him with a lightning bolt. But he shrugged it off, and told me a story:

"One of the most zealous advocates of my removal was Brother Jordan of Saxony. This Brother, on arriving in Rome for the first time, ran hither and thither from one holy shrine to another, and seemed like to burst from excitement and an excess of piety. One morning at dawn he forced his way into Gregory's bedchamber—none knows how—and frantically snatched the old Pope's bare foot from under the covers, to kiss.

" 'Ach, ach. . . .' Brother Jordan shouted, ecstatic. 'In Saxony we have not one sacred relic like this!' "

I laughed for the first time that day, and ceased to think of comets and the tower of San Miniato.

The loyal Pisans had invited me to spend Christmas with them, as they wished me to bridle the Conti and Visconti. These feuding families had much troubled the municipal peace. As I toured through the city I noted that the campanile, which was begun more than threescore years before, still was unfinished, and already had begun to lean. I offered to send engineers, but the Pisans were not much interested—as they seemed to think a leaning tower amusing. On Christmas Day I attended High Mass in the cathedral—though under the Pope's interdict it was a sacrilege. After the service, to the amazement of all present, I ascended the pulpit to speak to the people. I spoke slowly, so that every word could be memorized:

"Many are the examples in history which prove that states are ruined chiefly by their own divisions. You must live as good citizens and think of the welfare of your commune. If you disturb the peace, destroy your unity and your strength, we shall be the first to overthrow your city—not from hatred, but to prevent your falling under the yoke of our enemies. We adjure you to peace, for peace is our aim, the most ardent goal of our life—not only for you, but for our Realm, for all of Italy, for the Empire, for the whole world. . . ."

I marched toward Rome as a new prince of peace. My son King Enzo joined me. I was advancing into the Pope's domain only to reclaim the lands which I myself as Emperor had given to the Papacy, and my purpose now was to bring them peace. To Jesi, my birthplace, I wrote with such emotion that it might have been a second Bethlehem: "Arise, O our first mother, shake thee free from the foreign yoke. For we take pity on thy oppression and on the oppression of the faithful. . . ." To all towns I wrote: "Prepare ye the way of the Lord, make his paths straight! Take the bars from your doors that your Caesar may come, gracious unto you, but unto rebels terrible. Caesar—whose coming will silence the evil spirits whicih have so long oppressed you . . . !"

Everywhere I was greeted as a liberator—no, more—as the bringer of salvation. Town after town opened its gates. I was hailed as a king of kings. Before me went the Cross and the Eagle, and I gave my blessing to the thousands who bowed down before me. The Cardinal Giovanni Colonna, the Pope's General, came out with his soldiers from Rome, not to fight but to salute me. My progress was a triumphal procession. When I held court I sat upon a high throne, serene and benign as King David; and Pier della Vigna stood at my right hand, like an apostle of old, speaking for me, interpreting my wishes, issuing my benediction.

Thus we came to Viterbo, in mid-February, and I paused a

little before proceeding toward Rome. Word had come to me of the uproar in the city, the riots and turmoil. The Papalists did nothing to ease the tension as they spread rumors that the Antichrist would turn the Basilica of San Pietro into a stable for his Saracens . . . would revive the rites of pagan times . . . would make himself Pope or declare himself God. To all this the people of Rome paid little attention, but coursed and surged through the streets, shouting joyfully: "*Ecce Salvator! Ecce Imperator! Veniat, Veniat Imperator!*" They were ready at last to open for me the gates of Rome.

Gregory, abandoned by many of the cardinals and by most of the people, stood alone. Yet, as hourly I drew closer to the city, this Gregory, who so many times had fled Rome, refused to flee. He had lost all power, but it was in his mind to die before the advancing Beast as a martyr might die. In the violence of his hatred he would yield nothing. He would stand eerily upon another Calvary, his vestments swirling about him in the hurricane of change, calling down the wrath of Jehovah upon all who defied him.

It was the twenty-second day of February, the *festa* of the Chair of San Pietro. The Pope prepared exactly as usual. A splinter of the True Cross and the heads of San Pietro and San Paolo were carried in solemn procession from the Laterano to the Basilica of San Pietro. Through crowded streets and masses of excited people the procession wound its way—the crucifix in advance, then the banners, the censers, the few cardinals in robes, the heads of the two saints borne aloft, the emaciated old Pope pacing along under his canopy. And the people jeered and mocked, while Gregory, oblivious, muttered and mumbled under his breath, "*Tu es Petrus, et super hanc petram aedificabo Ecclesiam meam . . . Et portae inferi non praevalebunt adversus eam. . . .*" His eyes burned in deep sockets; he truly believed that the power of Hell could not prevail against him.

Suddenly, as the procession paused, he turned to the crowd in majestic dignity and pointed to the heads of Petrus and Paulus, crying out, "Here before you are the true antiquities of Rome! For their sake is your city venerated! The Church—the sacred relics! Protect them—it is the duty of Romans to protect them! I have done all that one man may; but I flee not! I await the mercy of the Lord!"

He took from his own head the tiara, and laid it upon the

relics. "O Holy Ones!" he cried again. "Defend ye Rome if the Romans will not defend her . . . !"

There followed a moment of silence, of reverence, of awe. Then weeping, sobbing, screaming, the mob swirled about the aged man, beating their breasts, tearing their hair. They ripped from their clothing the Imperial Eagles they had so proudly worn, and snatched up crucifixes on every hand. Shouting "*Petrus, Petrus!*" they rushed toward the walls, not to open the gates but to defend them for Gregory.

With two shrunken skulls the fate of all Europe had been balanced. And the venerable Pope stood transfixed and astonished at the miracle he had wrought.

8

ROMA—the harlot, they call her. Roma—fickle as a woman, they say. I had thought to embrace her, but as she turned on me, I was forced to pass her by. It was not to conquer Rome that I marched toward Rome: it was to be hailed in Rome, the Pope's own lair, as the saviour of peace. To have attacked Rome would have defeated my whole purpose, even had I been prepared to sustain a major siege. Disconsolate and dejected, I marched around Rome and headed southward to the Kingdom of Sicily.

Among my followers the whole atmosphere of triumphant exaltation vanished. Despondent, they plodded onward through an emotional morass more burdensome than the mud of Lombardia; every step of their feet was leaden. And for once, even Piero, who usually responded to my resilience, reflected the general mood. Not for a moment did I reveal my own bitterness. I could not drive from my head, however, thoughts of the changed course of history had I been victor, without bloodshed, over the potentate who sought to dominate by spiritual means the temporal life of men. For me a black day. How would it look, I wondered, from the perspective of centuries? That not I alone had been the loser . . . ?

But one course of action was possible for me: prepare to return. Could I so direct the stream of events that a second opportunity would be offered to me? But a second time I would return in such force that even by a miracle I could not be denied a victory. If need be, I would level the walls of Rome—at whatever cost. At once I began to make preparations.

I sought meanwhile to arouse my people by calling a special meeting, a grand *parlamento* in Foggia—as I had been five years absent. Each town was to select a mayor as a delegate. From these men I wished to hear their grievances; then they were to return to the towns to help organize the Realm against the threat of the Church's military invasion. I wished all to understand clearly the issues at stake.

At about this time Simon de Montfort, who had married my wife's sister Eleanor, arrived at court. He was followed, a little later, by Isabella's brother, Richard of Cornwall. They were enormously impressed with my palace at Foggia, with its fountains, pools, gardens, mosaics and antique statuary. It was, I think, more elegant and luxurious than any palace they had ever seen, and they were hard pressed not to reveal their awe. But like all the English I have met (including Isabella), their greatest enthusiasm is their reserve—though I understand they have their bawdy moments. Only when I produced exceptionally beautiful dancing girls, who performed on rolling spheres to the accompaniment of tambourines and castanets, did I draw from my guests their unguarded approval. De Montfort, however, was impressed in another way—by the *parlamento*. He would, he said, give thought to the calling of such a gathering in England at Westminster. The time might come.

By early summer, my forces reorganized, I was prepared to move from my base at Capua against the Papal States. But representatives of the German princes arrived in Rome to implore the Pope to peace—as the thudding hoofs and spine-freezing war cries of Mongol cavalry already were to be heard in Europe. The Germans appealed for unity of Pope and Emperor against the imminent threat to all of Christendom.

I myself was well aware of the characteristics of the Mongols, as the Muslim world was no less threatened than the Christian —and the Arabs had taken pains to advise me of this peril. Most Christians had heard vague rumors of a mighty king in the Orient, whose name was Genghis Khan. Mistakenly they thought of him as a king like Melchizedek, or the legendary Prester-John; the Jews were even more misguided, thinking that King David was returning as the Messiah, for the year was 5000 of their calendar. Actually Genghis Khan had died some years before, and his son Ogotay had assumed his role. I had, in fact, once received a mission from these strange people inviting me to pay homage to the Great Khan. I instructed the messengers to return with the ironical reply that I "applied for the post of Falconer at the Great Khan's court."

As I wrote to the Kings of Europe, the Mongols of the

Golden Horde were "a wild people, lawless and ruthless; but they have a lord whom they call *Lord of the Earth* and they obey. The frame and body of the Tartar is small and undersized; but powerful, broad-shouldered, hardy and enduring. They plunge into any danger at a sign from their leader. Their face is broad, their gaze is sinister, they utter a terrifying cry. For armor, they wear untanned hides of oxes, horses, and asses, stitched with iron. These Tartars are incomparable archers. To swim lakes and rivers they ingeniously use inflated skins. Their horses are content with roots and leaves and bark when other fodder is scarce—yet they are swift and long-enduring." I did not add that the Tartars enjoyed piling up mountains of skulls; this was a fact already well known. Alas, this letter repaid me ill: it was immediately whispered by my enemies that the Emperor who knew so much about the Tartars had called them into Europe to destroy all Christians!

My own written appeal to unite was issued thus: to "Germany, rising with rage and zeal to battle, and France, that mother and nurse of chivalry; warlike and bold Spain; fertile England, valorous on land and sea; Allemania full of impetuous warriors; seafaring Denmark; untamable Italy; Burgundy that never knows peace; restless Apulia; the piratical and unconquered islands of the Grecian, Adriatic, and Tyrrhenian seas; Crete, Cyprus and Sicily; bloodthirsty Ireland and nimble Wales; Scotland abounding in lakes; icy Norway—and every noble and renowned country lying under the star of the West..."

But the Pope was singularly unimpressed with the Mongol threat. He laid down impossible conditions for peace which I could not accept; and I dared not leave Italy so long as he continued to whet his knife for me.

"Oh God! how much and how often have we been willing to humiliate ourselves," I said publicly, "in order to prevail upon the Roman Pontiff to desist from giving cause of scandal through out the world by his enmity against us—or place the bounds of moderation upon his ill-advised violence—that we may govern our subjects in a state of peace. But he has ordered a crusade against me, an arm and advocate of the Church, which he might better have ordered against the Tartars. He exults in the rebellion of our subjects, who are conspiring against our honor and fame; and as it is our most urgent business to free ourselves from enemies at home, how shall we repel these barbarians as well . . . ?"

The most-western princes followed the Pope's cue, and the best I could do was to authorize the formation of a defensive army "to meet and check the attacks and violence of the barbarians." I placed the army under the nominal leadership of my not yet thirteen-year-old son Corrado, King Konrad IV. In coming months the Mongol tide continued relentlessly, and after the subjugation of Russia, Hungary was overrun. In the end it was left for Austrians, Bohemians, Poles, Slavs, and Germans to meet them on the battlefield; but it was the death of Ogotay which saved Europe. The Tartars had advanced to within seventy-five leagues of Wien.

The Papal policy of subordinating all else to my defeat was costly elsewhere too: in the Holy Land it brought about the loss of Jerusalem to Christendom. An abortive campaign against Syria had been begun by the Christians; it resulted in a crushing defeat. Though I was hard-pressed at home, I sent Ruggero di Amicis from Sicily to Egypt to negotiate with the Sultan Malik Salih, the son of al-Kamil—who had died two years before, to my great sorrow. My envoy was successful in recovering Jerusalem for me and for Christendom. Thus once more in the eyes of the world I—not Gregory—was the protector of the Holy Land.

Proposal, counterproposal, talk, pleading, prayers—all were in vain. The dogged and vindicative old Pope held fast to his single aim: he would see me destroyed or die. To him nothing else mattered. Muttering and dissatisfied, the German princes went home. So also the envoys for peace sent by King Louis of France and King Henry of England. Useless, all useless. With a certain weariness, once more I turned to war.

This time I would crunch the Papal States in bands of iron. I would apply pressure first in the north, then in the south. I gave the order to march.

9

FOR THE first time in years I fell ill. I was touched by a fever while crossing marshy land near Ancona; but as I wrote to Bianca, I so "overcame it by the might of my spirit that we were delayed only on the day of crisis." Secretly I felt more than a twinge of regret at having left the palace in Foggia. Was I to be driven ever thus by the Pope like a slave by a taskmaster . . . ?

The situation in the north had become very fluid, and I had suffered additional reverses. I decided to pick off a number of key towns before tightening the squeeze on Rome. Within a few days and with little difficulty I took Ravenna, which had shifted allegiance, and prepared to attack Bologna. But Faenza, to the south, threatened my rear, and I thought to take so small a town at smaller cost. Its Papal forces were under the command of young Count Guido Guerra, a notorious sodomite and excellent soldier. His garrison had been augmented by Guelfs from Bologna and Venezia, and the defenses strongly reinforced. In August we encircled the walls. In November we still encircled the walls. I paced the floor of my tent. I could not now afford another Brescia.

So we built a winter camp and settled down to starve them out. The weather was cold. Our wooden huts were small protection against the *bora*, the winter wind which blows unhindered across the Adriatic. But we had much fuel, and the town had little. Slowly the walls were crumbling as my engineers dug undermining tunnels. Food in Faenza was running low. But in camp money was running lower. I was hard put to it to pay the mercenaries and meet my obligations to other levies. Even the volunteer troops from the loyal towns had to be paid after a certain number of days. All had to be kept armed and well fed. I had taxed to the last possible tax; as a temporary expedient

I issued leather money. So great was popular faith in me that these leather coins were as readily accepted as silver or gold.

A group of soldiers from Schwyz who had crossed the Alps in midwinter to aid my cause I paid not with money but with a charter naming them free men—subject to my personal protection. At this they were delighted, for Rudolph of Hapsburg had sought to force them to become his vassals. They talked of joining with the men of Unterwalden and Uri for their defense; and this I encouraged, as they controlled the northern approaches to the newly discovered St. Gothard Pass.

Ostensibly I was calm, patient. People were amazed that in the midst of warfare I edited the text of an Arabic treatise on falconry translated for me by Maestro Teodoro. But I was busy with a number of other things. The war galleys of Venezia had ravaged and burned the coastal towns of Vasto and Termoli, a quick and daring maneuver literally under the prows of my own fleet. In reprisal I arranged for the Emperor of Nicaea to raid nearby possessions of Venezia, for the Sultan of Tunis to break off all commerce with them, and for the Dalmatian pirates of Zara secretly to be subsidized against them. Finally I hanged Pietro Tiepolo (who had been bound to the Milanese *carroccio*), the son of their Doge, in full view of their fleet coursing off Brindisi. Thereafter, attacks ceased.

Vastly more important were the letters I poured out to all the sovereigns of Europe, and to many princes of the Church. Pope Gregory, perhaps recalling the phrase in King Louis' letter stating that only a General Council could depose me, had convoked just such a gathering for the coming Easter—"to settle the arduous business of the Church," as he said. Not only were hostile prelates invited, but also all the leading nobles who had rebelled against me. It was obvious that the arduous business of the Church was chiefly temporal. "We cannot recognize the competence of such a tribunal which is justly suspect," I wrote; and therefore I refused safe conduct to all delegates to the Council in Rome. My warning could not have been more precise. Yet no one believed me. No one believed that any ruler—even so powerful an Emperor as I—would dare lay hands on delegates summoned by a Pope. Gregory pursued his course unflinchingly. At considerable cost, he arranged for his delegates to be transported by sea from Genova. Quietly I alerted the Imperial fleet and my friends the Pisans. Did the Pope who had bewitched a Roman mob also expect to command the waves of the sea . . . ?

Meanwhile I sat, firmly, patiently outside the walls of Faenza. Famine shrouded the town, and the rats fled the hunger of the inhabitants. Before dawn one day the gates furtively opened and gaunt packs of women and children were shoved out. I refused to permit them to pass, and the gates were opened to receive them back again. I reminded the people of Faenza that they had insulted my mother when she passed through their town in an advanced stage of pregnancy, "injuring her palfrey and venting their rage upon the brute beast." And "they murdered one of my knights clad in Imperial armor, thinking they had killed me, their Lord." Let the Papalists turn to the Pope in their hour of need for sustenance—let them be saved by a miracle. "Since you would not in prosperity return to your allegiance," I told them, "I will give no heed to you in time of trouble." Let them surrender. But they were afraid of my wrath.

For eight months they defied me. The walls were completely undermined, the town itself half-destroyed. Food was exhausted. Suddenly from tunnels my men appeared in the central piazza, and the end was at hand. With a benevolent smile I received homage from the starving wretches of Faenza. They expected death. But I surprised them: "We enter the town with overflowing gentleness and with the outstretched arms of inexhaustible clemency . . . so that you may know that nothing is juster and easier to bear than the yoke of Empire." Then I fed them. To the Papal town of Benevento, which fell to my forces in the south almost simultaneously, I extended the same forgiveness. All Europe was amazed.

Two weeks later, at the end of April, the Papal delegates prepared to sail from Genova. Of Germans there were none, and of Italians only representatives from the rebel towns. But the English, French and Spanish chose not to disobey the call of the Pontiff. When the English, however, looked at the assembled ships, overcrowded and some unseaworthy, they hastily changed their minds. They preferred to be ashore than afloat. The others, under the urging of the Papal Legate Gregorio da Montelungo (whose zeal never flagged), placed their faith in Heaven and took to the waves in thirty-three transports and twenty-seven creaking galleys.

Meanwhile, at Pisa, under the general command of Enzo, twenty-seven galleys of the Imperial fleet joined an equal number of Pisan vessels, and, on signal from friends in Genova, set out to intercept the Genovese ships with their holy freight. For a week my fleet lay in hiding, part near the island of Montecristo and part near the island of Giglio. The sun shone clear, the sea was calm, and the benevolence of God seemed to favor the Papal ships—though in fact it favored mine. On the *festa* of the Elevation of the Cross they were sighted from the topmast of my largest galley.

On the first encounter the weight of the prayers so overburdened the Genovese vessels that three sunk outright, with all hands, holy and otherwise, drowned. Among them was the Archbishop of Besancon. And so billowy were the clerical robes that all the others were blown off course, and with three exceptions, fell captive to my fleet. Only the Spaniards escaped. Ever so briefly blood dyed the waters. Loud were the cries and lamentations, piteous the pleas for mercy, vigorous the invocations of the name of God and the Pope. All to no avail. The hundred high-ranking Church dignitaries, and the four thousand miscellaneous men required to transport and protect them, were hustled to Pisa under guard aboard their own ships. Among them were three Papal Legates, two cardinals, four important abbots, and archbishops and bishops enough to furnish a score of chessboards. And much gold, wrung from various lands. My first reaction at the news was delight. My second was a solemn statement to Gregory that his defeat was a judgment of God upon him. Europe was impressed, amazed, and aghast.

It was my firm intention to help God provide another judgment quickly, for already too many precious hours and years had been spent in this enterprise. I would repeat the march to Rome, but this time I would not halt until the person of Gregory himself fell into my hands. Once again I turned south.

And once again Cardinal Giovanni Colonna deserted the Pope, this time without possibility of reconciliation. He had charged Gregory to his face with being untrustworthy, with having spoken falsely when he asserted that he wished peace. "Heaven help us," he said to the Pope, "that there should be such fickleness of speech in the mouth of so great a man as you—and that faithless words should be sent to so great a Prince. To this fickleness and faithlessness I will by no means consent but strongly oppose . . . !"

"Very well!" screamed the Pope, "I will no longer consider you as my Cardinal!"

"And I," replied Cardinal Colonna, "will no longer esteem you as my Pope!"

The encirclement of Rome proved astonishingly easy. From Terni I moved to Rieti; then to Tivoli, with its memories of the Emperior Hadrian and the oracles of death forecast for Piero and me. I took a special satisfaction in the destruction of Castel Monteforte, a carefully planned refuge for Gregory and his kindred, built with funds collected for the Crusade. Gregory's nephews who fought against me, I hanged; and one tower alone was left standing. By mid-August I was in Grottaferrata in the cool Alban Hills, so close to Rome that its hot ocher glow was easily visible in the distance. Pier della Vigna wrote my statement to the world: "The path of peace, which base obstinacy has hitherto blocked, will now be opened." After fourteen years of struggle, the circle was almost complete.

Then Gregory played his last card—an ace. Word came panting from Rome that the Pope was dead.

Gregory—once again—had triumphed.

10

"HE IS DEAD through whom peace was banished from the earth and discord prospered," I proclaimed. "For his death—though by him so deeply injured and implacably persecuted—we feel compassion; that compassion would be more profound had he striven to establish peace between Empire and Papacy. God, we trust, will raise up a Pope of more pacific temper; him we will defend as a devout son, if he follow not the fatal crime and animosity of his predecessor."

To take Rome now was to take empty air. In the eyes of the world my conflict was with Pope not Church. To have seized San Pietro and its treasures would have destroyed at a single stroke that enormous sympathy and support for my cause which existed all over Europe. The Church itself I dared not touch: to most men of Europe the Christian doctrine was as vital as breath to the body, for they were filled with spiritual fears to be negated and guilts to be atoned. All that I had asked of the Papacy, so to speak, was a division of spheres of influence. Again and again, I had repeated my own dictum: "The affairs of the secular power should not be subordinated to the Church."

Frustrated, I turned on my heels and marched back to Apulia. Only Bianca, welcoming me at the palace in Foggia, seemed glad at the turn of events. "It's the pause that makes the music, my Lord," she said, soothing me with a proverb.

At first I was too restless to attempt to relax. Until the character of the new Pope was known, I dared not disband my armies, dared not turn with full concentration to some of the peacetime projects I had in mind. Meanwhile, events in the College of Cardinals were a grotesque parody of all that a Sacred College should be.

The Sacred College was hardly more than a frazzled remnant

of itself: two cardinals I held in prison; Cardinal Colonna was in the Holy Land on a mission for me; and of the remaining ten, six favored peace and four favored continued war. The necessary two-thirds majority for the election of a new Pope was therefore impossible.

The cardinals themselves had been seized bodily by Matteo Orsini, one of the most powerful Papalist nobles of Rome, and forced into confinement to speed the selection. It occurred to him that the more uncomfortable the cardinals, the more rapidly they would act. Being himself a brusque man, he ordered his soldiers to drag the cardinals—some of whom were old and ailing—through the streets to the top floor of the Septizonium on the Palatine Hill. All that remained of this ancient building was a tower, recently damaged by earthquakes and as yet not repaired. There, without water, beds, latrines, or other necessities of life, Orsini confined the cardinals—men used to the utmost in luxury. On the roof, which was broken, Orsini's guards relieved themselves, performing their natural functions, and the cardinals were assailed not only by stench in the heat of autumn, but continual leakage of urine and offal. Soon all were sick, and one of the peace party died. But no matter how great their sufferings, neither side was converted: each side chose a Pope of its own.

Thereupon Orsini threatened to exhume Gregory's corpse and place it among them until another Pope was elected. Overcome with fright, they chose, after two months of this mockery, one of their own number, Goffredo Castiglioni of Milano. Despite his origin he was not unacceptable to me; and, though Orsini was vexed that a militant Guelf had not been selected, he released the exhausted cardinals from their confinement. Goffredo, who took the name Celestine IV, was never consecrated; his health had been undermined, and he died on the seventeenth day of his pontificate.

Horror racked the cardinals at the prospect of another such gathering, and all save three fled Rome. Then Colonna, approaching, was seized by Orsini and thrown into prison. Now the deadlock was complete. In the interests of the Church, I released the two cardinals I held; one was a bitter enemy, and when admitted to my presence promptly hurled the excommunication at me; the other, Otho of England, I won over to my cause. But no meeting followed. The months stretched on and on, became one year, then two.

I sent this message to the cardinals: "Your mother is dying, but in your discord you take no notice." Most anxiously I longed for a rapprochement with the Church. I wanted to be absolved. I wanted permanent peace. But I would have been well advised to accept gratefully the short interregnum fate was kind enough to allow me. For all too soon *peace* was to become nothing more than a word and a memory.

I was not so optimistic as to cease or even slow construction of the new fortifications I had planned. At Lagopesole I initiated a vast enclave to shelter many troops and all needed equipment for long defense. It would be, I thought, impregnable. But my architectural joy was the octagonal edifice I had designed and was now building, called Castel del Monte. Not far from Andria, its massive bulk—an octagon with eight octagonal towers—was to rise in solitary splendor on the highest hill of the wide plain called the *Murge*. It was to be one of my "places of solace." To such a place I could retreat in safety when all ordinary burdens seemed unbearable and I wished to think in quiet, or seeking union with nature, ride across the windswept land with falcons.

This castle I designed with mathematical precision, drawing on all my knowledge of Roman, Norman, Byzantine, and Arabic architecture. Around the octagonal courtyard were to be two stories, each of eight spacious rooms with vaulted ceilings, delicate columns of fluted marbles, floors of mosaic, gothic windows, and vast semiconical fireplaces. Everywhere were to be carvings—the capitals of the columns, the mensoles, the keys to the vaults. In certain towers were to be cisterns and plumbing facilities, and in the courtyard, under antique statuary, a fountain was to flow. Notable was to be the simplicity and harmony of line, though for the main entrance I conceived a quasi-Roman pediment and gateway, flanked above the door with two roaring Byzantine lions. But I dared not depart so far from the architecture of my own times as to omit the portcullis; however, I arranged it so as to be completely hidden until dropped into place. As an additional defense of the door, the entrance steps flared out to right and left—making direct assult with battering ram impossible.

As I watched the toiling workmen, moving in a line at a slow and rhythmical pace from the quarry to the scaffolding with stones slung in sacks draped from their heads, or carrying sand and mortar in baskets on their bent left shoulders, they seemed tireless. Their short strong bodies were naked except for a twisted length of cloth about their loins, and their sun-bronzed muscles glistened with sweat. Pausing to rest, they lay together in groups in the shade, singing, or eating bread, oil, cheese, fruit, and drinking wine. For how many thousand years had they looked, moved, rested thus? And when the Castel del Monte was finished, I would say: "I built it." They built it. But in truth, each of us was helpless without the other. The stone was as nothing without first the conception, and then the hands to fashion it. Else it remained inert and formless in the earth, of no use to man.

In the bright light and stark shadows cast by the Apulian sun, I thought my handiwork most beautiful—though already I found it touched by melancholy. What grim history, in years to come, would these walls see?

II

TWICE in short succession the angel of death brushed near me. I dreaded the thought of a third. First to be taken was the Empress Isabella, in miscarriage. She bled to death. She was only twenty-seven. I had become very fond of her sweet and girlish ways—for gradually she had ceased to be so restrained with me. In my sexual relations I had been careful not to frighten her, obliterating from my mind those satyr embraces I had seen in the carvings from antiquity. Isabella liked toys and strange musical instruments, and with these things I surrounded her. I buried her in Andria, in the same crypt with Yolanda, that they might keep each other company.

A deeper blow was the death of my son Heinrich, as he was being transferred from one prison to another. He rode his horse over a cliff in a compulsive fulfillment of the prophecy that he would die in a fall. Had he not known the soothsayer's words, he might not have acted at the thought of suicide—however desolate his banishment. He had not, as I hoped, responded to my efforts to make his prison more bearable—he read no books, composed no poems, sang no songs. Most of the time he sat staring at a barred window, or simply held his head. I had thought, not to pardon him, but to have him join me on some of the building projects I had in mind. Alas, too late! He was not yet thirty-two. He was buried in Cosenza in a marble sarcophagus. His shroud, at my orders, was made of gold and silver threads interwoven with eagles' feathers. This was my epitaph for him: "The pity of a tender father must yield to the stern judge: we mourn the doom of our first-born. Nature bids flow the flood of tears, but they are checked by the pain of injury and the inflexibility of justice. Neither the first are we, nor the last, who longs to weep upon the grave of an undutiful son."

The death of Heinrich inclined me more than ever to pay attention to my children. The elder girls I had married off, to sons of noble families. I wrote many letters to Corrado, so far away in turbulent Germany. It was important, I felt, that he should understand the true responsibility of kingship. "Famous extraction alone is not sufficient for kings," I wrote, "unless noble personal character is wedded to illustrious race, and outstanding zeal reflects glory on the prince's rank. People do not distinguish kings and Caesars above other men because they are more highly placed, but because they see farther and act better. As men they stand equal to other men by their humanity. . . . They are born as men and as men they die."

"As men they die—" In these days I thought much about death, for of late I had seen so much of it. And so much of it needless. Many people believed that I myself bore a charmed life, that I would live to be centuries old, or even that death would never touch me. Soothsayers often sought to ingratiate themselves by saying such things; my response was always the same—to thank them for their belief in the triumph of will over flesh. Oh no!—I had observed nature too closely not to understand that death is a part of life, that one continually supplants the other.

My observation of nature found expression in the book my son Manfredo urged me to write on the art of hunting with birds, *De Arte Venandi cum Avibus.* Though only ten, Manfredo had become as ardent a falconer as I, and we spent long hours together in the fields and woods. He begged and begged that I put on paper the things we talked about. For years I had been making notes on birds and their habits, ranging from the hummingbird's method of flight, to the crane's curved inner front toe which lies sideways on the ground to preserve its sharpness. I had learned that birds recognize the voices of mates, and some do not mate at all. I had noted, too, errors in extant works; for example, Aristotle assumed that waterfowl in V-formation followed a single leader—but from experience I knew that they changed their leader. I therefore sought to set down in a matter-of-fact way what I had learned about bird life in general and falcons in particular.

I began with the structure and habits of birds. I classified species, as to aquatic and terrestrial, rapacious and nonrapacious; noted breeding and feeding habits, methods of mating, manner of combat and defense, and geographic distribution. Migration was a subject in itself. Then I turned to bodily organs and their function, the skeletal structure, plumage, position and number of wing feathers, and the characteristics of flight. What I knew of diseases I included. Thereafter I discussed falcons in detail: their taking and training; the different lures to induce the falcon to return to the huntsman; the hunting of cranes with gerfalcons; the hunting of herons with the saker falcon; and the hunting of water birds with smaller species of falcons. I stressed that birds of prey are instruments in the hands of the master; the taking of prey is itself secondary.

If I had no facts to explain a particular phenomenon, I so stated, and left the question open. I was cautious about advancing theories without incontrovertible supporting evidence. I proved that barnacle geese are not hatched from barnacles, as commonly supposed; and I dismissed the legendary Phoenix as incredible. Sometimes I permitted mysef a speculation: Do vultures have no feathers on their necks because they thrust their heads deep into a carcass while eating? And I wondered how migrating birds sense the force of the coming winter, though I found no answer. I observed that falcons catch cold from overheated hoods, so I invented a perforated hood for ventilation, and described it in detail.

"*Presens opus aggredi nos induxit et instans tua petitio, fili Karissime Manfride. . . .*" Thus I phrased the dedication to Manfredo. I stated at once some of the points I wished to stress:

> THIS present work . . . prompts us to correct the many errors made by our predecessors who, when writing on the subject, degraded the noble art of falconry by slavishly copying the misleading and often insufficient statements to be found in the works of certain hackneyed authors. With the object of bequeathing it to posterity, we now offer a true and careful account of these matters between the covers of this monograph.
>
> As the ruler of a large Kingdom and an extensive Empire we were very often hampered by arduous and intricate governmental duties; but despite these handicaps we did not lay aside our self-imposed task, and were successful in committing to writing at the proper time the elements of the art. Among other things, we discovered by hard-won ex-

> perience that the deductions of Aristotle, whom we followed when they appealed to our reason, were not entirely to be relied upon—more particularly in his description of the characters of certain birds. . . . In his work, the *Liber Animalium,* we find many quotations from other authors whose statements he did not verify and who, in their turn, were not speaking from experience. Entire conviction of the truth never follows mere hearsay. . . .
>
> The author of this treatise, the august Fridericus Secundus, Emperor of the Romans, King of Jerusalem and of Sicily, is a lover of wisdom, with a philosophic and speculative mind.

And of course illustrations were essential; so Manfredo and I turned to pen and brush, to indicate for the artists precisely what we wanted. To our astonishment, when we had finished, we had drawn 915 birds, 170 human figures, 12 horses, a sailing ship, a rowboat, a swimmer and two bats.

Manfredo, I noticed, had drawn also two kings, robed and crowned and seated on separate thrones, awaiting falconers.

"And who are they?" I asked. "They appear to be twins."

"One, noble father, is you," he answered solemnly. "And the other—is Manfredo. For some day I wish to be a king: a king exactly like you . . . !"

12

For manfredo I dreamed great dreams. If Enzo was my own image, Manfredo was the image of his mother, Bianca. He was like her in so many ways besides appearance—he had her charm of manner, her intuitive understanding, her quick intelligence. If but one of my legitimate sons had been his equal, I would have been well content. He was, of course, as much the apple of his mother's eye as of mine; and her influence on him certainly equaled mine.

It was Manfredo who discovered for us the brilliant young doctor, Giovanni da Procida. For some time past, Bianca had not been well, suffering from headaches and sudden spells of dizziness. None of the court physicians had proved of any use whatever; but he contrived a way of applying heat to the back of her head, which seemed to relieve the pain. But this is to anticipate.

The court chamberlain had recently bought a new slave girl, by name Restituta, for service in the palace; young Manfredo had become friendly with her. She was pretty and vivacious. She came, she told Manfredo, from the Island of Ischia, of a good family, but had been taken by pirates and sold into slavery. Nobody had attempted to verify her story. One day a strange young man appeared, seeking her; she was, he said, his *fidanzata*. His home was the neighboring Island of Procida. But how could he reclaim a slave from the palace of the Emperor? He was only a young doctor who had just finished his studies at Salerno, and had no friend at court. Weeping, Restituta told her troubles to Manfredo, and Manfredo came to me. At once I freed the girl, restored her to her betrothed, and questioned the young man about his studies. I found him exceptionally gifted; he had a rational point of view toward medicine similar to my own.

I tried him on a few cases and was so impressed that I offered him a post as a court physician.

Such were the few facts. But how rumors distorted the story! It was told abroad that Restituta was so languorous and beautiful that I myself bought her from pirates for my harem. Her lover, after many adventures on sea and land, had traced her to my palace—where, fortunately, she had remained a virgin due to the fact that I had been indisposed. The young man, in despair at finding her the King's slave, had contrived to enter the palace by night, lying with her. But alas, I had discovered them sleeping together, nude and entwined; I controlled my impulse to kill them on the spot, and ordered instead that they be bound to the stake, naked, and burned. And only the timely revelation of their noble identity saved them from the flames, clothed them, earned my pardon, and assured their wedding. Such is the romantic embroidery of the popular imagination! But what a charming tale. . . .

The events in my own life at that time were not without an element of romance. I decided to marry Bianca. Her protracted illness had worried me, and in her letters I detected notes of false cheerfulness. I wanted to marry her for the most extraordinary reason: I wanted to make her my wife. I thought it unwise, however, after our living together such a length of time, to make my proposal too abrupt. One night in spring I sought her in a garden, not unlike the garden where I had seen her first. Now, as then, a fountain trickled and spattered with idle, playful dabblings. The air was warm and flower-scented; moonlight brushed a marble faun with iridescence. I sighed, not from burning need, but from the accumulation of memories.

"My Lord," Bianca said, "what troubles you?"

"My heart—" I said.

She glanced up in alarm. "Oh no! Not pain—?"

"Pain, but not pain," I answered. "The fires of youth become the embers of age. It is my only regret, *cara mia,* that I did not take you to my bed when I was very young indeed."

"My Lord Federico," she said, smiling, "it is better for a woman that ardor lasts. I have no complaints. . . ."

"I am pleased that you are pleased," I said, and placed my hand above hers in mock shyness. "But I have thought to give you a gift to express my pleasure: all the lands of Tricarico, Monte Scaglioso, Gravina—and the honor of Monte San Angelo. . . ."

"Such great estates—for me! I am humbled, my Lord, by your generosity." Then she permitted herself the hint of a frown and a curious wistfulness. "But this last—the honor of Monte San Angelo—is that not part of the dower of the Queens of Sicily . . . ?"

"It is, Bianca."

"But I—am not the Queen of Sicily."

"No—but I wish us to be married—"

"Married? My Lord! To me? I am not of royal blood. . . ."

"I do not want you for my Queen; I want you for my wife."

She gazed at me in bewilderment. "After so many years . . . ?"

It was then that I took her in my arms and kissed her as I longed to so many years before.

Of course we were aware that marriage of excommunicated persons, under the laws of the Church, held no legal sanction. To many, the very idea was shocking and sacrilegious. To me, it was meaningless—for marriage was not a sacrament but a form of social approval of biological necessity. I wanted Bianca for my wife because she had been a wife in truth to me. Of Queens I had experienced more than my fill. My feelings for Bianca were those of a man, not those of a "divine scion of a race of kings." It was good to lay my head upon her breast, to feel the touch of her gentle fingers upon my brow. . . .

For reasons of state we were married secretly in a private chapel, with dear Berardo, majestic and white-maned, performing the ceremony. Rarely have I seen him in so happy and exalted a mood. Attendants we had very few: our children Manfredo and Costanza, the Marquis Lancia, the singer of love songs, Giacomino Pugliese, the trustworthy Andrea Cicala, the much-honored Ruggero di Amicis, the dashing Riccardo, Count of Caserta, who had married my daughter Violante, the new young poets Folco Ruffo and Jacopo da Morra, brought up "as my sons and from whom nothing was concealed"—as I said, Maestro Teodoro, who gave us a good augury, Taddeo da Suessa, Pier della Vigna, and, for good luck, Doctor Giovanni da Procida and Restituta, his blushing bride.

It was the young doctor's gift we treasured most highly: a vial filled with a secret love potion—which, if ever tasted, would bring Eros from far away. We smiled, for we thought that we would never have need of it. . . .

Nor did we ever—for Bianca died in her sleep that night. I went alone into the garden so that my tears could flow unchecked.

13

"We are no mere man; we have the place of God upon the earth," declared Innocent IV—for that was the name assumed by Sinibaldo Fieschi, the new Pope.

By this statement I should have been forewarned, but I was not. As the urbane Cardinal Fieschi, of Genova, Count of Lavagna, with whom I had played chess, he was Ghibelline; as Pope Innocent IV, he was Guelf. Soon I was to cry out: "No Pope *can* be a Ghibelline!" After twenty-two months of maneuvering, pleading, threatening, the Sacred College had acted at last, and provided a head for the decapitated body of the Church. I welcomed the election with joy; Sinibaldo Fieschi, I thought, was a man with whom I could deal.

This Fieschi had none of the majesty and mysticism of Gregory IX, none of the fire, none of the ecstasy of personal courage. His age was about my own. His very appearance fitted his character—he had a long thick nose, high cheek bones, clean-shaven cheeks of bluish hue, a pointed chin, heavy arched eyebrows over cold hard eyes, a tight mouth. He was calculating, devious, shrewd, avaricious, and realistic. In the Papal Curia he had shown himself an able diplomat. Like all his family, he had one interest: power. Like many members of his family, he had used the priesthood as the path to power. The Papacy was his ultimate goal. Since I had not opposed, but welcomed, his election, I thought to find in him gratitude. I could not have been more wrong; I failed to appraise the effect of the Papal elevation upon him—one of the most disastrous failures of my life.

He was, certainly, a man of ice. With bitterness I have wondered what the designated cardinal saw from beneath the perforated chair of porphyry, on which the Pope was seated during a part of the coronation ceremony in the Laterano. To avoid the scandal of another Pope Giovanna and the son she bore, proof is thus made of a new Pope's sex. This Innocent, I swear, must have revealed not the normal warm-blooded organ of a male, but an icicle and balls of snow.

But if he was cold, he burned with ambition. Hardly had the tiara been set upon his head, before he issued this pronouncement: "The Lord Jesus Christ . . . has established in the Apostolic Throne not only a pontifical, but also a regal monarch, committing to the blessed Petrus and his successors the government of both a celestial and an earthly empire."

The earthly empire could only be mine.

The first shock came when the new Pope refused to receive my ambassadors, saying that he could not treat with excommunicated men. Before I could negotiate for peace I was therefore forced to sue for a favor; I had to beg that my envoys, Pier della Vigna, Taddeo da Suessa, and Archbishop Berardo, be released from the ban. Then, with a show of magnanimity, Innocent granted my request. The maneuver rankled, but I had resolved to let nothing interfere with the progress of peace.

The Pope proved elusive. At one point Piero returned to me in despair. "His Holiness says *yea* one minute and *nay* the next," Piero complained. "And half the time we cannot find him—he hides in a back room in the Laterano because he is afraid to face Gregory's creditors who pound on the palace doors. He shies at shadows, and is guarded every minute of the day and night. He acts like a man who believes his life is in danger. . . ."

"From whom?" I said.

Piero shrugged his shoulders. "Has he other peer in the world than you, Imperatore?"

More and more with passing time I turned to Piero as an *alter ego*, the one person who best understood me and in whom I had implicit trust. With Bianca's death our association resumed, not the old intensity, but the old intimacy, and we were hardly apart day or night. In Piero I found some surcrease for my sorrows, and with Piero I flung myself afresh each day into new activity, in an effort to forget. Ever gnawing at my mind was the thought of peace, denied me by one man, and one alone: the Pope.

"Piero, listen," I said, "concede, concede, concede—but bring back peace!"

Innocent's answer was not peace but a sword. And the sword was wielded by the military Cardinal Raniero of Viterbo, one of my most virulent enemies, whose sole intent was war. Papal elements in Viterbo, north of Rome, suddenly rebelled, under Cardinal Raniero's guiding hand, and drove my supporters into the citadel. My reaction was violent and rapid. Astonished at the quickness of my arrival before the walls of Viterbo with an army, the Cardinal wrote of me: "He leaped like a lioness robbed of her young or a she-bear bereft of her cubs. Clothed in the fire of his wrath he rushed like a midnight tornado; like a courier for speed he rode, and with no royal pomp, mounted on a red horse, to punish the town."

Piero organized the troops. One wing was commanded by my son-in-law the brave young Riccardo, Count of Caserta; the other wing I myself commanded. I swung off my horse, seized a long shield, and led the first assault. It was useless. The town was too well fortified, and could not be taken by storm. Once more I was forced into the tedious and costly business of a siege. But adversity dogged us. After siege engines had been brought, the wind veered during the first assault and our towers were set to blazing by our own Greek fire. Once more I had to begin from the beginning.

At this moment the Pope chose to soften; he was under heavy pressure for peace, not the least of which came from King Louis of France. As an evidence of good faith, Innocent sent as his representative my friend Cardinal Otho of England, whom I had released from imprisonment. The Pope's first request was abandonment of the siege of Viterbo, to which I agreed if my half-starved garrison in the citadel was allowed to go free unharmed. This all affirmed, and the citizens of Viterbo were bound by an oath. Nevertheless, as my men marched through the town they were massacred by the forces of Raniero; hardly one escaped alive. Cardinal Raniero indeed hated peace.

Again I exploded. Though I held no illusions about the capacity of cardinals for treachery, I was profoundly shocked. Under the circumstances, it was unthinkable that the truce should have been violated. "What bond will hold among men . . . if no respect is paid to the honor of spiritual fathers?" I wrote to Innocent. "What expectations can we have of success if human good faith is so despised?" I swore to revenge Viterbo even if I had one foot in Paradise. Promptly Innocent expressed himself as full of regret, announced that he would fine the town, and placed the responsibility for chastisement in the hands of—Cardinal Raniero.

I tried another tack. I called to me secretly that Bernardo di Rossi of Parma who had served as my envoy to the beleaguered Brescians. It so happened that he was married to Innocent's sister, and I thought to make certain appeals to the family interests of the Fieschi. Di Rossi was noted as a fine figure of a noble, imposing, self-possessed, gracious. I found him overly well-fed, ruddy-cheeked from too much wine, self-satisfied—even, I thought, unctuous. But without doubt he had the ear of the Pope when no one else was present to listen. I made it clear to him that, provided a formula could be found, I was prepared to grant even extreme concessions for peace.

Di Rossi listened gravely and said, "Has not the same message been given to His Holiness by your envoy Pier della Vigna?"

"A very similar message," I answered.

"Then how does your Majesty expect me to accomplish more than Pier della Vigna—a man, it is generally said, who is Petrus, and closer to God than the Pope?"

I frowned. "What do you mean by that?"

"Oh, it is a compliment, my Lord," di Rossi smiled. "I mean only what has been said."

I was gravely troubled by this interview. I did not like the too smooth response, the innuendoes about Piero. I had long known, of course, that Piero was disliked by many nobles of my own court. He was considered a commoner, a *parvenu.* What was the Pope's view of Piero?—the Pope, himself a nobleman? Certainly as Sinibaldo Fieschi he had held scorn in his heart always for those without noble blood: they were chattels, to be sold and bought. In my own life there had been no single person more important than Pier della Vigna. It was hard for me to realize that he was seen in ways other than the way I saw him. I would have given much to know the Pope's private estimate, for Innocent was unquestionably aware of my relationship to Piero, his value to me, and the love I bore him.

Suddenly my representatives reached a provisional agreement with the Pope. I was delighted, for I was most anxious that my name not appear once more on the ban list published on Holy Thursday. I had yielded much: I would not contest the right of the Pope to have excommunicated me; in Lombardia I would accept the *status quo ante;* I would return the Church lands; I would release my clerical prisoners; I would accept many lesser humiliations. In my name, Piero and Taddeo swore to the provisional treaty. In a sermon the Pope referred to me as "a devoted son of the Church." At last I began to draw deep breaths of relief; I could feel the tension leaving my body.

Too soon. Piero, riding hard, came to me exhausted. He looked like a man who has not slept for a week—drawn face, haggard eyes, gray skin. "Imperatore, Innocent plays cat and mouse with us!" he said. "Now the Lombards say they will accept no peace unless the Pope has unlimited powers as a mediator. And the Pope says he will not withdraw the ban unless you first restore the lands of the Church. . . . !"

To accept such conditions as these would have been madness. I looked again at Piero, who had been driven beyond the limit of his strength. But one possibility remained: a personal meeting with Innocent. Surely once more we might play chess together, and talk as reasonable men . . . ?

I suggested to Innocent that we meet at some convenient town south of Rome, in the Campagna. He first declined, then abruptly accepted my invitation, but chose the town of Narni northeast of Rome, on the Via Flaminia. I was mystified by this variability, and a new unease began to creep upon me. What slippery new tactic was in the Pope's mind? I made cautious inquiries; I learned nothing. I went therefore in good faith to a town in the vicinity of the appointed meeting place, and waited. The Papal court, meanwhile, had left Rome and moved up to Civita Castellana, rather far from Narni—and there, inexplicably, it paused. The time was June, and the quiet of early summer lay over all the land.

Cardinal Otho came to me to arrange the final details for the meeting. I brushed all difficulties aside, and he returned to the Pope. In a few days he reappeared with new problems: what would be the seating arrangement, how many secretaries, what menus, what protocol, what this, what that . . . ? Obviously the Pope was stalling for time. More than two weeks slipped through our fingers with nothing resolved. I demanded to see the Pope at once; but His Holiness had gone to nearby Sutri, curious to examine some Etruscan monuments uncovered there.

It was Piero who brought me the news one golden morning at dawn—news just received by courier from a crestfallen Cardinal Otho.

"Imperatore, wake, wake!" Piero cried. "Innocent has fled in the night, disguised in the armor of an ordinary soldier. Already he is aboard a Genovese galley and out to sea!"

All had been long prepared, the secret well kept.

I beat my temples with my fists. "O God! O God! I groaned. "I had him in checkmate—and he has overturned the board!"

14

It was put out at once that Innocent had fled to escape capture; that I sought his life. "Our soul is escaped, even as a bird out of the snare of the fowler," said Innocent from the deck of his ship as he landed in Genova. The galley was decorated with gold brocade and silken banners, and flew a flag with the cross. Innocent was accompanied by an entire fleet—arranged by the Fieschi family. Bells pealed and choirs intoned, "*Benedictus qui venit in nomine Domini.*"

When all this was described to me, I made a wry face. "It is written: 'The wicked flee when no man pursues,' " was my comment. Then in a manifesto, I said: "Who in his senses would believe that we seek to injure the Pope—whose death at our hand would bring endless strife upon us and our successors. . . ?" I determined to continue my conciliatory attitude, to continue to seek peace, to do nothing which might further inflame the situation.

It was clear that Innocent would only pause in Genova, though he was perfectly safe in that city. He planned to quit Italy, to escape completely from my proximity, that he might be free to pursue his course without hindrance of any kind. He petitioned the Kings of Aragon, France and England for permission to reside in their territories, but all declined. He then decided on Lyons, which was a free city under the rule of its Archbishop. After a serious illness which was whispered to be caused by my poison, he set out in a litter to cross the Alps. It was early October, and thunder boomed every day for fifteen days. Some of Innocent's newly created cardinals thought they heard the hoofbeats of my approaching troops.

The Pope's purpose in Lyons was a foregone conclusion. Hardly had he arrived in December before he sent out a call for a General Council, to be convoked on the Festa of San Giovanni the following year, for the purpose of deposing the Imperator Fridericus. This time I could not interfere with the delegates. The Church was preparing to turn all her might against me with an overwhelming singleness of purpose: "We must crush the great dragon," were reputed to be Innocent's words. Though recently the Holy Land had been overrun by the Khwarazmian Turks, and Jerusalem again had fallen, Innocent paid little heed. His thoughts were concentrated on the Christian Infidel.

Now came spewing out against me pamphlets, manifestoes, and all the old rumors, refurbished, more vitriolic, more violent. Cardinal Raniero, a man who foamed at the mouth, had been designated the Pope's viceregent in Italy; he was the chief author. Such words as these were the words spread against me:

> THE Beast in his fearsome stiff-necked wrath despises the ban and gulps down punishment like water from a brimming goblet, scoffing at the power of the Keys—this Prince of Tyranny, this overthrower of the Church's faith and worship, this destroyer of precept, this master of cruelty, this confounder of the earth, this scourge of the universe, this transformer of the times. He is like unto the fallen angels who aspire to be the equals of God and seat themselves on the mountains of the most High. Like Lucifer he essayed to scale the heavens to establish his throne above the stars. . . .
>
> Cast him to the ground before the face of the kings, that they may see and fear to follow in his footsteps! Cast him forth out of the holy place of God that he may rule no longer over Christian people! Have no pity for the ruthless one . . . ! Belshazzar the Babylonian defiled the vessels of the temple of Jehovah, and lost his Empire and his life. This Criminal deserves no less to lose his Empire. . . .

And so it was clearly implied that I, also, deserved to lose my life. The baleful Cardinal Raniero was releasing not only the hounds of hate but the demons of death. I wondered how long it might be before the same would be true of the Vicar of Christ . . . ?

I spent my fiftieth birthday not in celebration, like all my Realm, but in writing out a list of concessions to the Pope. I was tired, not of life, but of this endless struggle with an amorphous hydra which no sooner lost one head than grew another. To defy or defeat a single Pope was meaningless; the intrinsic policy of the Church did not change. It was by no means my intent to struggle with the Church; that was the role of heretics and martyrs, and I had no wish to be either. I craved peace more than sex, more than power, more than glory. In the ripeness of my years I longed to think, write, and experiment. I would be surrounded by a brilliant young court of philosophers, artists, poets. The elegance and culture of Greece and Rome would live again.

My daughter Violante wrote me to ask why must I always be embroiled with the Empire: had I not all any man could wish in my own Kingdom of Sicily? So anxious was I for peace that I dallied with the idea of abdicating the throne of Empire in favor of my son Corrado. Another appealing thought, which whispered and beckoned, was travel in the East. I would go to the Orient and never return—perhaps as far as India, perhaps as far as China. Oh, I ached to see the world! Not long since I had betrothed my daughter Costanza to the Emperor of Nicaea. In one of my letters to him, I indulged myself with a bit of wistful dreaming: "O happy rulers of the Orient—who fear neither the dagger of the rebel nor the superstitions invented by priests . . . !"

The list I drew up for the Pope was an abandonment of all I had fought for over the years. I would concede to the Church all the territories I had given by edict and retaken by force; I would yield unconditional authority to the Pontiff to arbitrate the Lombard conflict; I would release all ecclesiastical prisoners with indemnification; I would not challenge the right of excommunication and I would do penance; I would lead a crusade against the Turks to reconquer the Holy Land; I would remain at least three years, and only with Papal permission return earlier; I would forfeit my Kingdom and private estates if I failed to fulfill my vows; and I would appoint kings as my guarantors.

Could I have prepared a more abject surrender? If Innocent declined to accept such submission, on whatever pretext, the world would clearly understand that his sole purpose was war. There was a chance, a long chance, that he would accept; but I did not believe it. Like a man ordained to die, quietly I placed all my affairs in order—so little time was left. In the spring, on Holy Thursday, I received my answer. In Lyons, the Pope repeated my excommunication and added the name of my son Enzo.

I called a meeting of the German princes for the early summer in Verona, to precede the General Council called by the Pope. The ostensible business was to deal with the troubled situation in Austria, though chiefly I wished to sample the temper of the princes. It had been proposed that I marry the heiress of the Austrian dukedom, the sixteen-year-old Gertrude, and create a new kingdom. But Papal Legates had so frightened the girl with tales of my harem, that she refused in hysterics to come with her father to meet me. I felt a certain relief. She would have been a suitable queen for my son Corrado. He was a dutiful boy, and now, at seventeen, was fully mature. He was serious, stable, and dull. I admired his honesty and bravery. He was orderly but not analytical, nor had he the slightest mercurial touch. I embraced him and praised him, and sent him back to the Germans. We were not kindred spirits at all. I feared for his future.

Not for a moment did I consider appearing in person before the Council in Lyons; who were these ecclesiastical harlots to judge me? Piero was deeply hurt that I did not include him in the delegation sent to Lyons. After the departure of my two deputies I noticed his long face. Finally, becoming impatient with its continuation, I called him to me in my private studio, a room filled with the books I carried with me, and asked the cause of his depression.

Hesitating, he plucked with thin fingers at the silver and scarlet thread which embroidered his dark blue tunic—a rich and beautiful garment, for he had not lost his taste for fine clothes.

"How does it happen, Imperatore," he said, pausing,—"how does it happen that you did not select me to help to plead your cause before this critical Council? Am I less skilled in the law and language than Taddeo? Or less vigorous than the venerable Archbishop Berardo who now approaches eighty? Are the Alps less high for them than for me—or am I less trustworthy . . . ?"

The injury was so patent in his tones that I felt utmost contrition. I should have explained in advance what I planned to do, or asked his advice or even acquiescence. As always, I had absorbed him wholly and thoughtlessly, and had given so little attention in return.

"Oh Piero," I said in a voice chastened and apologetic, "I assumed you would understand, knowing my feelings for you—but of course there are limits to communication without words. I am guilty of obtuseness, because naturally, after so many deputations to the Pope, you would expect to be chosen again. But think, Piero my dear friend, how this meeting differs from all the others . . . ?"

The sulkiness had not left his face. "It differs in that its importance far exceeds all the others. It will be a turning point in history: chroniclers will date time from it—the Empire before the Council of Lyons, the Church after the Council of Lyons! Isn't this true?"

"True, alas—too true. But my Piero, what is said at the Council of Lyons—ill said or well said—will not change the result, for the decision has long since been reached in secret. Why then should I risk you?"

"Risk me?"

"Risk your life. Sharp are the daggers in Lyons, dark the alleys. Potent is the poison brewed by Ugo Borgononi, the Pope's own penitent, renowned as a chemist—I myself have read his treatise on the sublimation of arsenic. You are tired, perhaps ill; I would not trust you to a single doctor in Lyons! Piero! Piero! Innocent well knows that to destroy you would be little short of destroying me. Could I survive that blow, after all the others? Piero—however brusque or cruel I may be, never forget that you are my other self!"

His drooping shoulders straightened, and he reached out to take my hand and kiss it. "Imperatore, my Lord, and my friend Federico," he said softly, "always you have my love and devotion!"

I seemed to awake for the first time to the gray in the once black curls, the deepening lines in the fine and sensitive face. He appeared, to my amazement, much older than I, yet our age was the same. I must take better care of Piero, I thought; I must be careful not to lose him. It was a selfish thought—but its genesis was a profound and abiding affection. For a long moment I gazed into the depths of Piero's expressive eyes. The warmth of their response, I hoped, would never change. Yet somehow I felt that all was not well with him; indeed he was exhausted, but I sensed a fatigue of the spirit more corrosive than fatigue of the flesh. Acid trickled in little drops from some hidden spring within, burning and stinging. He broods, and magnifies some fancied wrong, I thought.

"Piero," I said suddenly, almost sharply, "in what lies ahead, I shall have great need of you!"

Then for the first time in all our years together, he avoided my glance. And, coward that I was, I could not bring myself to ask him why.

15

FROM VERONA I rode with my cavalcade of exotic beasts, through the turbid heat of summer, to Torino; and thence, as prearranged, with a small force into the foothills of the Alps to await the coming of messengers from Lyons. Already I knew that the Council was poorly attended, having drawn only a fraction of the two thousand prelates who came to the Lateran Council of the preceding Innocent. A few Italians, the English, the French, the Spanish—one hundred forty all told. Such was the composition. And of them all, Cardinal Raniero and the Spaniards who had escaped capture were the most vehement against me. My supporters, except the Patriarch of Aquileia, quietly resisted the Pope's summons and failed to arrive. But for Innocent, the number was enough; his only need was an audience.

At last my waiting was ended. In that still and expectant hour before dawn, a lathered courier arrived with the final report from Taddeo and Berardo in Lyons. Shivering with the mountain chill, and with shaking hands, Piero brought the document to my tent. By candlelight we read it together.

The proceedings had begun with the "*Veni Creator Spiritus.*" In the cathedral the Pope had celebrated Mass, then taken his seat upon a raised throne, wearing his most splendid robes of scarlet and gold. The nave was filled with rows of archbishops and abbots. The Pope rose and spoke: "I have five sorrows, which I may liken unto the five wounds of Christ. These are the Tartar invasion; the schismatical spirit of the Greeks; the heresies which have crept in among us; the seizure of Jerusalem by the Turks; and the active enmity of the Imperator Fridericus to the Church which he is bound to protect." Then the Pope wept, and his hearers were also moved to tears.

Only the sins of the Emperor were discussed. The English

rose to protest excessive money-gathering by the Pope's representatives. They were brushed aside. The first charges against the Emperor were listed by Cardinal Raniero: all the long-familiar crimes, presented with a mouth dripping venom. Envoys of the French and English Kings rose to protest. They were brushed aside. The Patriarch of Aquileia rose to protest. He was threatened by the Pope with loss of his ring if he did not subside.

Taddeo rose to deny the jurisdiction of the assembly: "I appeal from this Council, from which so many great prelates and secular princes are absent, to an impartial General Council. I appeal from this Pope, the declared enemy of my Lord, to a future, more gentle, more Christian Pope." Taddeo's objection was brushed aside.

But Taddeo was allowed to answer the charges, one by one. He did so with fire and telling effect, stabbing the lies and half-truths of Raniero with fingers like rapiers. He revealed the intransigence of Gregory, the duplicity of the Curia, the hatred of Innocent. He produced for examination documents with the seals of Emperor and Pope. But all was brushed aside. The promises of the Pope were conditional, said the Council; the promises of the Emperor, absolute.

Then the Pope summed up. He deleted only the outright charges of sodomy, murder of wives and son. The Emperor had been proved guilty of perjury, breach of the peace, sacrilege and heresy. He had not fulfilled the treaties sworn with the Church; he had defamed a Pope; he had broken peace with the Church; he had occupied the territories of the Church; he had seized prelates as prisoners; he had expressed friendship with the Saracen kings; he had placed his wives in the charge of eunuchs whose castration he had overseen; he had permitted Muslim worship in the Temple of the Lord in Jerusalem; he had used Saracen warriors against Christians; he had betrothed his daughter to the schismatic Emperor of Nicaea; he had used assassins against princes; he had celebrated the holy mysteries as an excommunicant; he had kept a harem of Saracen women; he scorned the morals of a Catholic prince; he associated with heretics; he gave no alms and did no pious deeds; he had built neither church nor cloister; he was sunk in sin and in league with the Prince of Darkness.

Innocent rose from the throne and gathered about him the cardinals, each bearing a lighted torch. In the hushed cathedral the Pope intoned the sentence: "We, therefore, having maturely and carefully deliberated with our brother Cardinals and the holy Council on the wicked deeds of the said Emperor; and inasmuch as we, unworthy as we are, hold on earth the authority delegated to us by the Lord Jesus Christ, who said to us through the person of the holy saint, Petrus, '*Whatsoever ye shall bind on earth shall be bound in Heaven, and whatsoever ye shall loose on earth shall be loosed in Heaven,*' do hereby declare the above-named Prince, who has rendered himself unworthy of the honors of sovereignty, for his crimes to be deposed from his throne by God, to be bound by his sins and cast off by the Lord, and to be deprived of all his honors. And we do hereby sentence and deprive him."

Then to the cardinals the Pope presented, one by one, blood-red hats, to remind them constantly of their holy mission, saying, "Whosoever loves justice should rejoice that vengeance is thus declared against the common enemy, and wash his hands in the blood of the transgressor."

Weeping and beating his breast, Taddeo cried out, "Now will the heretics rejoice, the Turks prevail, the Tartars arise in their might. O day of wrath, of tribulation, of agony!"

Innocent began to chant "*Te Deum laudamus,*" and all his supporters joined their voices. When the hymn was finished the Pope took up a lighted torch, and, with the cardinals, beat the torches against the cathedral floor to extinguish the flames.

In an awesome voice the Pope declaimed his final malediction: "So be the glory and the fortune of Fridericus extinguished upon earth!"

When Piero and I had finished reading the documents, dawn was breaking on the glaciered peaks and filtering roseate light into the misty valley of the Po.

"Call the princes and the knights and all the troops," I said in a remote, stern voice, "—and open the chest with my crowns."

And in a little while, in the full bright light of dawn, with banners waving, all had gathered before the royal tent of striped purple and white. A trumpet sounded and the curtains of the entrance were pulled back by the Saracen guards. I was revealed in gleaming royal armor seated on a throne. A ruffle of drums echoed and reechoed from the rocks.

"Bring me my crowns," I commanded, choosing to speak in the first person.

Then from among the many I selected one, and set it upon my

head. I rose. "This is the Crown of Empire," I said. "Pope Innocent IV in vulgar presumption would take it from me. But as my right to the crown is derived from God alone, neither this Pope nor his puppet Council nor the Devil can remove it from my head! The Pope himself preaches heresy, and opens wide the gates of Hell to release the dogs of war. He himself brings misery, suffering, anguish, bloodshed, and death. He sets himself above kings and equal to God. He is a false Vicar of Christ. He himself prepares the way for the Antichrist. Thus the Pope himself has released me from allegiance to the Church and reverence for his Holy Office. He alone must bear the consequences in the eyes of God and man. Therefore, go ye forth and repeat my words to the world:

"Let those who shrink from my support have the shame as well as the galling burden of slavery. Before this generation and before the generations to come, I will have the glory of resisting the Papal tyranny.

"TOO LONG HAVE I BEEN ANVIL—NOW I SHALL BE HAMMER!"

And a crash like thunder sounded from the drums. . . .

VI

IL MARTELLO DEL MONDO

I

UNDER the Gothic arch of a window in the Castel del Monte, overlooking the empty plain of the *Murge*, I recline on cushions, writing. My aging wolfhound, Omar, is with me. I am wrapped in a silken coverlet, for in autumn the vaulted rooms are often chill, and the vast thickness of the castle walls resists the heat of the sun. A small fire flickers in the floor-to-ceiling semiconical fireplace. The serrated rays of the late afternoon sun shaft through the leaded glass of the window, touching with light and shadow the Gothic forms, giving substance and *animus* to the yellow and gray stone. I have been ill, and now I am engaged in a slow convalescence. I listen to the trickling fountain in the courtyard below, but it does not cheer me. I am very lonely. . . .

Five years have passed since I caught the Pope's javelin in my hand and hurled it back again—five years drawn straight from the Apocalypse, as I foresaw. But though I foresaw a ravaging death for the many, I did not foresee the torturous death of a few. And in this last lies my greatest sadness, for to save my own life—as I thought—I myself became an instrument of torture. In my life, this tragedy is out of all proportion to the comedy, a sorrow out of all proportion to the joy. Hence my bitterness. There are times now when I weep for days on end; but the tears are fruitless, and the lamentations atone for nothing. What is done is done. The dead are dead. I live, but I am cursed by life. For when the joy of life is finished, life is finished. But I do not die. I continue, fiercely, my defiance of the Pope, his armies, his plots, his threats of damnation. I have proved impossible to defeat, very difficult to kill, to his infinite frustration. It is, in truth, only my hate for the Pope and his works, which keeps me alive. The hate which consumes me can be slaked only by his utter annihilation . . . or mine.

One of Innocent's cardinals wrote wonderingly about me: "The stones hurled by the Papal catapaults against Fridericus turn to straw; he lets the rays of the sun fall upon him, and he fears the God of the lightning as little as an archer with his bow."

In these five years I have hardly touched pen to paper, but my sword from its scabbard I have drawn many times. Now in an interlude of quiet—how long?—I must compensate for the lacks of the past. The story of a life is not completed until it is finished; and this story, like the three Fates, I will spin on the loom until the thread breaks.

The whole of Europe, the whole of Christendom, has watched breathless as the struggle of titans progresses, and all Christendom is divided in two. To some, Innocent is the "Heretic Pope"; to others, I am "the Scourge of God." But to all, enemies and partisans alike, I am known as *Il Martello del Mondo*—the hammer of the world. And, freed by the Pope of all restraint, as a hammer I have struck blow after blow, resounding to the ends of the earth. How else would I react to a man, priest or no, who declares to the world that he has sworn "to destroy to the last descendant this race of vipers"? Moreover, I have cried out for reform of the corruption in the Church itself, and in so doing have sounded many a responsive chord. I have been urged to pursue the hierarchy so relentlessly that they will "hide their tonsures with cow dung if no other covering can be found."

Along with the sword, the lance, and the ax, I have used words. It is better to capture men's minds than to destroy men's bodies. I spoke first to the kings, then to the peoples. Straightway from the foothills I marched to Torino, and with the help of Piero issued a manifesto to all princes. I did not deny the authority of the Pope in spiritual affairs, but, as always, I challenged the rule of the Pope ever secular affairs. I challenged the legality of the Council. And I stressed that the primary allegiance of all priests is to the Pope, not to the temporal sovereign or state of origin. Hence no state can trust the loyalty of the Roman clergy, I said, for all have sworn their blind and absolute obedience to the Roman Pontiff.

> YE single kings of single countries—what have ye not to fear from such a High Priest who dares to depose us . . . us, whose Imperial diadem is given of God, and who holds sway over illustrious dominions?

Neither the first are we, nor yet the last whom priestly power opposes and seeks to hurl from the seats of the mighty. And the fault is yours who give ear to these hypocrites of holiness. . . . These who call themselves priests now turn oppressors, grown fat upon the alms of the fathers and of the sons. Although they themselves are the sons of loyal subjects, they render no reverence to emperor or king once they are ordained as priests.

The humiliation of the other kings and princes will be a little thing, if the power of the Roman Caesar, whose shield bears the brunt of the first onslaught, should crumble under perpetual attack. . . . We adjure you, nobles and princes of the earth, and cry the alarm, not because our own weapons are unavailing to ward off such shame, but that the honor of all is touched when insult is offered to any one. . . .

And the kings gave thought to this problem, so that not one recognized either my deposition or excommunication—even the sniveling Henry III of England, called by Innocent, "our vassal, or rather our slave," and who so feared the Pope in all things that he sent gold at every demand. As for King Louis IX of France, twice in person and once through a deputation of bishops he protested Innocent's policy.

At Cluny he went with his mother Queen Blanche to remonstrate with the Pope; but he left in a fury at discovering that the most Christian of Christians was less Christian than he thought. Later, he urged Innocent to cease my persecution, that I might aid him with his Crusade; but the Pope refused. King Louis replied, "If, as may be foreseen, these policies gravely affect the Crusade, the guilt will be yours." And, as foreseen, the Crusade was so gravely affected that it was a disaster, with the saintly Louis himself taken prisoner. At once I intervened in his behalf, in spite of my hosts of worries—for the commander of the Saracen forces was my old friend Fakhr ad-Din (with my Eagle on his shield!).

Meanwhile the rapacious policies of Innocent were bearing more than golden fruit. He had enriched not only himself but his relatives and hordes of hangers-on. He had so crammed the Church offices of Lyons with his kin that the canons told him to his face they would not lift a hand if the hostile people drowned his relatives in the river. In disgust at the money-hunger of the Papal court, the Archbishop of Lyons retreated to a monastery; and Innocent in delight promptly filled the vacancy with Philip of Savoy, who had never taken Orders. The Pope's multitude of nephews were awarded dioceses in France and England from which they collected revenues without ever making an appearance. All men talked of the vast wealth of the favorite nephew, Percivalle, who became famous as the richest priest in Christendom. Another, a mere youth, Guglielmo, Innocent named a Cardinal, and kept him close at hand as a kind of bodyguard of treasure.

Once more Pier della Vigna turned his pen into a lance and wrote a long satirical poem in Latin about the Pope's insatiable hunger for gold. The Pope's devices to raise money were the greatest scandal of all scandals. He extended the system of benefices to absentee holders, to reward anyone who was of service to him or paid enough. Dispensations could be bought for any sin, any crime. Indulgences were granted, for a fee, to those who were unable (or unwilling) to join the official Crusade against me—and also for merely listening to a sermon against me. Holy Church stank of usury and simony, and the peoples of all lands groaned under the Papal demands for more and yet more money. "If you offer a priest your hand, he seizes your arm up to the elbow. . . ."

I thought of the teachings of my contemporaries San Francesco d'Assisi and Sant' Antonio di Padova, and addressed myself to the world as follows:

> SUCH is the way of Rome: Under words as smooth as oil and honey lies the rapacious blood-sucker—the Church of Rome is like a leech. She calls herself my mother and nurse, but she is a stepmother, and the root of all evil. The whole world pays tribute to the avarice of Rome. Her legates travel through all lands, binding, loosing, punishing, not to sow the seed of the Word, but to subdue all men and wring from them their money. . . .
>
> The primitive Church, founded on poverty and simplicity, brought forth numberless Saints; she rested on the foundation laid by our Lord Jesus Christ. The Roman Church now wallows in riches—what wonder that the walls of the Church are undermined at the base and threaten utter ruin. Unite! Unite and overturn this tyranny. . . . This danger is common to all!

Not one, but many manifestoes I wrote thus, and I said that "to take from the priesthood their treasures which are their burden and their curse—this is a labor of love." Many were the manifestations of sympathy and support I received on this issue, and, not least, from among the mendicant orders themselves—for many were those who sincerely believed the Francescan doctrine of poverty and simplicity. My words so stung the Pope that he specifically ordered the mendicants to go out and preach a Crusade against me, at the same time secretly instructing them not to mention the Crusade of King Louis. I was to be termed again and again "The Antichrist," and my deeds painted blacker than pitch. "Kill, kill the Antichrist!" was their war cry.

So, on the mendicants too I turned my wrath: "These caricatures of angels, who under the mask of religion creep about like reptiles, speaking and acting evilly, ought to be seized and punished with the torment of fire!"

All the forces of disorder, which I had controlled with such difficulty, were now released and magnified a hundredfold. Everywhere I found little or great groups of Papalists springing up around me. Every flame was fanned by the priests into a conflagration. In every loyal town the Church's agents sought to organize, openly or secretly, hostile groups to seize control. Conversely, in many towns controlled by Papalists, the common people rallied to my cause against the Pope. Thus in every town, confusion, suspicion and hatred reigned. When I left Torino and marched southward, I was inundated with rumors of treachery and rebellion in a score of towns. It was like dropping a ball of mercury into fire.

With Enzo I met and defeated contingents of the Lombard armies which had been sent by the Pope to harass me, but all decisive engagements were refused. I was forced to rely heavily on the services of such mercenary overlords as Ezzelino da Romano and the one-eyed Marquis Oberto Pelavicino, two *grandi signori*, who had remained loyal to me. Pelavicino was even more menacing in appearance than the hairy Ezzelino. A cock had plucked out one eye while Pelavicino lay in the cradle, and the other was frightening. It "glittered like a black coal," people said, in a swarthy face ringed with grizzly black hair and beard. These were men who believed in nothing and were interested only in their own power, sustained by whatever means. But since they were powerful as well as ruthless, they were useful to me.

I had to take help where I could find it—for the opposition was equally ruthless and equally avid for power.

At every bend of the road I discovered the hand of the Pope —military units organized and commanded by priests. With each fresh assault, my wrath grew; but again I took first to the pen:

> WHENCE have our priests learned to bear arms against Christians? To don coats of mail instead of sacred garments, to wield a lance instead of a shepherd's crook, to carry the bow and arrows of bitterness instead of their writing reed, to think lightly of the weapons of salvation? What assembly of God-fearing men has commanded this and sealed it with its seal?
>
> If anyone doubts this, let him behold the cardinals and archpriests in the land where we hold sway. One calls himself a duke, another a margrave, yet a third a count. Here is one who commands an army corps, there one who guides a fleet. And why is this? They are prepared for war: they have breastplates, weapons, and banners. Did the first disciples of Christ so arrange it?
>
> O foolish multitude! Ye attribute holiness unto them, ye create saints unto yourselves as imaginary as the giants of myth! These are not holy men, but famished wolves . . . !

Hard grew my heart, ruthless my methods. I told myself that mercy was a word I must learn to forget. I commanded that all Papalists found armed should be executed. Any town I entered must give hostages. Messengers caught bearing letters from the Pope would lose hands and feet. I lined the banks of the Po with three hundred Papalists of Mantova, dangling from gibbets over the water. On the walls of Reggio I beheaded one hundred, for their tonsures had been covered by helmets.

With sorrow I resolved on a policy I had avoided all the years of my reign. Now I had been left no alternative: I unleashed bloody terror.

2

UNEASE increasingly took hold of me. My temper and my patience wore thin. Even my closest intimates (except Piero) became afraid to approach me without first ascertaining my mood. Everyone became suspicious of everyone else. Spies abounded. Restraint surrounded each man like a coat of armor, and the old comradeship was no more. Privately I mourned this state of affairs, but my mouth tightened, my fists clenched. I drove my aides at a pace which few men could bear. I would have transformed them, if possible, into Furies in my relentless attacks on the Pope.

With the coming of winter I moved down the coast of the Tyrrhenian Sea to Grosseto in Toscana. It was warmer, closer to Sicily, and my communications by sea were secure. (Also the hawking was good in the marshes of the Maremma). Yet I was close enough to the north and east to observe events at something like first hand. As uncertainty grew upon me, I thought it wise to shift my administrative officers from post to post. Among the most important towns were Parma and Fiorenza, controlling key passes across the Apennines. With some misgivings I had shifted Bernardo di Rossi, the Pope's brother-in-law, from his post as *podestà* of Parma, to Fiorenza. Despite his tie to the Pope, he gave every evidence of continued loyalty to me. I moved Tebaldo Francesco, one of my most brilliant vicar-generals, to Parma, and sent Pandolfo da Fasanella to Fiorenza to work with Bernardo di Rossi. Then in a monastery near Parma some of my men discovered documents which involved Bernardo di Rossi in Papalist activities against me. When I moved to apprehend him, I discovered that he had fled with some Guelf knights to Milano.

Smarting from this treachery, I recalled Pandolfo to court because he had been associated with di Rossi, and sent Piero to Parma to help Tebaldo stabilize the situation there. To Fiorenza I sent my son, Federico of Antioch. Federico was now nineteen, intelligent, energetic, and so handsome and pleasing in manner that his associates quickly forgot his lameness. Since certain activities were barred to him, he had become an expert with crossbow and javelin, and his *canzoni* were among the most graceful and beautiful of all the poets. His face, in certain lights with certain shadows, remained the face of his mother Balian—and for this alone I loved him. Moreover, and just now most important, I could trust him—for in return he loved me. So successful was he that he became greatly esteemed by the people of Toscana, who called him "King of Fiorenza" or simply "Re Federico." Such was the fulfillment of my promise to Balian.

Tebaldo and Pandolfo had been among that crop of young men who had grown up at court like my sons, had been educated at the University of Napoli, and specially prepared for the great responsibilities I placed on their shoulders. They had been away from me for some years, however, and now I wanted to resume my contact with them. In the early spring I thought to recall Tebaldo to court from Parma, and Federico too, and have all join in a general reunion. The vicar-general of the Marche, Jacopo da Morra, one of my favorites among the young poets and also witness of my marriage to Bianca, was already at court. Taddeo and Berardo had long since returned from Lyons. Of my sons, Enzo was to arrive within a few days. His marriage had been annulled by the Pope, and now he was constantly in the field with my armies. He had developed into a military commander of marked ability. Riccardo di Theate had been ill (as he was so often), but he managed to appear—though he hardly spoke to anyone. Only Manfredo was missing; but, as he was not yet fifteen, I kept him in Foggia for safety's sake. Enrico, the child of Isabella, was still too young to consider.

I was planning a sumptuous banquet with music, songs, and dancing—I wished to revive, if I could, some of the old feeling which had been so chilled by the Pope's war. I wanted to reduce tension and suspicion, increase harmony, and weld into an even more cohesive force that group of young men on whom I had lavished such pains—and for whom I held such affection. Indeed they were second sons; on the lap of more than one I had rested my head. It is not too much to say, I think, that I loved and cherished them all.

The banquet was set for mid-March, and by that date only Tebaldo was not among us. I was at a loss to explain the delay, as the passes from Parma were open. The dawn that day broke strangely obscured, with masses of dark, drifting clouds; and by noon the sun was extinguished, the earth darkened, and blood-red rain began to fall. At once the astrologers united to proclaim that some dreadful and portentous event was impending. Men huddled together in fright, casting apprehensive glances at the swirling, blackened sky. I examined the rain, and found in it traces of ash and red mud, and concluded that a portentous event had already occurred—a massive volcanic eruption of which as yet we knew nothing, possibly our Etna in Sicily. I explained what I thought, but only Piero, Enzo, and Federico of Antioch appeared to believe me. The banquet, I said calmly, would take place as planned. Privately I sighed, because I found catastrophies of nature easier to explain than the superstitions embedded in men's minds.

It was evident that a pall had been cast over our festivity. As the guests began to assemble that evening no laughter or talk could be heard. Except for the silence, we began just as always, washing our hands in basins brought by servants. I gave the signal for music, thinking thus to bring cheer; but the musicians were so quavering that they played at odds with one another. Then I noticed that two seats, one to the right of me and one to the left, were empty. I frowned. What could have happened to Tebaldo and Jacopo, that they should be so late? A chamberlain approached, and spoke in an undertone to Piero; then he, who sat always on my right, leaned over and whispered in my ear. We rose together and went into an antechamber.

A distraught messenger awaited us. He had come by swift sailing ship from my son-in-law Count Riccardo di Caserta, bearing secret documents, he said, of such importance that he was charged on pain of death to deliver them—else he would never have braved this night brewed by witches. He was wailing of the demons he has passed and conquered, while I was busy breaking seals and reading the first lines.

I scanned again what I had read, and then again. "Parricides!" I cried aloud. "It cannot be . . . !"

Then I saw in my mind the two empty chairs. I reeled from this blow. Nonetheless, I refused to believe until I myself talked to the groom who had saddled their horses at their urgent command, and had seen them vanish through the muddy rain in the direction of Rome. Hours had passed; to overtake them now would be impossible. If they were not guilty, why had they panicked at the ominous portents from the sky, and fled from the court?

I was to die under their daggers at table this night. And Enzo as well.

Such was the plan, revealed by a conspirator who suffered from the pangs of his guilt. But it was no simple conspiracy. Conceived by Bernardo di Rossi, it involved Francesco in Parma as a leading organizer, for he had been promised the Kingdom of Sicily under fief from the Pope. In the island of Sicily, Ruggero di Amicis, and on the mainland, the greatly beloved Andrea da Cicala, were to revolt, simultaneously with invasion of Papal forces by sea. In the north, the Papal armies under Cardinal Raniero were also timed to invade. The Bishop of Bamberg, fresh from Lyons, had forecast to his flock in Germany that I would shortly die at the hands of my own courtiers. Tens and scores of persons were involved; and the leaders were the young men I had known best and trusted most.

First I wept, believing, disbelieving, believing. This might happen to others, but not, not to me! Daggers in the hands of these boys who had romped at my feet. We had eaten together, hunted together, been swimming together, talked of love and life and philosophy together—why, I knew them better than my own sons. Daggers in their hands? Impossible!

One day I had been given by the Marquis Malaspina a blooded horse—but it was a rickety old palfrey barely able to run. All the spectators were astonished, but I understood. Now this Marquis was one of the traitors. My young men were afraid. They were afraid of my decline and the rise of another power of which they held no part. Better to be on the safe side, they thought; better to join with the strongest before too late. The rewards were so tempting—so grandiose and alluring. The Pope promises . . . promises . . . promises. The weaker ones began to crumble, and the stronger feared to be left behind. Cowards . . . !

These two whose hands were to drive the daggers to my heart—were they more afraid of the sky or of me? But if they were not afraid of me, let them fear me now! For as my wrath mounted, I became indeed like a vengeful Beast risen out of the sea: I would not rest by day or night until I had delivered them over to the punishments reserved for parricides under Roman law. That night, when at last I found a fitful sleep, I dreamed that I reclined by a pleasant fountain, and two parallel lines of dancing girls came toward me gently waving their arms. They were balanced on rolling spheres, and as they passed they turned to savage beasts—lions, leopards, panthers. Snarling, they lashed out and raked me with their claws. But quickly I turned and knocked the spheres from under them; with screams they fell, writhing, to the blood-soaked earth. I awoke gasping. Henceforth I wore chain mail by day and much of the night. My sword was always at hand.

Even as I took ship for the Realm, word came that Cardinal Raniero, unaware that the plot had not succeeded, had begun his invasion—only to be severely defeated. But news of the failure preceded me to Sicily, where the conspirators already had spread lies that I was dead. The risings had collapsed, for no support had been found among the people; and the news of my arrival was the end. The traitors had taken only one town and two fortresses. Only the citadel of Capaccio, not far from Paestum, below Salerno, held out till my arrival. But at Capaccio, made desperate by guilt, the conspirators refused to surrender. Perhaps they were misled by Papal agents into believing they were not alone; one letter of encouragement from the Pope I intercepted. Once again I was forced to besiege. Though I cut off the water supply and augmented my striking power with more and more catapults, the siege dragged on into midsummer; but of the outcome I held no doubt. I would reduce this fortress stone by stone, even if all the men and all the riches of my kingdom were required! My vehemence was without bounds. I would grind to dust the twenty-four towers which surmounted impregnable cliffs of yellow stone; if need be, I would undermine the cliffs, and level the mountain to the plain!

In the hours when assaults were not in progress, I rode to the magnificent ancient Greek temples at Paestum. I had noticed in the church in Capaccio a Madonna holding child and pomegranate exactly like the Hera the Greek woman had described to me when I was a boy. Capaccio itself was founded by the people of Paestum when the fevers grew too deadly in the river valley. I thought to relieve the tiresome days by an inspection of the site where Greeks had worshiped the goddess so long before the Christian era. Here, at the mouth of the river Sele, wrote Strabo, Jason voyaged with the Argonauts, to found a sanctuary to the Argive Hera. To my dismay I found a lime kiln in operation, and several temples partially destroyed. I gave orders to stop this savagery at once, but who can supply the missing stones quarried with such loving care?

I liked to sit in contemplation among the ancient temples which remained, now overgrown with foliage and dyed with yellow lichen. Once they were tinted in rich reds and blues, and echoed to the music of lyre and chanting chorus. To my ears came only the sounds of cicada and occasional bird calls and the soothing wash of nearby waves on saffron sand. My favorite time was sunset, when the sun gilded the majestic Doric columns, and, through the long colonnades of the peristyle, extinguished itself in a blaze of glory in the wine-dark sea. So each day Apollo drove his chariot in splendor until the last moment of his allotted span; and so would I. I was grateful to those gods whose worship had produced such harmony and beauty; for the joy of man and the beauty of his handiwork were surely the chief ends of life. All else was naught. Here the men had vanished; but the handiwork remained, radiant with the spirit—a soul?—which its creators had breathed into it. I knew them; I felt them; I admired them and loved them for what they had left behind. In my own way I too had tried to make gifts to posterity: and perhaps some day men would sit among the ruins of my palaces and castles, and feel something of what I felt now. Among all animals, only the minds of sensitive men can span the centuries and communicate with one another. If I feel bitterness for the disasters of the present, perhaps for the future I can rejoice. The Greek temples are ruined; but they are not failures.

So my sorrow was equal to my wrath. Not for a moment, however, did I permit the sorrow to bend me from my purpose. Stern justice must be dispensed, a justice which would have meaning in lands so inured to cruelty that quick death by hanging or the headman's ax was considered a favor. So damnable a crime as parricide must be punished by all four elements: earth, air, fire, and water. And such punishment would be understood, remembered, feared. To men of my own time I would behave like a man of my own time: I would forget the past and cease to think of the future.

In the menacing heat of a July morning, the citadel showed a white flag. Parched, filthy and unshaven, starving, the one-hundred-fifty defenders were paraded before me. To my amazed senses I recognized among them Tebaldo Francesco, Ruggero di Amicis, Andrea da Cicala. They would not meet my contemptuous glance. I did not speak to them, but had them set apart. The other leaders of the conspiracy who had fled to Rome had been richly rewarded by the Pope; these here would receive a different treatment. The lesser conspirators I disposed of quickly: some were dragged across the stony earth by horses; some were hanged in the air; some were burned by fire; some were sewn into sacks and thrown into the sea. I sent all to their deaths unabsolved, with the taunt that their clerical friends could take care of them on the other side.

For those chief traitors, whom I once loved and now hated, I reserved the punishment of mutilation of their strong young bodies; amputated were one hand, one foot, the ears, the nose, and the tongue. Their eyes I spared that they might see the horror of honest people who gazed at them as they were paraded on asses from town to town through all the countries of Christendom.

Tebaldo Francesco was preceded by a sign which read:

> Let the punishment of this accursed criminal instruct your minds and spirits by the sight of the eye—for what is seen makes more impression than what is heard. Let no forgetfulness dim what ye have seen: the just judgment of a parricide.

And upon his head was tied a Papal bull—so the whole world might recognize that the true author of the plot to murder a Christian king was the Vicar of Christ.

3

These events produced in Italy a vast cynicism about the Church, and in Germany a vast sorrow. In France and England the chief reactions were continued fretfulness at the insolent demands for money. But the machinations of Pope Innocent IV had hardly begun. As diplomat, puppeteer, and master of intrigue, he had few equals. As his cause, he said, was holy, all means were suitable to his end. He slipped his hand with equal ease into mailed gauntlet or velvet glove. His genius lay in his ability to recruit others, by pleas, or threats, or artifice, or gold, to do his bidding. He did not always succeed.

Innocent, who so abhorred the slightest taint of the infidel, chose to approach the Sultan of Egypt, urging rupture of the agreements made with me. I laughed heartily when the Sultan, the son of al-Kamil, sent me a copy of his reply to the Pope:

> We have received your ambassadors, Holy Father of the Christians, with honor. They have spoken of Christ, whom we know how to glorify better than you do, and of your desire to give peace to the peoples—a wish ever in our heart. But do not ignore that in the time of the late Sultan, our father (may Allah glorify him), a sincere friendship existed between us and the Emperor of the Romans. If we are to treat with you, his agreement is necessary; therefore we will instruct our envoy at the Imperial court to inform him of your proposals.

The crafty Pope, having failed to take my life in Italy, now turned his attention to outflanking me from Germany. His means were unexcelled. By a series of threats, expulsions, and new appointments, he preëmpted the German Church for himself. In the beginning, many of the German clergy had reacted like the

Bishop of Brixen, who barricaded the streets against the Papal messengers, or the Archbishop of Salzburg, who ground a Papal letter to pieces under his feet. But dozens of depositions quickly turned the tide; henceforth all elections were strictly forbidden, and all oppointees were creatures of the Pope. The lay princes were another matter; but they were so divided among themselves that it was obvious I could not depend on them for long.

In an audacious maneuver, Innocent first turned his attention to my son Corrado, and attempted subversion. But Corrado was no Heinrich, and resisted all the most toothsome blandishments of the Pope; and for this I shall forever honor him. Then the Pope sought another candidate to stand for election as Emperor, and found him in that ever-hungry Heinrich Raspe of Thuringia, whom I had appointed as Regent before Corrado came of age. The Landgrave Raspe, however, being a cautious man, declined the honor until the Pope had laved him with twenty-five thousand silver marks—enough to make him rich whether king or no. Then three archbishops and a handful of other clerics—without a single secular elector—proceeded to meet near Würzburg and choose Heinrich Raspe as Emperor. Mockingly he was dubbed by the people, "Rex Clericorum."

This "Rex Clericorum" soon found himself an army, for the Pope was willing to pay for the whole enterprise, and challenged Corrado to battle near Frankfurt. Corrado, whose forces were much larger, thought to settle the matter once and for all, and accepted the challenge. As the battle began, two-thirds of Corrado's army went over to Raspe, under the leadership of a Swabian noble who had been paid six thousand marks and promised the Dukedom of Swabia by the Pope. Corrado was defeated; but he rallied his forces for another day, and the battle decided nothing. Then to the extreme vexation and mortification of the Pope, his "Emperor" died—and all the costly intriguing had to be done over again. This time candidates were even harder to find, and Innocent had to be content with a young Dutch boy with rank no higher than count: Wilhelm of Holland. He was a creature of the Archbishop Sigfrid of Mainz, a pretty little fellow, chubby-cheeked, a splendid acolyte. I feared his sword as much as his candle.

This warfare by attrition I found very tiresome, and conceived a plan to end it. I myself would go to Germany with a powerful army—by way of Lyons, to pay my respects to the

Pope. The prospect of physical danger always made Innocent feel nervous indeed—so perhaps in fright he might listen to reason. If he did not—! Yet for all its simplicity, the plan was daring and dangerous. It was Piero who suggested that Italians cross the Alps—for the first time since the days of ancient Rome. I would have relied on forming an army in Germany, but this thought was much more appealing. To obtain passage through the Alps to Lyons, I made a number of agreements with various nobles, and to the daughter of Count Amadeus di Savoia I betrothed my son Manfredo. The route once secure, I turned my attention to Italy. I divided its administration among my sons, and Ezzelino da Romano, who now was a son-in-law. I had become afraid to trust anyone who was not linked to me by blood—with one exception: I made Pier della Vigna protonotary of the Imperial court, and placed the entire realm of Sicily under his jurisdiction. In my absence he was to act for me; his power was so great that it was almost my own. Yet on his head he wore no crown. Piero had become at last that apostolic Petrus which Bernardo di Rossi had so cynically implied.

All was arranged, all was prepared. In the spring following the plot against my life, I moved by easy stages from the Realm to Torino. From Torino I sent my advance guard ahead to begin the rigorous march over the Alps; I myself would follow shortly. News came to me that the Pope was in a panic, that frantically he sought haven once more from varied kings—to no avail. Already towns along the way to Lyons were jammed with curious people, waiting to see pass the "Hammer of the World." Behind me all Italy seemed tranquil, and I breathed relief.

It was the omninous calm before the storm.

4

MESSENGERS ARRIVED from Enzo on foam-flecked horses; with the greatest reluctance I opened the dispatches. My eye at once caught the name of Bernardo di Rossi, and I groaned. On Sunday morning June 16, a group of seventy Guelf knights under the leadership of di Rossi, disguised as pilgrims, with arms under their cloaks, entered the gates of Parma. My *podestà*, the well-known poet Arrigo Testa, and leading Ghibellines were engaged in a wedding festivity. All were filled with good cheer and wine. At a signal from di Rossi, the town Guelfs rose, and cut my forces to pieces. Arrigo Testa was killed, and Parma lost. Immediately, by prearrangement, Guelf reinforcements poured in from the Guelf towns, including a powerful contingent from Milano under the leadership of my old enemy the Papal Legate Gregorio da Montelungo.

How like Innocent to defend his breast by striking me in the back: so I thought as I rushed to join Enzo, who was near Brescia, and march together against Parma. The defection of Parma was a grave blow at a critical moment; it controlled the only western pass over the Apennines available to me, and its loss severed my communications with the Kingdom of Sicily. I could not possibly cross the Alps without Parma secure in my rear. Innocent had struck at my most vulnerable spot. But worse, the loss of Parma was the signal for Guelf risings everywhere. At night, wherever we turned, literally, we saw flames. In every town and hamlet, once more the priests had taken to arms.

On the second of July we reached Parma. Its defenses bristled with all the might the Guelfs could give it. I climbed a shielded observation tower and gazed across the walls. Even from a distance it was easy to see that the *duomo* and the baptistry were the military headquarters of the town. The romanesque baptistry I observed with a certain acrid distaste, because it had been built by the Bishop Obizzo Fieschi, another of the Pope's many relatives. Its octagonal shape the Bishop had relieved by columns of diverse forms, for to the clerical mind symmetry was the symbol of death. Now another Fieschi had indeed brought death to Parma; I could not permit it to remain in Guelf hands. Both its practical and its symbolic value were too great. So the Guelfs, with their many reinforcements, felt safe from assault, safe from death. We should see. . . .

Outside the walls, before the eyes of the amazed defenders, I built a new town. Using a Roman-style plan, I laid out streets, squares, markets, walls, eight gates, drawbridges over a moat, a canal bringing water, and finally I added a small, very fine Greek bronze of the Winged Victory. My astrologers were consulted for the right hour of the right day to begin construction; the Guelf astrologers, to lift flagging spirits in Parma, observed that Cancer and Mars were in close conjunction, a clear sign the new town was doomed. I ignored their prediction, and named my town "Vittoria." I minted coins with its name. The watching world—and certainly the Pope—was no less amazed than the defenders of Parma.

I was prepared to wait in Vittoria until the Judgment Day for the fall of Parma. I moved in with menagerie, dancing girls, chancery and armament. Actually I could not afford to mass here the necessary forces to take the town by assault, for my armies were everywhere in desperate motion, attacking, defending, besieging. I sent troops to open La Cisa Pass, and to a dozen towns—one day Ghibelline, the next day Guelf, the next day Ghibelline. I sent troops to encircle Parma widely and block all supplies by land or river. I sent troops to hold all bridgeheads along the Po. I tried every device to paralyze all movement of the Guelf forces, and isolate them from one another. And the Guelfs of Parma, who had confidently expected continued reinforcements and supplies, found themselves facing a long winter siege without adequate fuel or food.

I laid waste their countryside, burning the property of their clergy and nobles. Their cows wandered unmilked, their pigs were butchered, and their geese revolved tantalizingly on our spits. That ruddy, overfed face of Bernardo di Rossi, would now assume, I hoped, a lean and hungry aspect. As for Gregorio da Montelungo, my wish was that he might become too weak to bear armor over his cassock. Let him hear the rattle of his bones! And to remind all of their eventual fate, each day I hanged a number of prisoners in full view of the town. They swayed gently from their nooses in the light wind of evening. My confidence returned, and I felt that the expedition to Lyons was only a little delayed.

At length the bony finger of famine touched the people of Parma. They had no salt; they baked bread of linseed; their wine was watered; they ate roots and rats; they quarreled incessantly; they lied, stole, and seduced without hindrance. My spies informed me that one night the once plump friar Salimbene, whom I had befriended as a youth by returning him to his father in Parma, had escaped with the intent to flee to Lyons. I gave orders to permit his passage unhindered; I wanted the Pope to hear a firsthand account of his friends' plight.

Unrest grew. The common people were sick of the rule imposed by the Papalists. Day and night the only talk was surrender. But neither di Rossi nor Gregorio da Montelungo would permit surrender. Once, at a gathering of townspeople, a mendicant monk appeared, exhausted and smeared with the mud and dirt of the road. From his kit he produced a letter from a general-cardinal promising that help would soon come, and his news was greeted with wild shouts of joy. Poor fools, to be thus deceived by a Papal Legate—for Montelungo himself had written the letter just the evening before!

So passed two hundred and thirty-one days of the siege. Monday evening, the seventeenth day of February, a raw and rainy night, I spent by a warm open fire dictating corrections and additions to the master copy of my falcon book. It was, I thought, superbly illuminated, and was bound in velvet and silver with clasps of solid gold. My son Manfredo, now sixteen, was helping me. I was pleased with my work (and so was he), pleased that the respite of this siege had given me time to bring it almost to conclusion. From so much ill was some good obtained! We went early to rest, for we planned an excursion at dawn to the gravel beds of Taro with my falcons. It was a restful sleep, because my innumerable anxieties had given way to my interest in nature, and I felt relaxed in my writing.

At first light, cocks crowing, we set off well concealed by the river mists. I thought that our going was unobserved. Enzo was away on campaign, and in command I had left Manfredo Lancia. As Piero had remained in Sicily, Taddeo da Suessa was in charge of the chancery. Berardo was in Sicily too. Both because of winter conditions and the heavy demand for troops elsewhere, the garrison of Vittoria had been reduced to a minimum. I felt no concern: Parma was on the defensive, not Vittoria. Gradually the fog thinned, then lifted, revealing blue sky and my soaring falcons. The hunt was good; every bird performed as bidden, and I heaped praise on my falconers.

Alas, how little are we forewarned on the eve of our greatest disasters! We go for a sail on a tranquil sea: a sudden tempest splits our boat upon the rocks. We pause in the snow to admire a mountain view: an avalanche thunders down. We reach for a flower in the field: a snake strikes our hand. So it is with death itself, unless we are condemned as criminals and know our death in advance. We live; we live not. How fragile is the life of man!

Well content, though tired, we turned homeward. As we approached the plain where Parma lies, we saw ascending heavenward gigantic plumes of smoke. I guessed at once, for I had seen towns put to the torch. But I was not prepared in any sense for what had happened. We approached cautiously now, with a small body of Saracens well in advance, for the smell of danger was in the air. We saw them intercept a single horseman, and then they let him pass. It was Folco Ruffo, one of the youngest of my poets. His tunic and cape were wet but singed and tattered; his face was caked with blood from an ear half-severed from his head. When he saw me, he could not hold back tears; they streaked through the filth on his face.

"Doomsday!" he gasped. "Doomsday!" His words were only half-articulate. "Vittoria is sacked and burned! My Lord, flee, flee—great danger . . . ! Taddeo slain—they chopped off his hands . . . thousands dead, thousands prisoners . . . ! You, thank God, are saved . . . !"

In shocked silence we turned hurriedly off the road and hid in a grove of tall poplars, posting guards all about. In bits and pieces I got the story from Folco. He had escaped by hiding under an abutment of a bridge spanning the Parma River. There he had seen and heard enough to give a picture which was almost complete.

"In mid-morning the Papalists made a sortie outside the walls of Parma, in the direction opposite Vittoria," he said when he was calmer. "The Marquis Lancia rushed off with a sizable force to intercept them—I didn't go, as I had been sick in bed. It was a feint, but nobody knew it just then. I was cursing my luck when I heard frightful shrieking and screaming: the Porta dell'Olme opened and all the starving women and children of Parma came pouring out, a human tidal wave. They swept over our guards and brushed all aside. Arms were useless against them. They were followed by their men and a picked corps of knights under Montelungo, who waved a crucifix in one hand and a sword in the other. It was massacre—stark massacre. Our people were all cut off: Taddeo in the chancery, I at the entrance to a bridge. As I wore no armor, I jumped in the water, and the mob went howling by me. The women and children rushed for food; the men for booty and the Saracen girls; the knights for the chancery. It was Inferno! The fire had begun, but I was wet and freezing. I could hear cries from the Saracen girls, the camels' squeals, the elephant's trumpeting as it broke its hobbles and charged through the streets. Panic everywhere. I saw women with aprons full of flour, men stuffing jewels in their pockets, a priest with a roll of finest purple cloth, a little boy with an astrolabe, a bearded monk lugging off one of the dancing girls, arms and feet tied. A knight with your falcon book. Then Montelungo himself, carrying your bronze Winged Victory—he gave it to a priest at the bridge, and told him to be careful of it, as it was the heathen goddess the Emperor used in black-magic rites and prayed to . . . !"

I groaned aloud. So stunned was I that all seemed at first merely like a fanciful tale my poet was telling me. Taddeo slain? Oh no! But the blood was real, and so was the fury I saw in the eyes of my son Manfredo. "More—?" I said, controlling my own rage as I thought of Taddeo's beautiful hands.

Now Folco stared at the ground. "Such humiliation that I hardly dare speak—but better you learn this from me than from others. I heard a great hubbub, and I strained to see. People were shouting, 'Look, look at Cortopasso the cobbler!' I thought: what a nickname for a man—"Shortstride"! My Lord, there came tripping onto the bridge a dwarf, twirling the Imperial crown on his hand! Then he stopped and set it on his head, while the Papalists hooted and jeered, and a mendicant monk called out: 'Behold the King of the Demons!' My Lord Federico—I came near to drowning myself in my shame and my misery . . ."

"Enough!" I said. "We have heard more than enough. A doctor must be found for you and I must be off—"

"Your doctor was taken, my Lord," Folco wailed," he too! I saw Maestro Guido marched across the bridge in fetters!"

I kissed Folco gently. "You have earned the love of your Emperor," I said. Then I gave him over to my falconers to clean and bandage his wound.

"Come, Manfredo," I said in a tone grim and hard, "we ride to Cremona. In four days we return with an army."

I chose twelve men and the best horses. Into the gathering night with its mists we set off, spurred by hatred. The smoke of Vittoria was in my nostrils, its ashes in my heart.

5

All night we rode to Cremona, pausing only to rest our horses. When at last in the distance we saw sun rays gilding the pointed turret of Il Torrazzo, the tallest campanile in all Italy, we knew that our grueling torture soon would end. Then we heard the bells—to the others, a sound which brought joy; to me, the sound of a dirge. I remembered suddenly the tolling of bells at the death of my mother. Though I had been in the saddle for twenty-four hours—and now my years were past fifty-three—my exhaustion was not of the flesh. Must I always be denied peace . . . ?

We entered Cremona by the Porta Romana, in sad contrast to that triumphal entry after the battle of Cortenuova. The earliest risers were going about their business, and their astonishment at seeing their mud-bespattered Emperor and so tiny an entourage was equal only to their incredulity. The news traveled with the speed of sound, and a huge crowd gathered about me before the *duomo*. I explained what had happened; but I begged them to be of good cheer, for all was not lost. On the spot I called for a new army, and hundreds volunteered.

At the appointed meeting place with Enzo I did not dismount, in my urgency, but paused only for greetings. He was not wearing a helmet, and the wind blew his long fair hair as he approached.

"You have my promise, noble father," he cried out, "to strike two blows where one was struck before. My sword will not rest until we avenge di Rossi's infamy!" With one hand sheathed in a chain-mail gauntlet he attempted to brush away from his eyes the tears of fury.

As I had declared, on the fourth day I returned to Parma, and at the mere rumor of my approach, the Papalists abandoned their bridgeheads and withdrew behind the city walls. With Enzo and the remnants of Manfredo Lancia's troops I joined forces, and we bivouacked by the still-smoking embers of Vittoria. The people of Parma could not credit their eyes, and it was said that in my flight I had transformed myself into an eagle. This was all the more readily believed since among the two hundred cherished books they had stolen were charts and graphs of the heavens, designs of the planets, and representations of the signs of the zodiac—all thought to be magic—and a beautiful nude woman, symbolic of the moon. I trafficked with "Beelzebub and Ashtaroth, the Consuls of Darkness," said my enemies. Also vanished was my collection of oddities, such as a ceramic bishop bearing a big fish on his Bible; a bronze oil lamp (from remote antiquity) depicting a naked figure so doubled-up that wick and flame issued from the anus; a gilded bronze of a nude male (a Priapus from Greek Sicily?) with erection—his organ worn so smooth by the touch of pious worshipers that it had reminded me of the much-kissed toe of the statue of San Pietro.

I thought at first to resume the siege; but at a council of war we decided instead to fortify the pass through the Apennines, and leave Parma alone. This decision was dictated as much by financial as by military considerations, for the whole treasury was lost, with the monies collected to pay all my troops—plus jewels of immense value. My immediate task was to restore my finances, then launch another campaign. Shortly I found myself borrowing money at eighty per cent interest, and squeezing more taxes out of a Sicily already drained dry. Yet, when one of the Sicilian towns suggested a freewill collection, I declined the offer with thanks. I preferred for all to suffer alike.

As we withdrew from Parma's walls toward the pass, one great satisfaction was granted me: in a skirmish with our rear-guard, Bernardo di Rossi was thrown from his horse and killed. That smug face was smashed into mud. "This infamous traitor of long standing," I declared, "has at last met an ignoble ending." I gave thanks to my own battered Fortuna. From heaven di Rossi could no longer do harm.

But the real disaster inherent in the defeat and destruction of Vittoria was not the loss of the treasure, nor the loss of the men —but the loss of prestige. The legend of my invincibility was shattered like glass; no one had believed it so fragile. The facts that Enzo had seized a hundred provision ships on the Po; that Riccardo di Theate won an overwhelming victory over a leading

Papalist general, that I myself drove off a Milanese army—all meant very little. I was vulnerable. I could be defeated. I could be destroyed. Thus all the north of Italy fell deeper into civil war and chaos. The Guelfs rose in greater force than ever against the Ghibellines, and the Ghibellines replied in kind. Life was safe only for those families with the tallest towers, and the profiles of the towns came to resemble their crenelated walls. Thus we witnessed warfare not only between groups, classes, and towns—but between towers within a single town. Their owners slung stones and arrows and Greek fire across at one another, and onto the street below poured pitch or boiling oil. Streets became so unsafe that no one dared leave his house without an armed guard. The country villas were abandoned, and agriculture was extinguished except for small plots just outside the city walls. On the roads, merchants no longer dared travel except in large armed groups; even so they faced the constant danger of plunder or seizure for hostage. Such was the peace of God brought by Pope Innocent IV. Only Sicily remained tranquil and secure—and there my thoughts increasingly turned.

However, I returned for the summer to Cremona. I found my mercenary knights grumbling about pay, and the town levies sullen and lethargic. All ordinary people were sick of the war; only the priests showed enthusiasm. People said I had been cold-shouldered by Fortune. One day in whiling away time at dice, I thrice threw a six. My spirits thus lifted a little, I attempted some levity with one of the jesters.

"Messer Dallio," I said, putting my hand lightly on the hump of his back, "when do you intend to open this jewel case? You well know our interest in precious stones. . . ."

"Signore," he said, rattling his bells, "it will not be so easy to open, because the key was lost in Vittoria."

I took the blow without the flicker of an eyelash.

6

IT WAS evident that I could no longer leave events in suspension. Once more I must seize the hammer and strike sparks from the anvil. Thus, as is written, I girded up my loins, and prepared for new struggle. I would yet cross the Alps. I would yet squeeze this Pope until peace or his life juices ran out of his veins!

I sent for Pier della Vigna to join me; I needed his counsel —and I missed him. Then I undertook arrangements myself to marry the young daughter of Duke Albert of Saxony, for in the lower Rhine centered the chief German resistance toward me. I married Corrado to Elisabeth of Bavaria, ending the Hohenstaufen feud with that house, and securing the Brenner Pass in case of need; I married Manfredo to Beatrice of Savoia, thus securing not only Piedmonte but the Mont Cenis Pass into France. And slowly I was recouping my shattered finances. Even the instability of the north assumed a certain stability. Soon, soon, things would be going well again.

In the autumn I went to Torino to celebrate Manfredo's wedding, leaving, as usual, Piero in charge. To Manfredo Lancia I referred publicly as "our well-beloved relation," thus hinting at my marriage to Bianca. By my statement, the Marquis Lancia took precedent over the father of the bride. I was pleased for Manfredo that his bride was so young (fifteen, one year less than the groom), so pretty and so charming, and my thoughts turned backward to the girl Bianca. In all this new festivity, this music and dancing, I felt little joy and much loneliness. I decided to visit the Lancia home nearby in Vercelli for a rest.

As I had been slightly ailing, and had but little trust in most doctors, I felt that I could now spare the funds to ransom my own doctor, Maestro Guido, from captivity in Parma. I therefore wrote Piero to open negotiations with the loathed Gregorio da Montelungo, and warned Piero "to be diligent and attentive in the matter, as is customary with you." Back came an indignant reply: "Imperatore, the praise in your letter amounts to the exact opposite. Am I not always diligent and attentive in handling your affairs? Have I ever been careless and lazy? How does it happen that you seem to think I have changed my behavior at this point in life? Are the nobles again at work against me, speaking slander, attempting to poison your mind? My Lord Federico, whatever you wish done, I will do, but please—please do not insult me!"

How irascible and difficult he had become, I thought. How hypersensitive! It was nothing. I had meant nothing by my words. Or had I myself become far more irascible and difficult than I realized? I answered Piero in a most soothing tone: "My serious anger is reserved for such ridiculous accusations as those you bring against me, dear Piero. You well know that I place absolute dependence in you. How could you think that I would listen without skepticism to any voice except your own, which is so dear to me . . . ?" Confident that this problem had been solved, I went on to Vercelli, in search for peace within myself.

Vercelli was not a large town, and the Lancia palazzo was not grandiose—but harmonious and comfortable. With its small park of flowers and trees, it was in appearance a country villa. It was constructed of the long flat bricks constantly used by the Romans, and roofed with the terra cotta tiles which take on with age so rich a texture, a gray-green and yellow patina. Such houses become a part of the landscape, as if they had existed always, and would exist always. Not far away, on an inner courtyard, were the stables and storage rooms for wood and rice and wine. Over all was the odor of plenty and an atmosphere of peace. Most of my courtiers I had left in Torino, and when I arrived with Manfredo Lancia (Percivalle Doria was with me, too), I had the curious sensation of coming home.

It must have been, of course, that Bianca in idle moments had prattled to me of her childhood, had described the house where she grew up, had shared with me her nostalgia for a family life I never knew. What a wonderful insulation from pain is a safe childhood—how conducive to serenity and love! I went one day to Bianca's room, which had been so long unoccupied. I looked out her window at the view, I examined her crucifix of ivory and silver, I rummaged in her cupboards. I found some moldy dolls, a dusty schoolgirl slate, a copy of the *Aeneid* with many pages underlined. "It was not of my own will, Dido, I left you land. . . ."

I settled down in the Lancia house. In the early mornings, as the sun rose across the rice fields and made sparkling the dew, I went hunting with my falcons. In the late afternoons I watched the sunsets behind the distant Alps, magnificent with their golden glaciers. In the evenings I sat with Omar and other dogs before the great stone fireplace, sometimes in conversation with my friends, but most often intrigued by the flames. In the nights, I listened to the wind fingering the rustly leaves of the poplar trees—and, in winter, whistling through the branches.

I stayed and stayed. Autumn fog changed to winter snow. Christmas came and passed. Then the New Year, clear and cold. At last I stirred myself. I wrote to Piero in Cremona to prepare for me. I was coming back to the world.

Ill-starred day that I returned! Now on me in quick succession fell hammer blows which left me dazed—I, who had hammered at the world. These blows were not of my making, but were of my making—for no man can wholly escape responsibility for his own fate, however much he may resign himself to the stars. How hateful is the curse of retrospect, how painful the phrase "if only—" And how grievous the memory of power misused.

The first blow was the death of my son, Riccardo di Theate. His death left a serious gap in the structure of command of my armies, though his gifts most certainly were not military. He was never very well, but his death occurred under circumstances so mysterious, and with such violent pains in the belly, that I questioned whether the Pope had not set out to poison us one by one.

Far, far more hurtful to my cause and to my heart was the capture of Enzo. In an engagement which began as a skirmish of no importance, his horse was killed under him. At this moment arrived the main forces of Bologna, and he was taken with four hundred knights and twelve hundred foot soldiers. He was fettered and led by a golden chain into the town. When word was brought to me, I was frantic with fear that he might be executed, and I began at once, through every possible channel, to try to save him. I wrote, however, to make a brave face to the world:

> THIS misfortune—which we must so acknowledge—seems as in fable or nightmare terribly severe; yet our cause is not lost. We accept this reverse, in balance, as slight or even negligible. Nor is our proud head bowed. The accidents of

war are manifold; but our illustrious quiver is filled with many sons. We learn such news, therefore, with calm. Our powerful right arm will pursue all the more vigorously the destruction of our enemies.

With the Bolognese I took a different tack. I suggested exchanging Enzo for certain important prisoners I held, but my suggestion was refused. I offered ransom: I would lay a ring of silver all around the walls of the town. The offer was refused. Then I tried a direct appeal to the people of Bologna:

We read in history that the Goddess Fortuna knows many diverse acts. The evil fortune which at one moment presses a man to earth, the next moment may raise him to the heights. And from the heights he is again cast down, scourged, and pierced with wounds incurable. If today you see fortune smiling on you with unclouded brow, you would be wise to refrain from being puffed up. The greater the height, the harder the fall. Fortuna makes glowing promises, fulfills much, and in the end brings manifold misfortunes.

Therefore take warning. If you surrender Enzo, our beloved son, King of Sardegna and Gallura, we shall exalt your town above every town in Lombardia. But if you listen not to our command, then expect our triumphant and unnumbered army. The traitors of Lyons shall not deliver you out of our hands!

They listened not. They were, however, enchanted by Enzo's simplicity and nobility of manner, his lithe and handsome presence, the flowing golden hair under his flashing helmet. They thought of him as a youthful god of antiquity, who had fallen miraculously into their hands. He had friends, too, among the Bolognese, who worked incessantly to save him: the young Pietro Asinelli, whom he knew intimately, and the lovely Lucia Viadagola, who plead for him with the passion of love. At length, the Bolognese assigned him an apartment in the palace of the *podestà*—that very palace where I had been so welcomed when I first returned from Germany—and imprisoned him only at night. Then they swore an oath: they would not execute him, but neither would they ever release him. So the Pope, who wanted him killed, and I, who wanted him free, both had to be content.

"Fortuna . . . in the end brings manifold misfortunes. . . ." I would have done well to ponder my own words.

7

ONE NIGHT in Cremona, I paced sleepless, brooding over the decline of my star. Almost like a madman, I roamed aimlessly about the palace—lighted only by oil lamps or stray moonbeams. The corridors and marble pavements were chill with the damp of February; and I was so bundled in a woolen cloak that I was unrecognizable. The cloud of my breath was my only companion, for I had discarded my Saracen bodyguard. I longed for the warmth and sun of Sicily.

Now I recalled how, as a boy in Palermo, I had practiced the aspects of kingship secretly in the Royal Chapel, sitting on the throne and gazing out over an imaginary multitude. I sighed for the vanished years and all their fullness, and wished that I might once more begin—not over again—but at a beginning. What resolution lay before me? Only struggle, more struggle, and more struggle. I had become convinced that victory over the Pope was so elusive as to be impossible. In a death grapple one must die: which—?

So pondering, I wandered, as if retracing the steps of my childhood, to the throne room. It was not, like the Royal Chapel, a hall of splendid and glittering golden mosaics, but a room of short columns and round arches, decorated with horizontal bands of light and dark stone. It was a room replete with shadows, whispers and echoes, for like grandfather time it seemed to talk to itself. Cold moonlight sprayed through the leaded panes of the windows, and hung in suspension as if frozen in space.

And so hung I, for on the shadowy throne a man was sitting.

My first inclination was to shout in fury; my second to draw my dagger and fling it; my third to die, for now I recognized Piero. How could this be? What did it signify? I raised no challenge, I made no sound; like an adulterer about to be caught,

I shrank into my cloak and disappeared in the darkness. If Piero saw me, he made no sign, and certainly he did not know me. Any other man in the world, except my sons, I would have killed on the spot.

Now indeed I set to brooding. This riddle could have but one meaning: Piero sat on the throne as a king would sit, to feel how a king would feel. Why?

My gut contracted, my mouth burned, my head ached. Finally, toward dawn, I fell into sleep, but the margin between sleep and wakefulness was so thin that it was difficult to know whether I saw visions or dreamed dreams. I was walking alone, and turned suddenly, to see following me a fanciful creature such as are carved on cathedrals. The animal paused and crouched, and I saw that it had the face of a beautiful boy with large, burning eyes. It had followed me always, and knew all my secrets. As I stared, its body changed from rabbit to cat, from cat to dog, from dog to wolf. And the beautiful face changed to a scowling mask with empty eye sockets. I walked on, then once again turned; but now I was followed only by shadows.

By morning I was ill, and I summoned my physician. Piero's efforts at ransom had been more successful than mine, and Maestro Guido had lately returned from prison in Parma to court. Him I trusted, for he was a Fiorentino, and had been with me on many campaigns. He was a grave man, older than I, tall, bald-headed but retaining a ridge of dark hair, domed of forehead but marked by plentiful black eyebrows, and very nearsighted. As he was physician to the Emperor, his scarlet robe was trimmed with ermine, as was his cap. His distinguished, dignified manner lent confidence; he seemed very wise. Rather savagely, as if he were to blame, I told him my symptoms.

He looked in my mouth, felt my pulse, listened with his ear to my chest. "My Lord, you are tired," he said, "you need to relax from your tensions. I prescribe a blood-letting, a simple meal of pounded chicken and a draught of herbs I will prepare for you. Rest in bed for the day, quiet, with your bed-curtains drawn."

"No blood-letting!" I said stubbornly. "I have need of my blood—all of it."

The pounded chicken I ate without relish; my stomach, I thought, was too sore to take food at all. But I was less concerned with the pain than the enervation which had seized me. I seemed incapable of movement, and my mind was becoming a blank. What was this—death while in life?

When I had finished my chicken, Maestro Guido brought me his draught. It was hot, gray-green like some herbs, and its odor was not displeasing. Almost jokingly I said, as I swirled the mixture in the silver goblet, "Good Doctor, you have not, I hope, prepared for me a poison?"

He flushed. "My Lord, how can you say such a thing—even in jest!"

He had not answered my question. And the tone of his voice was most curious. I lifted the goblet to drink, and in so doing managed somehow to spill part of its contents on the side of the bed and the floor.

"I am clumsy with illness," I said. "Call a slave to clean up this mess." And while he spoke to a servant, I looked at my new guards. All four stiffened under my gaze. My faithful "Pietro" and "Paolo" had perished at Vittoria.

I made conversation. "Do you think Maestro Guido, I have spilled too much of the draught? Will this be enough?"

"Quite enough my Lord, quite enough. But you should drink before the medicine cools."

"As it touched my mouth, I found it too hot—hence I spilled. Better to cool for a moment."

Then my servant returned with a slave—a wizened old man much too infirm for this earth, I thought. "Here, *nonno*," I said, "drink some of this—I fear it is too hot for me."

The doctor's face changed from pink to ashen. "Oh—no, my Lord!" he cried.

"Drink!" I said.

The old man drank, slowly, and with a vague gesture gave the goblet back to me. As he did so, his head shook, his face paled and assumed the greenish pallor of death. He was seized by convulsions, gave one gurgling shriek, and died. I beckoned to my Saracens in the doctor's direction.

"My Lord!" the doctor mumbled, now livid. "Someone has made an error!"

"A small error," I replied, "easily corrected. Shall we mix a draught for you?"

"I do not know the formula!"

"This game, good Doctor, is ended. I shall now give you over to torture. I am anxious to discover where you studied chemistry.

In Parma, under the professor Gregorio da Montelungo? Or in Lyons—"

"My Lord," he said, his voice quavering, "torture is not necessary! If you will spare my life, I will tell you all you wish to know!"

"I make no bargains with men I cannot trust."

"Most gracious Majesty, most revered Majesty!" he shouted. "I am only the instrument of Pier della Vigna!"

"How generous is the Pope with other people's thrones!" I exclaimed. Then I realized what the doctor had said.

For a stunned moment I felt as though I had swallowed the poison brew; then I wished that I had. I could not abide living. I cried aloud in my despair: "This Petrus, whom I thought a rock, and who was the half of my life, has plotted my murder! My very bowels betray me! Where can I again be happy and secure? Whom can I trust henceforth . . . ?" I sobbed with the uncontrolled agony of the hopeless.

After a while, through aching eyes I saw that the doctor was groveling on his knees by my bedside. He slobbered as he rained kisses on my hand. "My life, your Majesty . . . pity . . . only spare . . . my life . . . !"

With one foot I kicked him aside, as I leaped out of bed, and the violent, savage anger of my prime suffused me. "I grant your life, such as it may be worth to you under the conditions I prescribe," I said with scalding mockery. "Your medicine is to be torture—slow torture, day after day, night after night, not enough to kill—but with no respite!"

I turned to the Saracens. "Take this man. Tell the executioners he is not to die until he begs for death—and even then to wait awhile, to be certain he pleads with truth."

Two guards took him, hanging limply between them. "And remember, good Doctor," I called after him, "your torture in no way equals mine—for you have poisoned my mind and my heart and with them I must continue somehow to live. . . ."

But neither my mind nor my heart seemed to function. In the empty emotionless tone of one who has lost all feeling, I spoke in Arabic to my two remaining Saracens: "Arrest the honored Pier della Vigna, and blind him. Do not injure his body. Blind him with hot irons. I cannot bear the sight of his eyes. . . ."

8

Already I was troubled by doubts. I wished to know more of the role of Pier della Vigna, for my spies had utterly failed me. So I, who had looked askance at torture, turned now to the wheel, the rack, the iron maiden, the spiked board, the steel cap, the weighted lash, the pincers, the thumb screw, glowing coals, boiling oil, red-hot irons. I tortured all (except Piero) who had been associated with the negotiations for my doctor's release, or who had been in contact with the Papal Legate Gregorio da Montelungo. I learned nothing. To Piero, I could not bring myself to speak. I dared not.

The doctor himself confirmed, in a final effort to avoid torture, that the source of his own instructions was Innocent. As to the reasons for his treachery, nothing was revealed. To all the kings and princes of Christendom, and to the world at large I wrote—without the assistance of Pier della Vigna—the following statement:

> This Pope, this Innocent, this priest, this shepherd, this peace-loving Holy Father and director of our faith—he is not content with unnumbered intrigues and degrading machinations in his efforts to do us injury. Now—to the shame and disgrace of his title as Vicar of Christ—he has just attempted to murder us by secret means. From a dagger in the hand of a traitor, he has turned to a poisoned cup in the hand of a physician. Let the Great Physician pass judgment upon him! And let men render judgment suitable to God . . . !

About Pier della Vigna I said not a word—at first. Already the news of his disgrace and arrest had spread through wild rumor, and everywhere I came upon sudden shocked silences.

Everywhere, too, was unease and horror at this revelation of instability in my camp. In some eyes I was a monster; others smiled with delight at the fall of my favorite. But fear was in the minds of all: who might be next?

I did not wish it to be known that Piero, whom I so treasured, could turn against my life. I myself therefore spread confusing accounts of his fall from grace. I wrote several letters implying that he had embezzled state funds in enormous amounts; I suggested that he was a swindler, who had misused for self-enrichment his great powers. Why, then, someone said, were his hands not cut off, if he had been dipping into the public purse? Or perhaps some sexual mystery was involved, and he had been emasculated? In response to such questions, I started the rumor that he had attempted assault of my favorite concubine. And this came back to me distorted into a tale that lecherous I had seduced the lovely young virgin he had chosen for a bride, and so he had assaulted me. What other cause was now left for so grievous a fall—except treason?

The people of Cremona, who had been aroused by the doctor's plot, now turned their wrath against my hapless ex-minister. Muttering crowds grew daily larger before his prison, and the rumor spread that he had betrayed me for years in the pay of the Pope. I increased the number of guards; but the crowds doubled and tripled, hurling stones and shouting, "Traitor . . . traitor . . . traitor!" In the pre-dawn hours of a wet, slimy morning, when the crowds had dispersed, I had him secretly removed to a dungeon in not distant Borgo San Donnino, where he would be safe. I had other plans for him; but now I chose to draw the veil over the whole affair. None knew except me and my Saracens whether Piero was in prison, whether he had been mutilated, whether he was dead or alive. I forbade, on severest penalties, that his name should ever again be mentioned in my presence. The name of Pier della Vigna was to be forgot.

I alone could not forget. In these days the words of Job were often on my lips: "All my inward friends abhorred me, and they whom I loved are turned against me."

I became harassed and haunted by fears. In every dark shadow I fancied an attacker; in every cup of wine I saw a skull. I multiplied my Saracen bodyguard many times over. I was never alone. I ate nothing which had not first been tested by someone among my retainers; thus meals became an agony for all, as each man feared daily for his life. A few dared to complain; I laughed in their faces, and called them incipient traitors. Had I not already known intimately men who betrayed me?

My irritability turned into unreason and injustice. No man was safe from my wrath; I flogged, broke teeth, and imprisoned for trivial and ridiculous offenses. My Saracen executioners became more frightening than demons; people crossed themselves when the Saracens passed. I had lost interest in rule by law or the administration of justice. I had ceased to be what Aristotle termed a just king, and had fulfilled his definition of a tyrant. I was avoided by all who could avoid me; I was left to brood alone. By the Pope's incantations I had been turned at last into the Great Dragon.

At length I shook myself and concluded that I must return to Sicily. Once there, I might again find bearings—like the invariable north polarity of the mysterious compass. Once again in my own land, I might once again know myself. Abruptly I announced my departure for the south, and all was confusion. Sorely I needed on my affairs the guiding hands of Taddeo da Suessa and Pier della Vigna.

At last, in March, things were ready. I missed the perfume of the dancing girls, the sly laughter of the eunuchs, the soft-shuffling pad of the camels, the trumpeting of the elephant. All were dead or in captivity in Parma. My caravan now, for all its banners, was like any other caravan, except for the heavy concentration of Saracens around my person. We marched sluggishly, without verve, tired before the journey was an hour begun.

In Borgo San Donnino we paused briefly to add a blind prisoner, but lightly fettered, to our company. For all his love of fine clothes, the prisoner was robed and cowled like a monk. His name was not announced. I myself did not see him, but I gave orders that he was to ride an *asino* with the baggage train. On either side of him I placed a Saracen guard and a drummer; the drummers were instructed to ruffle their drums each time the prisoner attempted to speak. When passing through towns, they were to drum without cease, but muffled. The drums were painted gaily with inverted triangles of yellow and red; but to the prisoner this meant nothing.

Snow still clung to the peaks of the Apennines, and sharp winds stung our cheeks and stole our breath. As we entered

finally into the valley of the Arno, lowering, rain-laden clouds hung over us day after day. I recalled once again the oracle of Piero's death and my own. My doctor, from Fiorenza, was indeed associated with both death and flowers. *Sub flore:* I avoided that town which the Italians call Fiorenza and the French call Florence. My thoughts were all inward; I saw nothing of the muddy road. Yet not for a moment did I forget the prisoner riding, head bowed, with the wagon train.

We came in due course to San Miniato, though long before we reached it we saw the darkening tower silhouetted against the opaque gray of the sky. Here, in the very tower where together we had gazed at a comet's brilliance, traced the constellations, and had known the closeness of man—here I would leave Piero to languish all the years of his life. How high the climb, how steep the hill, how dizzy the height of the tower! I felt like a man approaching the edge of the universe. Yet Piero could have no knowledge, no sense of this place. Only through words could he know . . . and the words would recall memories. Then he would see what his eyes could not see. And remember. . . .

It was just short of dusk when we toiled up the winding path toward the tower. The undulant river valley far below was lost in haze and mist and the first shadows of evening. Above, swirling dark clouds swallowed the top of the tower like spirits attempting to devour the earth. In the church lower down on the edge of the rock, vesper bells were sounding, heavy and clanging. From the belfry, black rooks in scores took to the air, circling, cawing, prophesying. The wind was strong, chill, dank—bending the tall cypresses and flailing their foliage. Everything seemed in suspension, neither in birth nor in dying.

Before the castellan's house the prisoner was dismounted, fumbling and awkward; and the castellan, wiping his hands on his leather jerkin, came out to lead the blind man away. In the door, the castellan's wife and small children watched with dilated eyes; three gray kittens romped at their feet and chickens pecked at the ground. When the woman saw the prisoner, she started. "God's mercy upon him!" she murmured, crossing herself.

I lingered to watch as the two figures, one stumbling at the steepness, began the final ascent. Slowly the blind one felt with his feet for each step, slowly moved upward. Impatiently the castellan nudged him, spoke words which were blown away by

the wind. They reached at length the platform of the tower, built of bricks which once seemed soaked in wine and now seemed soaked in blood. At the tower's base, the two men paused, teetering on the edge, bent forward against the fierceness of the wind.

In an abrupt, strong movement, as though bursting his bonds, the prisoner turned about and threw back his hood. I saw, in a last sliver of sun rays, the once beloved face. I stared in horror at my handiwork, at the seared cavities where the living eyes had been.

With one sleeve of his robe he wiped away the tears which streamed from the empty sockets, and cried out in the clear, well-remembered voice: "Imperatore! Imperatore! Hear me, *caro* Federico . . . ! Never, never in word or deed have I betrayed you . . . !"

In a single springing leap he flung himself outward into space and down to the rocks below. The oracle was fulfilled. Suddenly all was in shadow.

"He is lost—he is lost!" shouted the castellan.

Fool! I thought; it is I who am lost! And in the bitterness of my despair I murmured aloud: "He who came from nothing is returned to nothing. . . ."

9

EVERYWHERE I was followed by hordes of blind beggars—perhaps no more than usual, but I had become acutely conscious of their presence. In Pisa I could not shake them until I stepped aboard my galley, and with relief hid myself in the cabin. When we were clear of the reedy river and out to sea, I came on deck—but not before. I looked back at the fast receding coast, still oppressed by the weight of low-hanging clouds, and sighed. I too was oppressed, I thought, and would ever be. In this departure I sensed a finality. The major portion of my life was finished, and could never be retrieved. Nor would I ever return to this land.

The seas ran wild and turbulent, and the apprehensive captain said the ship might sink. He wanted to put in to the Island of Montecristo and wait for fair weather, but I bade him press on. I had no fear whatever of death in the waves, and the lives of the crew meant nothing to me. Gradually the storms abated, and we entered the Golfo di Napoli under the pure and limpid sky of springtime. Never had the harbor appeared so spectacular—an emerald sea sprinkled with diamonds—and I seemed to see it with the vision of Ulysses. On the far right was the dim jagged mass of Capri and the Sorrento peninsula: toward the center, the harmonious cone of Vesuvio, languidly puffing and steaming. On our left were the terraces, vineyards and castles of the volcanic Island of Ischia; and a little ahead, the Island of Procida, in one of whose pink-blue-yellow-white houses lived a physician I could trust—and would shortly summon to court. Then, in the distance—the Vomero, the Castle of the Egg, the tall feathery palms of the nymph Partenope, and home at last. . . .

Home at last! On the *molo* I was greeted by a small group

of courtiers and officials of the town, who made the usual excited buzzing over the arrival of an important personage in their midst, hoping, as always, to shine in reflected glory. For them all I cared not a fig, with the exception of Berardo. I fell into his blessed arms. He kissed me on both cheeks; and with his vast white beard—now he was nearly eighty-five—it was almost like being scratched by the brush of Jehovah Himself.

"Welcome home to the Realm, my son," he said.

"*Hòi*, good father Berardo, I am glad to come home—I am dog-tired, worn to the very bone!"

"I have but one question, just now," he said gravely. "What are your plans for the great gate at Capua?"

I understood him at once. "The marbles are to be left exactly as recently finished: my statue in the center, Taddeo at my left hand, Piero at my right."

Berardo drew a breath so deep that it gradually became a moan. "Then—he—was—not—guilty—?"

Now with Berardo I was compelled to confession: "He did not betray me—I betrayed him. He—was—not—guilty."

In an anguished, solemn voice, Berardo said, "Peace go with you, my son."

As I mounted horseback, and Berardo, shaking, entered his litter, we were assailed by blind beggars crying, "Alms, gracious lords, alms, alms, in the name of Christ's bleeding wounds, give us alms . . . !"

I tossed them coins from my purse, and with the edge of my sleeve wiped the tears from my eyes.

Thus it was, everywhere I traveled. I sought surcease in all my places of solace, but I found no solace. Outside the gates were always blind beggars. I tried the massive new castle at Lagopesole, with hunts in the forests of Monte Vulture. I tried the intimate small castle at Gioia del Colle, but I found no joy on that hill. I returned to Oria, but the memory of the passion with Balian jibbered and mocked. At Melfi I lingered awhile, evoking my fine code of justice and the lawyer-poet who put it in words. I danced with the shade of Bianca and reread my love songs. But always, everywhere, blind beggars. Only in the empty plain of the Murge, enclosed in the Castel del Monte's octagonal walls—a symmetry symbolic of death, remember?—could I find escape if not peace.

A year passed in this series of flights from myself. In these months my armies were everywhere victorious. Even the rancid old Cardinal Raniero was defeated and died. And another attempted invasion of Sicily was easily thrown back. Town after town returned to my standard—some willingly, like treacherous Viterbo, which by now had its craw overstuffed with gravel by the priests. At sea my fleets smashed the Genovese fleet; and the fleets of Venezia had lost all interest in fighting, for those eager merchants had acquired little gain from a Genovese Pope. In Germany, the anarchy had exhausted itself, and my son held his own; the towns began to turn to his support in efforts to free themselves from both lay and ecclesiastical princes.

Innocent had little stomach for continued fighting. His armies and funds were sorely depleted. In all lands the Church was in grave disrepute. All Christendom laughed at or deplored the remark of the Cardinal Hugh of St. Cher, made one day in Lyons, after Mass: "When we came hither, we found but three or four brothels. When we go, we will leave a whole city of nothing but whores." The greed of the Pope was now legend, for all Christians had suffered his extortion at first hand. The Pope's failure to support the Crusade of the saintly Louis had led not only to disaster, but to the bitterest resentments; at one point the Pope had attempted to divert crusaders from the Holy Land to attack Sicily! It would be, I thought, many long years before the Papacy recovered from the insidious harm Gregory, and especially Innocent, had done it; other times, other men, might bring it the reverence its due. Vast implacable forces had now been released, which neither he nor I could control. Reformation was not yet; but in the end it would come. The Church, by its deeds, destroyed itself. So it is not I, but this Pope and others like him, who must bear the judgment of centuries. He need fear me no longer; he had best fear the future instead. I myself am willing to undergo the ordeal of time. . . .

I felt ill. Often I experienced pain in the gut. I ignored the pain. I lost weight. My skin yellowed and constantly itched. My muscles became flabby, wrinkles formed in my neck and my face. I frowned much. My breasts sagged; my hair began to fall out; my pubic hair turned gray. Sporadically my body renewed its interest in sex, but I could think of no partner I desired. In the early autumn of this year I took to my bed. Now, in the Castel del Monte, I am convalescing.

Soon I expect to move on to Foggia, and thence to the castle at Lucera, for after these interminable wars with the "Christians," I find being surrounded by Muslims a relief. The Saracen men on my staff are handsome, quiet and self-possessed; and their women, when unveiled, have serene, grave and haunting faces. This does not mean, as the Pope often has said, that I am a convert to Islam. Indeed, to the orthodox of all sects, I shall always be the greatest of infidels.

I have been a law and a creed unto myself alone. And there lies the glory and the tragedy of my life.

10

At last I understand, I believe, the full truth of Pier della Vigna. I write now in haste, for I have been very ill, and lie in the shabby little Castel Fiorentino because I was too sick to return to Lucera. I was hawking on the promontory of Monte Gargano, in mid-November, when dysentery overcame me. For many days I have eaten almost nothing, and both weakness and waves of nausea assault me. Though Lucera on its height can be seen from my window, the distance seems to me as from here to the stars.

I was rereading, not long ago, the *Nicomachean Ethics* of Aristotle. The section on friendship particularly caught my attention. "Without friends," he wrote, "no one—even though he had all other goods—would choose to live. . . . Friendship stimulates those in the prime of life to noble actions—*two going together*—for with friends, men are more able to think and to act. . . . perfect friendship is the friendship of men who are good and alike in virtue." But "in the case of kings, men who are much their inferiors do not expect to be friends . . . for much can be taken away and friendship remains—but when one party is removed to a great distance, as a god is, the possibility of friendship ceases. . . ." One thing more: loving is more the essence of friendship than being loved, said Aristotle.

"Can two unequal ever equal be . . . ?" said the soothsayer. So it was impossible from the beginning, but not impossible—because in youth we bridged the gap which kingship imposed. In private, we *were* figuratively naked, the difference between us visible only to angels. Only slowly did the weight of a crown force us apart. It is also true that as Piero aged from both years and fatigue, I ceased seeing in him the same beauty, or feeling for him the same excitement. These things I did not comprehend;

Piero did. He became reconciled to loving more than being loved. How difficult always to be second best! And always to be almost a slave, at the beck and call of someone else, never to have the final say in anything! And to be taken for granted—as I took him for granted! No wonder he came again and again to complain. I thought of him as if he were a member of my own body—another brain, another hand, another voice—to be used as I used myself for my own ends. His happiness . . . ? Only at first did I consider it.

He was my friend; but I was not his. I depended on him, exploited him, and admired him for his value to me—thinking never of my value to him. Honors, riches, fame—these rewards I pressed upon him. Indeed, he was ambitious. Yet he would have been better rewarded with the happiness of love. This he preferred to all else. How could he any longer look into my eyes—when he knew that I no longer saw him?

Secretly he sat on the throne in Cremona, yes: certainly he had been tempted, certainly the Papal agents in Parma had offered him the Sicilian Kingdom. But this temptation he had rejected. His only guilt was that he sat on the throne in darkness and in secret, savoring the kingship he would never know—solely because of his love for me.

And the ending: how well Innocent understood my relationship to Piero! How cruelly astute! I have learned but lately of the lands and money given my doctor's family by the Pope. The wretched physician was instructed, I am sure, that he was to implicate Pier della Vigna if the poison failed. Thus the Pope's deadliest weapon had a double edge. If not myself poisoned, I would destroy Piero—and in so doing destroy myself. For in the moment of Piero's destruction, I would begin truly to love him again. "*Caro* Federico!" he had called out to me as he died. . . .

Too late. Too late too late too late. . . ! All between us is ended; and I too am finished. What was carved by my statue on the great gate at Capua?—IN WRATH WILL I DESTROY THE MAN WHO PROVES FAITHLESS. Ah—so . . . !

I am well aware that, fainting, I was borne to a place called *Fiorentino*. I have not forgotten the oracle, and I feel an obsessive need to fulfill it. When I asked about the blocked doorway to the nearby tower, I was merely amused when the castellan told me that it was a rusty old iron door to an entrance no longer of use. All castles have rusty old doors, I said that morning to Piero; and Italy is a land full of flowers. *Sub flore* . . . ! Where are the flowers, now in December? Not many, not many—but soon; for Christmas and my natal day thereafter will continue to bloom those giant red geraniums whose petals showered Palermo streets upon my coronation long long ago. This is the year 1250 of our Lord Jesus Christ. I shall be (perhaps) fifty-six.

Yesterday, calmly, I made my will. I called in many officials and gave many instructions, for I like all things—even death—to be orderly. First I disposed of the Empire, leaving it to the legal heir, Corrado; and to the little Enrico, the Kingdoms of Arles and Jerusalem. Of all my illigitimate sons, Manfredo was the only one it seemed appropriate to mention, as I awarded to him the lands I had given his mother Bianca, the title "Prince of Taranto," and named him Vicar of Sicily. For the others I made special arrangements. (Enzo remains imprisoned, writing poems, the toast of Bologna.) To the Church I returned all that was her due, holding in reserve the rights of Kingdom and Empire. I made many bequests to individuals, and one to a bridge—for I wished to be sure that a certain bridge is completed, as it is needed for commerce.

The witnesses included my doctor Giovanni da Procida; that admirable young poet Folco Ruffo who sings so sweetly; Count Berthold von Hohenburg, the last and only German at my Silician court; my son-in-law Count Riccardo di Caserta; my well-beloved son Manfredo, now eighteen; and the venerable ever-faithful Archbishop Berardo, who for me has been truly the representative of the Heavenly Father on earth.

I gave specific instructions for my burial. I am to be interred in the sarcophagus of red porphyry which has been awaiting me these many years in the Cathedral of Palermo—alongside my mother, my father, my grandfather Ruggero, and my first wife Costanza. I doubt if even Innocent will dare to remove my bones. I am to be dressed in robes equivalent to those I wore at my coronation as Emperor—for in spite of the Pope I retain my title and throne. Above an alb of linen, with Cufic inscriptions on neckband and cuffs, I will wear the tunicella of scarlet silk. An outer garment of red will be embroidered with pearls and closed with a precious jewel. I will wear shoes of red silk, and on my right hand a gold ring set with a large emerald. My sword belt is worked with silver and gold, and my laminated and engraved sword will lie beside me. I will wear a simple caplike crown of bronze and gold; and the Orb of Empire, a golden globe set with a circle of small emeralds and four huge pearls, will lie to the left of my head. If this seems an excessive concern with my wardrobe, think how long I must wear it! Nowhere about me will be any symbol of any religious faith—for in spite of the actions of men, my faith was in Man.

These instructions have been made light of by everyone; and even my doctor Giovanni da Procida joins in the collective deception. I am much better, he says; tomorrow I may perhaps rise from my bed. "Like Lazarus!" I told him. And he clucked in disapproval as loudly as any old hen.

A cold wind is blowing from off the Adriatic Sea, and clouds scud hurriedly inland like frightened sheep. We are in for a tempest, I think. The air is raw and cold, and I have great difficulty in keeping warm. Just now they have brought me hot pears baked in honey, for it is believed that baked pears revive an ailing stomach. It is fortunate that pears are plentiful now; I will have need of a whole pear tree! Spasms seize me from time to time, so painful that I almost faint from the agony. I gasp for breath, moan, clench my teeth. The color of my face I know, and I have refused the use of a mirror. Then temporarily the pain eases; my face relaxes, becomes tranquil. For an illusory moment I feel almost young again. But it is impossible by words to convey the sense of pain. I recall my observations on the battlefield as I watched calmly the agonized writhings of wounded men, and felt not their pain but only sorrow for them. I recall, too, that at the close approach of death the human mind mercifully ceases to function. I must not wait too long, therefore, to conclude all my affairs.

I repeat to myself with some satisfaction the lines written by the Emperor Marcus Aurelius, wishing they were my own, as they express my feelings so exactly:

> All that thy seasons bring, O Nature,
> is fruit for me!
> All things come from thee, subsist in thee,
> go back to thee.

For my part, what is to be said for life? Only that it is to be lived—to the bursting! I have embraced life with passion, as an embrace without passion is meaningless. Now passion has gone from me, and the kiss I feel on my cheek is the kiss of death.

Many times have I seen a priest rushing by with a ciborium, and I have thought: "How much longer must this nonsense continue?" Now it is my turn! I must, even now, pay certain attention to propriety, as is appropriate for a Catholic prince—not for my sake, but for the sake of my subjects who are sincerely pious, and for the sake of civil authority within the Realm. At the last moment (this evening?—or dawn, the hour of death, tomorrow?—tomorrow is, I think, the thirteenth day of December—I still mark time!)—at the last moment, I say, I will call the Archbishop Berardo to give me absolution and the Holy Sacrament. The Sacrament—my first memory of Berardo, my last memory of Berardo. He will administer to me, as so long ago to that other beloved and admired friend, Guglielmo, from whom I learned how to love.

The last rites of Holy Church! But of course the Pope will say that, as I am excommunicant, this ritual will avail me nothing. In the Papal camp will be rejoicing. I can hear them now, giving thanks to God for this great deliverance, while assuring the world that I sizzle and fry in the fires of Hell! What a joke on the Pope that I, unlike himself, feel no terror of Hell; therefore I shall die, unlike the Pope, without spiritual agony—though certainly with one anguished regret. As there was no pain in the nonexistence before birth, there can be no pain in the nonexistence after death. To me, this will be a relief. Verily, for the unborn and the dead, all is without form and void, and exists not. . . .

For me, a single problem remains: the disposition of this manuscript. I can entrust it to the hands of but one man alive: Berardo. I shall instruct him to place it in a chest I have conserved for the purpose—an Arabic casket of intricately carved ivory, depicting a pattern of lions and eagles, and bearing inscriptions extolling the glory and greatness of man. This chest he is to deposit in a secret niche in the Royal Chapel in Palermo, a niche I discovered as a boy. There, I hope, it will be safe for many years to come . . . while I myself rest secure in the snug womb of time.

APPENDIX

After Word

AMONG ALL the arrows in Federico's quiver, Manfredo was the best. He was described by Dante in the *Purgatorio* (Canto III) as the very model of an Italian prince: "*Biondo era e bello e di gentile aspetto.*" He made every effort to maintain the enlightened brilliance of his father's rule.

Within two years of Federico's death, Corrado gave up the struggle in Germany, and returned to Apulia, the land of his birth. Within another two, he was dead of a fever. The young boy Enrico, son of the English Isabella, had died a year after his father. Federico of Antioch was killed in battle. So the burden of the struggle against the Papacy fell entirely on Manfredo's shoulders. For sixteen years he managed to maintain his rule successfully in the Kingdom of Sicily, and partially in northern Italy. The policy of the Papacy toward Federico's offspring had changed not at all, though Innocent IV had died soon after Federico, and the Apostolic Throne was occupied by other men.

It was Urban IV, a Frenchman, who called to the aid of the Papacy the "needy and unscrupulous" (Trevelyan) younger brother of King Louis IX of France—Charles, Count of Anjou. He was a heavy-jawed and heavy-handed man. To Charles the Pope offered the crown of Sicily, and to his soldiers the Pope offered remission of sins and plunder—for the campaign was elevated to the level of a Crusade. With an overwhelming army of thirty thousand men, in February of 1266 Charles marched from Rome with the Pope's blessing.

Manfredo's ranks had been seriously depleted by treachery and by desertions, due to the hostile preaching of the mendicant friars. In the battle of Benevento, his ranks were thrown into confusion by the unexpected French device of stabbing horses. When he saw that the battle was lost, he deliberately sought death. After three days his body was found. It was slung over the back of an *asino* and carried to Charles's tent—where it was recognized with tears by Manfredo's captive comrades-in-arms and wife and children. He was thirty-four. Excommunicate, he was buried under a cairn of stones on the bank of the Liris River.

In triumph, Charles entered Napoli. "The Kingdom soon found that he had come to chastize it with scorpions." Such was the evaluation of Charles's iniquities by the Guelf chronicler Sabas Malaspina. The new King's spoils-hungry agents "spread themselves over the land like a swarm of locusts." The Church flourished anew. And the people groaned and wept for the lost days of Federico and Manfredo.

Into prison for life were thrown the wife of Manfredo, his youngest daughter, and his three sons. For thirty years the sons were held in chains in the Castel del Monte, and then transferred to the Castle of the Egg in Napoli harbor until their death—though some chroniclers assert that one finally escaped and fled to Egypt. Meanwhile, the son of Corrado—Corradino—left behind in Germany, had reached the age of fifteen. He was said greatly to resemble Federico in spirit and appearance. After the death of Manfredo, he crossed the Alps and marched with a small army to Rome to claim his heritage. He was wildly hailed by the people of Rome; and in Apulia a rising of Saracens against Charles made success seem imminent. But Corradino was betrayed, captured, and sold to Charles. At the age of seventeen, in October of 1268, this last grandson of Federico was publicly beheaded in the market square of Napoli, on the orders of Charles and with the consent of the Pope.

Witness to all these events was Enzo, imprisoned in Bologna. His songs and poems had yearly grown more tragic. In 1270, when he was over fifty, he attempted to escape in a wine cask; but he was betrayed by a lock of his own hair, it was said, and apprehended. Two years later, he died. The Bolognese voted him a funeral at civic expense; he was buried as a king.

Among the people, hatred for the regime of Charles steadily increased. A plan was conceived to call Don Pedro III of Aragon to the throne of Sicily—as Don Pedro earlier had married the eldest daughter of Manfredo, Costanza, who had become the last hope. The go-between in the negotiations was that same Giovanni da Procida who had been Federico's physician in Apulia. At the hour of vespers, on the evening of March 31, 1282, the people of Palermo suddenly rose against the French occupation force of Charles, and slaughtered them. Not one of the two thousand men is said to have escaped. Such was the "Sicilian Vespers."

So to the throne of the Island of Sicily came a new Costanza of Aragon as Queen—the granddaughter of Federico. Thus history turned full circle. But the mind and heart of Federico was no longer there; now the island's history, like the regime, was without significance.

And in all the rest of southern Italy, Charles and reaction reigned.

Notes

Some of the place names used in this book have changed since medieval times, as follows: Fiorenza to Firenze; Monte Malo to Monte Mario; San Germano to Cassino; Castrogiovanni to Enna; Agobio to Gubbio; Suessa to Sessa; San Felice to San Fele; Borgo San Donnino to Fidenza.

PROLOGUE

A number of the gold coins showing the profile of Federico II today exist in good condition in various museums. A stylized symbolic "portrait" often has been reproduced from the illuminated manuscript of *De Arte Venandi cum Avibus*. In the museum at Capua, copies can be found of a portrait bust of a handsome young boy, "perhaps Federico Secondo." The style, however, bears little, if any, resemblance to that of the thirteenth century. An imaginary oil portrait hangs in the restored castle at Oria. In the museum at Barletta, a recently discovered bust is said to be a portrait of Federico. It is tempting to accept this sculpture as authentic, as it portrays a strong and virile face at the prime of manhood. Some experts claim, nevertheless, that the carved inscription (on which the identification is based) is of a later date than the sculpture itself. After Federico's death, his enemies did a thorough job of destroying all physical representations of the Emperor—though fragments of the Great Gate at Capua remained as a target for the invading troops of Napoleon.

A word is in order about Federico's own literary style. He tended to be simple, direct, and lucid in most of his writing—though he could, when he wished, use all the high-flown imagery and flourishes of his period. His letters range from the utmost in formality to the intimate and almost chatty. He was not only given to such maxims as those found in the Falcon Book, but relished the use of such phrases as: "I never raised a pig, etc.," "It would take a pick-ax to drive any sense into his head," "Can't see a crow in a bowlful of milk," "Let him scratch where it itches." All are authentic. Above all, he had a great sense of suiting his style to the occasion, except when he deliberately wished to shock. No comment is needed on the power of his later manifestoes.

PART I

Chapters 1-8, 11—Very little precise information survives about the childhood of Federico. Perhaps the opening of the Vatican's secret archives would throw much light on this phase of his life. The letters all exist as quoted. The existence of Federico's tutor Guglielmo Franciscus was fact; his other childhood friends fictional, as described. He must, however, from the few facts available, have lived a boyhood very similar to that portrayed—as so much of the behavior of his later years was derived from ideas acquired in childhood. The date of the elevation of Berardo to the Archbishopric of Palermo is also uncertain, though it occurred while Federico was very young. For reasons of simplification, Berardo is introduced as officiating at the first coronation of Federico. Berardo's flight from Palermo and return has no historical confirmation.

Chapter 13—The story of the three rings occurs in the *Novellino*, a collection of stories which appeared in the thirteenth century, and which had great influence on writers in succeeding centuries. The story of the three rings was popularly ascribed to Federico; hence, it is included. Federico himself appears as a character in other stories, as do some of his associates.

Chapter 14—The time and place of the beginnings of Federico's archaeological activities are unknown. As Sicily is one of the world's richest archaeological areas (its cultures date back to the Upper Paleolithic period) it is reasonable to suppose that Federico's curiosity was very early aroused. The Greek and Roman remains, however, are the most obvious, and he could hardly have escaped them. His most notable discovery occurred in later life, when he uncovered the mausoleum of Galla Placidia in Ravenna. Such interest in antiquity was one of the hallmarks of the dawning Renaissance; in Italian, *Rinascimento*.

Chapter 17—Otto's dream about the young bear is on record.

PART II

Chapter 4—The time and place of Federico's first meeting with Pier della Vigna and Bianca Lancia are unknown. The letter written to the Archbishop Berardo by Pier della Vigna first called Federico's attention to Piero's existence; its date is uncertain. As Manfredo Lancia was active in Federico's behalf while Federico was in Germany, it is entirely possible that Federico first met Bianca at the time he met Manfredo Lancia. Unknown, however, is Bianca's and

Manfredo's blood relationship: they may have been cousins, or even niece and uncle. Piero did not rise to prominence in Federico's service until after the coronation at Rome; from the very beginning he was called "the Emperor's favorite." Dante, in Canto XIII of the *Inferno*, has Pier della Vigna say that "scarce another soul had any part in his (Federico's) most secret thoughts." The liaison with Bianca did not begin until about the time of the proclamation of the Constitution of Melfi. As the relationship of Federico and Pier della Vigna in a sense foreshadows the Renaissance relationship of Lorenzo the Magnificent and Angelo Poliziano, so Bianca Lancia foreshadows the educated and emancipated women of the Renaissance. (Above phrase from the *Inferno* as translated by John Ciardi. The lines quoted from the *Aeneid* were translated by C. Day Lewis, and are reprinted by permission of the Harold Matson Co.)

Chapter 7—The fragment quoted from the Emperor Julian was translated by T. F. Higham, from *The Palatine Anthology*.

Chapter 9—It is probable that the incident at Charlemagne's shrine followed, rather than preceded, Federico's coronation at Aix-la-Chapelle. This is the sequence given by chroniclers. The sequence has been reversed because of the dramatic significance of Federico's taking the Cross for the Crusade.

Chapter 10—It was to Hermann von Salza, Grand Master of the Teutonic Knights, that Federico issued the "Golden Bull of Rimini" in 1226, authorizing them to Christianize the heathen Prussians—who, in the words of a chonicler, "knew neither writing nor books."

PART III

Chapter 4—Federico's experiment with religious self-determination and resettlement of Muslims succeeded admirably until the eventual triumph of Papal forces. Then the Saracens were massacred, and Lucera was returned to Christianity. Recent restoration efforts within the walls of the fortress have uncovered skulls in such quantities as to permit stacking like the round stone shot for catapults. Though the fortress was enlarged by Charles of Anjou, the sections built by Federico are today largely in ruins.

Chapter 5—Federico's meeting with Francesco d'Assisi has no documentary confirmation, and has been considered more legendary than factual. The legend of the Saint's temptation has been very persistent, however, and tends to be confirmed as fact by the discovery of a commemorative plaque, dated 1635, during recent restorations of Federico's castle at Bari. The account of San Francesco's conversion of the wolf of Agobio can be found in Section XX of the *Fioretti di San Francesco*.

The translation of the Saint's poem is by Dante Gabriel Rossetti.

No other translations of the early Italian poets have been used in this book, though Rossetti rendered a large number of their poems into English—including one by Federico II. A successful translation is, in fact, almost impossible, as the cadences of thirteenth century Italian and modern English are so dissimilar. The Italian language is itself an old language (its first known written use was at Bologna in a document dated 961), but it is much closer in form to modern Italian than Middle English is to modern English. Since the poems contain many recognizable words, the best choice was to leave them intact in their original rhythm and beauty. As for the sonnet, specialists on medieval Italian literature consider either Jacopo da Lentini or Pier della Vigna the inventor.

Chapter 6—Federico's journey to the north of Italy occurred after, not before, his marriage to Yolanda. For dramatic reasons the sequence has been changed.

Chapter 7—The whole affair with "Balian" is completely shrouded in mystery. Even the true name of the mother of Federico of Antioch is unknown. Legend attributes to the seduction of his wife, the bitter hostility of Walter de Brienne toward Federico. This hostility carried on beyond the grave, as Walter de Brienne joined the invading forces of Charles of Anjou. For his own reasons, Federico appears to have made every effort to keep the affair secret, though his love poem addressed to "the flower of Syria" appears to imply much. Federico of Antioch was in fact the only one of the Emperor's children to have a physical blemish sufficiently important for the chroniclers to record.

Chapter 12—Several Arab writers reported the details of Federico's tour of the Holy Places of Jerusalem, including incidents and conversation.

Chapter 13—The details of Federico's visit to the "Old Man of the Mountain" are entirely unknown.

PART IV

Chapter 1—Of the two Greek bronze rams which Federico placed over the gate of his Castello Maniace in Siracusa, one may be seen today in the Museo Nazionale in Palermo; the other has disappeared. The Great Gate at Capua is said to have been the model for the Triumphal Gate of the Castelnuovo in Napoli—to be seen today in a good state of preservation. It was built by Alfonso the Magnanimous of Aragon, as a monument to his victory in Napoli in 1442 over the Angevins (whose regime had lasted 176 years).

Johannes Maurus, the son of a black slave woman, displayed such marked abilities that under Manfredo he rose to be Grand Chamberlain and later Treasurer of the Realm.

Chapter 2—Neither the date of Michael the Scott's arrival at

Federico's court, nor the date or place of his death is known with certainty—though probably he died in Germany. The questions presented to Michael the Scott by Federico are all authentic—as was, say the chroniclers, the trick about the height of the sky.

Chapter 3—The species of bird Federico calls "*praeneus*" has not been identified. The experiment with the cuckoo is described in *The Art of Falconry*.

The questions sent by Federico to savants of the East actually were composed some years later than the time indicated. All Federico's scientific experiments were recorded approximately as described, with the single exception of the experiment on the dog, which has been added. The goblet tossed into the sea is the subject of a poem by the German poet Schiller, titled *Der Taucher*.

Chapter 5—Because of the historical importance of the Constitution of Melfi, restoration of the castle at Melfi is now said to be planned. Though it has been damaged by earthquakes, the Hall of the Three Domes remains intact, as does the secret passageway described.

Chapter 6—Though historians generally credit the thirteenth century with the invention of buttons, quantities of buttons have been found at Pompeii. They seem to be another case of re-invention of an invention.

Chapter 10—The Landpeace of Mainz did not precede, but followed, the Jewish ritual murder trial. The change has been made for structural reasons. This is the same period that Federico visited Marburg, to attend the re-burial and canonization ceremonies for his kinswoman Saint Elizabeth.

Chapter 11—"Sumer Is Icumen In" is the oldest known song with English words. It dates from the thirteenth century. Matthew Paris was the recorder of Isabella's remark about the eunuchs' faces.

PART V

Chapter 1—The famed "Donation of Constantine" was revealed by the scholarship of Lorenzo Valla, in 1440, to be one of the greatest forgeries of history. The Papacy responded by hauling Valla before the agents of the Inquisition in Napoli; but Valla was saved by the protection of King Alfonso the Magnanimous.

Chapter 3—The negotiations of Pope Gregory IX to arrange a wedding between his niece and Federico's illegitimate son Enzo are very obscure. The reasons for Federico's refusal have never been historically explained.

Chapter 4—All extraordinary natural phenomena were interpreted as signs and portents, good or evil as the case might be, in relation to the struggle between Emperor and Pope. Federico's excommunication took place a few weeks before the eclipse of the sun; but, as the excommunication itself was not generally known for some time after the event (due to the slowness of news dissemination), the eclipse and the excommunication were closely related in people's minds as harbingers of doom. For this reason, no violence is done to history by having them occur on the same day. As for the other natural phenomena related to particular events in Federico's life, the comet appeared shortly before his advance on Rome, and blood-red rain fell shortly before the conspiracy against his life by his intimates.

Chapter 9—Federico's grant of freedom to the men of Schwyz was the beginning of the modern Swiss Confederation.

Chapter 10—The Castel del Monte stands today in solitary splendor atop a hillock in the Apulian plain. Despite the fact that it has been stripped of its furnishings, its statuary, its mosaic pavements, most of its marbles, and even of its fireplaces, it remains one of the architectural wonders of the world.

Chapter 11—Federico's book, *Of the Art of Hunting with Birds*, is considered a monument in the history of the biological sciences, and has been called "the beginning of experimental science in the West." Its illustrations are remarkable for their precision and detail, and may have been influenced by Persian drawings. It perhaps was used as a source book by Albertus Magnus, and remained a definitive work until quite recent times. It also stimulated other works which attempted scientific methodology, such as *Horse Healing*, by the Calabrian Jordanus Ruffus—the first veterinary treatise of western Europe. (The excerpts quoted from *The Art of Falconry* were translated by Casey A. Wood and Marjorie Fyfe, and are used by the kind permission of the Stanford University Press.)

Chapter 12—The popular tale of how "Gianni" da Procida saved his Restituta from the clutches of Federico may be found in Boccaccio's *Decameron*, the sixth story on the fifth day. This "Gianni" and Giovanni da Procida, the young physician at Federico's court, whose name was later to figure so prominently in Sicilian history, must surely have been the same person. Boccaccio, however, places the scene of Restituta's near-seduction by the King in Palermo.

The marriage of Federico to Bianca Lancia is one of the hypotheses of history. The external evidence is strong that he did so. His gifts to her—most unusual—are on record, as is his statement that Manfredo Lancia was his "well-beloved relation." Further evidence is the fact that Manfredo, his son by Bianca, was the only illegitimate child mentioned in the final will—and the only child granted a title in that document. There can be no doubt that Bianca Lancia was the only woman in Federico's life who held his affections over a long period of time. The date and place of her death are not known.

Federico's definition of marriage has been precisely stated according to his own often expressed opinion.

Chapter 13—Pope Giovanna (in English, "Joan") was thought to have been one of the tenth-century Popes who ruled under the name of Ioánnis or Johannes (in Italian, *Giovanni*). She was said to have assumed the name of "Johannes Anglus" as a young girl, and thereupon disguised herself in male clothing to be with her lover in a Benedictine monastery. Through her expert knowledge of Greek and other learning, she rose eventually to the Papacy. Her secret was not discovered until, in the midst of a procession to the Lateran, she gave birth to a child. In the time of Federico, Pope Giovanna was universally credited as fact. In the year 1404, at the coronation of Innocent VII in Rome, Adam of Usk reported that Pope Giovanna's "image with her son stands in stone in the direct road near St. Clement's." Today, the account is said by Church authorities to be legend, though it received learned support as late as the eighteenth century.

Chapter 15—The proceedings of three sessions of the Council of Lyons have been condensed into one, for reasons of simplicity and clarification.

PART VI

Chapter 1—The actual date of Federico's famous "Reformation Letter" is uncertain, and has aroused considerable discussion among historians. It is generally presented as having been written after Federico's first excommunication by Gregory IX, on the authority of the contemporary English chronicler Matthew Paris, who reports it as directed to the King of England. This dating has come into question because of the tone and force of the letter. It is at variance with Federico's temperate response to the first excommunication, and is much more in keeping with the powerful attacks on Innocent IV made by Federico after the Council of Lyons. Hence it is presented here as belonging to the later period.

Chapter 2—Extant documents of the cardinals leave no doubt whatever that Pope Innocent IV personally organized the conspiracy against Federico's life.

Chapter 3—In reading the Sultan's letter with the phrase about Muslim glorification of Christ, it must be remembered that the Koran respects Jesus Christ as a true prophet.

Chapter 4—The copy of the "Falcon Book" which was taken as booty from Vittoria was later sold to Charles of Anjou, according to some historians.

Chapter 6—The capture of Enzo, and probably the death of Riccardo di Theate, both occurred about a year after the time indicated. The date has been advanced for structural reasons.

Chapters 7, 8—The true reason for the disgrace of Pier della

Vigna is one of the mysteries of history. Despite the fact that many historians state he was associated with the doctor's plot against Federico, no evidence supports this view. Many others say that he embezzled state funds at a critical time, but the evidence is slight. Modern research has shown that at no time did he intrigue with the Pope. Many contemporary rumors were current, and many subsequent theories have been advanced as to what actually happened. Known with certainty is the fact that Federico suddenly chose to obscure the whole affair. Dante, in the *Inferno*, presents Pier della Vigna as proclaiming his own innocence, the victim of envy. Modern research has also established that the blinded Pier della Vigna committed suicide at the tower of San Miniato al Tedesco, on the road to Pisa. For his suicide, Dante assigns him to the seventh circle of Hell, transformed into a thorny tree whose leaves are eaten by Harpies.

Chapter 10—The sarcophagus of Federico II in Palermo Cathedral was opened in 1781, in the presence of many officials and an artist. The content was carefully recorded, while the artist made detailed drawings—still available today. Early in 1962 the sarcophagus was again opened. According to one of the observers, Federico's face was remarkably well preserved—"like a saint."

Selected List of Sources

Allshorn, Lionel: *Stupor Mundi* (Secker, London, 1912)
Amari, Michele: *I Musulmani in Sicilia* (Bompiani, Milano, 1942)
Bernini, Ferdinando: *I Comuni Italiani e Federico II di Svevia* (Societá Editrice Internazionale, Torino, 1950)
Carcani, C.: *Constitutiones Regum Regni Utriusque Sicilae, Mandante Friderico II Imperatore* (Napoli, 1786)
Caruso, Giovanni Battista: *Storia di Sicilia* (Stabilimento Tipografico Lao, Palermo, 1875)
Casertano, Antonio: Un Oscuro Dramma Politico del Secolo XIII (Libreria del Littorio, Roma, 1928)
Cocchiara, Giuseppe: *Federico II Legislatore e il Regno di Sicilia* (Fratelli Bocca, Torino, 1927)
Coulton, G. G.: *Medieval Panorama* (Cambridge University Press, London, 1938)
De Blasiis, Giuseppe: *Della Vita e delle Opere di Pier della Vigna* (Stab. Tip. del' Ancora, Napoli, 1860)
De Stefano, Antonio: *Federico II e le Correnti Spirituali del Suo Tempo* (Roma, 1921)
——: *La Cultura alla Corte di Federico II Imperatore* (Fanichelli, Bologna, 1950)
——: *L'Idea Imperiale di Federico II* (Vallecchi, Firenze, 1927)
Di Blasi, Giovanni: *Storia del Regno di Sicilia*, Vol. II (Palermo, 1846)
Durant, Will: *The Age of Faith* (Simon and Schuster, New York, 1950)
Fillitz, Hermann: *The Crown Jewels and the Ecclesiastical Treasure Chamber* (Kunsthistorisches Museum, Vienna, 1956)
Frederick II: *De Arte Venandi cum Avibus*, translated as *The Art of Falconry*, by Casey A. Wood and Marjorie Fyfe (Stanford University Press, Stanford, Calif., 1943)
Gabrieli, Francesco, editor: *Storici Arabi delle Crociate* (Einaudi, Roma, 1957)
Haskins, Charles Homer: *Studies in the History of Medieval Science* (Harvard, Cambridge, Massachusetts, 1924)
Hughes, P.: *A History of the Church* (London, 1948)
Huillard-Breholles, A.: *Historia Diplomatica Friderici Secundi* (Paris, 1852)

——: *Vie et Correspondence de Pierre de la Vigne* (Paris, 1864)
Kantorowicz, Ernst: *Kaiser Friedrich der Zweite* (Berlin, 1927); English edition, *Frederick the Second*, translated by E. O. Lorimer (Constable, London, 1931)
La Mantia, V.: *Legge Civile del Regno di Sicilia, 1130-1816* (Reber, Palermo, 1895)
"L'Illustrazione Siciliana": *VII Centenario della Morte di Federico II*, Numero Speciale (Arte Grafiche, Palermo, 1951)
Mann, Horace K.: *Lives of the Popes in the Middle Ages* (Kegan Paul, Trench, Trübner & Co., London, 1915)
Masson, Georgina: *Frederick II of Hohenstaufen* (Secker & Warburg, London, 1957)
Moisè, Filippo: *Storia dei Domini Stranieri in Italia*, Vol. V (Batelli, Firenze, 1842)
Molajoli, Bruno: *Castel del Monte* (L'Arte Tipografica, Napoli, 1958)
Momigliano, Eucardio: *Federico II di Svevia* (Mondadori, Milano, 1948)
Monteverdi, Angelo: *Studi e Saggi sulla Letteratura Italiana dei Primi Secoli* (Ricciardi, Milano-Napoli, 1954)
Nassi, Giulio: *Letteratura Italiana del Medioevo* (Editrice Universitaria, Firenze, 1955)
Paolucci, Giuseppe: *La Giovinezza di Federico Secondo* (Barravecchio, Palermo, 1901)
Paris, Matthew: *Historia Maior* (ed. Luard, London, 1872)
Pepe, Gabriele: *Lo Stato Ghibellino di Federico II* (Laterza, Bari, 1938)
Rondoni, G.: *Dove Si Uccise Pier della Vigna* (Bollettino della Accademia degli Euteleti in San Miniato, Agosto, 1919)
Ross, James Bruce, and McLaughlin, Mary Martin, editors: *Medieval Reader* (Viking, New York, 1949)
Rossetti, Dante Gabriel: *The Early Italian Poets—Part I, The Poems of Dante Gabriel Rossetti* (Oxford University Press, London, 1959)
Salimbene di Adam: *Cronica* (Bernini, Bari, 1942)
Saracino, Emanuele: *Federico II di Svevia e L'Apulia* (Scuola Tipografica, Molfetta, 1960)
Schipa, Michelangelo: *Sicilia e Italia Sotto Federico Secondo* (Archivo Storico delle Provincie Napoletane, Napoli, 1925)
Shearer, Creswell: *The Renaissance of Architecture in Southern Italy —A Study of Frederick II of Hohenstaufen* (Heffer, Cambridge, 1935)
Testa, Francesca: *De Vita, et Rebus Gestis Federici II* (Panorini, Bentivenga, 1775)
Trevelyan, Janet Penrose: *A Short History of the Italian People* (Allen & Unwin, London, 1956)

Ullman, Walter: *Medieval Papalism* (London, 1949)

Università di Palermo: *Atti del Convengo Internazionale di Studi Federiciani–VII Centenario della Morte di Federico II* (Palermo, 1950)

Volpe; Volpicelli; Della Corte; Pazzini: *La Vita Medioevale Italiana nella Miniatura* (Bestetti, Roma, 1960)

Wahl, Rudolph: *Wandler der Welt* (Salzburg, 1947)

Waldburg-Wolfegg, Hubert: *Vom Südreich der Hohenstaufen* (Schnell & Steiner, München, 1955)

Willemsen, C. A. and Odenthal, D.: *Apulia–Imperial Splendour in Southern Italy*, translated from the German by Daphne Woodward (Thames & Hudson, London, 1959)

ABOUT THE AUTHOR

Joseph Jay Deiss, a descendant of an old American family, grew up in Amarillo, Texas, and attended the University of Texas, where he took both B.A. and M.A. degrees. He became one of the highest-paid U.S. executives in the field of public relations. He left business temporarily to write his first novel. In 1954 he left business permanently, to devote his entire time to writing, and a novel based on the upper echelons of big business shortly followed.

Preparation of *The Great Infidel* required more than five years. For the research it was necessary for Deiss not only to learn to read modern Italian (at school he had studied Latin, French, and Anglo-Saxon), but to pick his way through thirteenth-century Italian. He became so absorbed in the medieval art of hawking that he even acquired a falcon to observe its behavior.

The writing of this novel began in an abandoned goat hut in the Aeolian Islands, near a town built twenty centuries before Rome was founded. It was finished in a coastal tower which served as a refuge against the Saracen raiders of the early Middle Ages.

Deiss has traveled widely in Europe and South America. He is married, and divides his time between an eighteenth-century colonial house on Cape Cod and a fifteenth-century Italian villa on the Mediterranean. His novels have been especially acclaimed by critics throughout Europe, and have appeared in many editions—including British, Italian, French, Dutch, Yiddish, German, Hungarian, Czech, Swedish, Russian, Swiss, Rumanian and Greek.